Critical Praise for
NIGHT CALLS

"Uncommonly enlightening . . . Eisenberg writes with rare candor about the risks and rewards of his practice." —*John Barkham Reviews*

"A winning chronicle about a physician whose sense of wonder has survived despite experience, technology and law suits . . . Disarmingly frank!"
—*Publishers Weekly*

"One doctor's odyssey . . . very revealing!"
—*Philadelphia Inquirer*

"Henry Eisenberg is a rarity: a physician with the courage and maturity to expose himself and his profession and offers remarkable insights into what life is like on the other side of the doctors desk . . . with honesty and humor!" —*South Bend Tribune*

"Illuminating . . . moving!"
—*News Journal* (Mansfield, OH.)

"Explores the gynecologist's delicate relationship with his patients. And he admits to a few all-too-human reactions of his own." —*The Star*

"Candid!" —*Book Alert*

"Eisenberg's revelations are engrossing and revealing!" —*Midwest Book Review*

NIGHT CALLS

The PERSONAL JOURNEY of an OB/GYN

HENRY EISENBERG, M.D. AND
ARLENE AND HOWARD EISENBERG

B

BERKLEY BOOKS, NEW YORK

This Berkley book contains the complete
text of the original hardcover edition.
It has been completely reset in a typeface
designed for easy reading and was printed
from new film.

NIGHT CALLS

A Berkley Book / published by arrangement with
Arbor House Publishing Company.

PRINTING HISTORY
Arbor House edition / August 1986
Berkley edition / March 1988

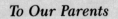

To Our Parents

Gender Note

Women are wearing stethoscopes in place of necklaces in growing numbers these days, and the ob/gyn is no exception. But as we write this, the vast majority of ob/gyns are still males. After writing ''he or she'' and ''his or her'' several dozen times, the authors (one of them female) arbitrarily decided to use ''he'' generically for the ob/gyn, in part because, given the specialty described, we had no alternative but to use ''she'' for the patient. We believe our decision will make this book easier to read. But feel free to mentally slip an ''s'' in front of the physician ''he'' wherever it appears.

—The Authors

Contents

x   Contents

In Appreciation

The first thirty years of my life were spent as a student—first learning the alphabet, and then the ABCs of medicine. During that busy time, I was too busy to notice how little I had learned about myself and about those around me—except for the anatomy, physiology, or pathologic states.

I was blessed with two wonderful parents, memories of whom I still cherish many years after their deaths. They made it possible for me to become a physician and thus to serve people in a way that few are privileged to do. I'm grateful that they let me know how much I was loved and for their showing me, by example (though, with ob/gyn training happening simultaneously, it took a while for their imprint to take), how to be a loving parent.

The person who showed me how to be fully human was Madalyn, the young woman I met during my internship, who twenty-eight years later is still my teacher and coach—about life and particularly about matters relating to women. She is also my wife and best friend.

Her affinity for people, her caring, her zest for life and joy, and her unparalleled willingness to be honest are the qualities that make a relationship with her very special—for myself and for all who know her.

If I were a violin, I'd want every string fully functional, so my music would be rich and complete. Madalyn's strings are like that, and so is her song—sad when it needs to be, sweet and beautifully joyful most of the time. To be in harmony with her is to harmonize with life. I thank her for her love, support, and understanding through all the years of sudden summonses to spend long hours with other women. I thank her, too, for bearing and mothering three wonderful sons: Jordan, Bruce, and Ned.

I've learned, too, from each of the many women who've shared life's most intense experiences with me—births especially, but sometimes death. As long as I practice medicine, I'll try to be worthy of their special trust and confidence. Most of my practice years, I've been fortunate to have the strengths of a very special ob/gyn reinforcing mine. Jack Yoffa was still in medical school when we met. I knew right away—and told him so—that if he happened to choose my specialty, I'd welcome him as my associate. His hair was black then. There's silver in it now. He is the fine and caring physician I knew he would become.

With nuclear families exploding geographically in all directions, brothers today are often separated by gulfs of real and psychological miles. Howard and I were. First by five years, then by interests, occupations, new families, and distance. He became a writer. I became a doctor. Then, his writer-wife, Arlene (to whom I'll always be indebted), suggested: Why not combine the two and become brothers again in fact as well as name? This book—years in the "Why don't we?" stage, one year in the writing—became the magnet drawing all of us together, not only in the writing but in the heart. We used to shake hands. Now we hug. That's a special dividend that's made us—and, we're sure, our parents—very happy.

Something else that's made us happy is our good luck in drawing one of those rare and precious editors who takes the time not only to read, but to ask tough questions about, the books for which she takes responsibility. In the publishing business, flags—little yellow tags stuck to pages in need of remedial English or rethinking—are signs of caring. Arbor House editor-in-chief Ann Harris cares. She adorned our manuscript with enough flags to meet the needs of United Nations Day, and her twenty-five or so single spaced pages of challenging questions forced us to do better time and again.

We thank you, Ann, for your initial enthusiasm in acquiring this book from our hard-working agents, Elise and Arnold Goodman. And, more important, for not forgetting it—busy though you were with the rest of the catalog—when it needed your deft touches and fine critical mind. We're grateful for your perfectionism and your determined pursuit of excellence.

From prologue to epilogue, we're finished. May you who pick up this book enjoy the reading as much as we enjoyed the remembering and the writing.

—Henry Eisenberg

PART ONE

BECOMING

Prologue

"Madalyn . . ."

"Yes, Henry." My wife's brown eyes are tightly shut, her lips pressed firmly against the pillowcase. The words roll slowly and reluctantly from a corner of her mouth.

I slide forward in our bed and ruefully inspect the snow-tipped evergreens in the backyard. The tumbling flakes are plumper and thicker than when we went to sleep, and the wind is singing a winter song. If I were a schoolboy, I'd rejoice, but it's a long time since I enjoyed the luxury of playing hooky. I think of the years of 3 A.M. phone calls, the nights of leaving a warm wife for an icy garage.

No sympathy was called for or needed then. Each mission was an adventure, and I was what I wanted to be. But today somehow I want no more of it. "Madalyn," I challenge illogically, "why can't I stay in this nice warm bed with you and not have to get up and go to work?" I flop back and tug the blanket over my head.

I know that clinging to my wife and ducking under the covers is more than just a desire to stay warm, to be a little boy again enjoying a snow day, to sleep a little longer because emergency surgery kept me up late last night. I don't want to get up because I am troubled by vague fears. The fear of being responsible for the lives of other human beings, of the potential for catastrophe in every move or decision I make. The fear that if something goes wrong, even if it's beyond my control, I could lose my home, my practice, everything.

Madalyn is wide awake now. "You're tired of doing this, aren't you?" she asks, suddenly understanding.

"More than tired. Scared," I reply fiercely. "Getting out of bed isn't the fun it used to be. And I'd like not to get out of bed this morning. But I don't have a choice."

"Would you like to stop being a doctor? Could it be time to start thinking about retirement?"

I have always loved ob/gyn. I've loved it even more since the women in my life—first my wife, then my patients—toppled me from my pedestal and taught me that doctoring is more than just knowing the right diagnosis and making the right cut with my scalpel. Since I discovered the joy of delivering babies in partnership with their parents instead of all by myself.

No. I don't want to stop being a doctor. But a little voice within me keeps whispering, "Quit. That's the only way you'll get rid of the fears . . ."

1

Flunking Out:
The Journey Begins

Winter 1952

WAKING AND SLEEPING during my first six months at medical
school, the thought most often on my mind wasn't of retiring
voluntarily, but of being involuntarily retired. Suddenly and
without warning. By the very professor whose signature on an
acceptance letter had brought me there in the first place.

I shuddered whenever Dr. Armstrong so much as looked at
me, but especially when I heard the sound of his voice. He
would pad stealthily up behind me (or so, in my paranoid state,
it seemed) as I stood carving and slicing uncomprehendingly at
a cadaver on the anatomy table. "What," he would ask
ominously, his cultured British tones shattering my concentration as hammer shatters goblet, "is that in your hand, doctor?"

Too often, I didn't know. In Introduction to Anatomy and
other premed courses, I had relied with considerable success
on rote learning. The way I passed exams on dogfish anatomy
was by drawing maps of the circulatory and respiratory
systems and memorizing them. It had worked on fish and small
mammals, and I had been confident it would work on people.
But I quickly discovered that it was no longer enough just to
draw maps.

Human anatomy meant studying the unfortunate cold, gray,
stringy three-dimensional body that Fritz, hunched and sardon-

5

ic and looking as though Central Casting had chosen him to preside over the anatomy lab, had waiting for us on the slab each morning. It meant seeing and understanding how things related and fit together in God's marvelously intricate, ultimate jigsaw puzzle. We started at the abdomen, the least complex area, then moved to the head and neck, then the chest cavity, and finally the extremities, down to the sinewy tendons and ugly toes. I even had trouble with the abdomen.

The gene for three-dimensional perception seemed grievously absent in my brain (I couldn't differentiate tissues on a slide under the microscope, either), and I didn't get much besides blood- and fat-stained from my cadaver. I fell back desperately on Plan A, earnestly memorizing sketches representing the human body into the early hours of the morning—not easy, since something else I lacked was a taste for black coffee. But my neatly drawn blood vessels were only lines on a flat surface, their interrelationships uncertain. So when Dr. Armstrong quizzed me, I didn't have the answers.

How could a doctor practice patient care without understanding how his patients' bodies worked? I was sure that, sooner or later, I would find a note in my mailbox informing me that I'd been banished to Siberia—the grim summer semester makeup class at the University of Michigan, where you either earned a B in anatomy or didn't bother to return. Or even worse: a form letter stating that I was not *materia medica* and had been summarily flunked out.

But maybe it didn't matter. It was entirely possible that I wasn't going to live long enough to graduate. I had developed a nerve disorder that had all the indications of being terminal. Twitches rippled embarrassingly at the corners of my mouth and eyes, skidded across the backs of my hands, and, most conspicuously and uncontrollably, jerked my left thumb as if with invisible strings. Not just a nerve, the whole thumb.

My thumb's spasmodic movements were random and unpredictable, mutinously ignoring my desperate commands to cease and desist. It wiggled and fluttered back and forth as if stimulated by an electric current and unable to stop contracting. I kept my hand in my pocket to hide its scandalous behavior.

After weeks of twitching that I had absolutely no ability to control, I went in quiet desperation to the student health service. The outcome, I knew, was going to be a terrible blow to my parents, who had been overjoyed by my admission to medical school and the prospect of my becoming the family's first physician. Though uncertain of the exact diagnosis, I was absolutely certain of the prognosis: terrible. One possibility was early MS. Or it could be some other demyelinating degenerative disease of the nervous system of which the twitching thumb was only the first symptom, precursor to deeper and more painful twitches that would advance inexorably across my palm, then up my wrist and arm, leaving it ultimately limp and useless. At the very least, I'd never be able to do surgery.

I had a long anxious wait at the health service, staring enviously at students with ordinary ills: colds, sore throats, pink eye. When at last my name was called by the gentle middle-aged lady doctor, I smiled wanly, took a deep breath, and followed her into the maze of examining and consultation rooms. In the privacy of her tiny office, I stammered out my secret fears, as if sharing them would rid me of whatever was wrong.

She shook her head and smiled sympathetically. She knows, I told myself. She knows what it is already. But she obviously wanted to be certain, and did an exhaustive physical. When, at last, she put her hands on my shoulders, and looked me straight in the eye, I stiffened, prepared for the worst. "Son," she said, "your condition isn't terminal. It's situational." She continued to talk, but my mind, like a stuck phonograph needle, hung gratefully on "isn't terminal . . . isn't terminal . . . isn't terminal."

"You're suffering from a case of good old-fashioned medical school syndrome," she was saying when I tuned back in. She went on to explain that I could expect to develop demoralizing symptoms of other diseases as I moved forward through the curriculum. As for my twitch: It would go away as soon as I stopped being so anxious.

In retrospect, it's reasonable to believe that a lot of my fellow students were walking around with their hands in their pockets, too, but at the time I was too humiliated to notice.

Unfortunately, there was no getting away from the twin well-springs of my anxiety: the good Dr. Armstrong and his anatomy lab. As much as I was relieved to learn that I was going to live, there were moments, usually in his presence, when I wished myself dead. As much as his questions, I feared his periodic ritual invitation offered on the blackboard: "Table 5, tea and cookies in my office Friday afternoon at 4 P.M." "And, oh yes," he'd add aloud (dry smile, astringent British medical school humor), "don't forget to bring your stool."

At these tea parties, he would ask us how things were going and throw in some anatomy questions. I had my own ritual. I stared intently down at the scuffed tips of my loafers. I glanced critically up at the mottled paint of the ceiling. I thoughtfully scanned the tea leaves in my cup—certain they predicted a dark professional future. At all costs, I avoided meeting Dr. Armstrong's keen glance.

He was the chairman not only of the anatomy department but of the medical school admissions committee as well. I feared that his X-ray blue eyes would pierce the flimsy facade of belonging that I had erected, that he would see through and inside me, that he would of an instant recognize that he had made a mistake: that one Henry Malcolm Eisenberg did not deserve to be there.

I have, of course, no way of knowing what Dr. Armstrong actually saw when he chanced to look in my direction. If he saw or concluded anything, it may well have been that I was a rather shifty-eyed chap.

Feelings of inadequacy and self-doubt were not new to me. Influenced by a birthday subscription to *Popular Mechanics*, I had decided at age thirteen that the end of World War II had created a magnificent opportunity for people with skills and imagination to design the housing that postwar America urgently needed. I thought I could be that kind of person, that I would be a civil engineer and build housing developments. Somewhere I learned that the way to get a running start was to transfer from my neighborhood junior high in the Bronx to Brooklyn Tech, two boroughs and several subway train changes away. I was not discouraged. For an empire-builder, three hours a day of underground travel was a trivial sacrifice.

My grades were good enough to qualify me, and I passed the entrance exam for the elite school with little difficulty. But something went unexpectedly wrong in my first drafting course. With each passing day, I saw with greater clarity and despair (ominously foreshadowing anatomy courses to come) that I lacked the three-dimensional imagination the craft required. Our instructor allowed us to move about freely and, like a plant seeking sunlight, I found myself gravitating with increasing frequency and frustration toward the window. Elderly men sat on benches in the park across the road, idly feeding bread crusts to the pigeons, and I wished myself among them. Anything was better than confronting the reality that I was incapable of passing drafting—that my dream of rebuilding postwar America was beginning to look more and more like the rubble of postwar Europe.

Two weeks after arriving at Brooklyn Tech with hopes and spirits high, I rode the subway home with transfer papers in my school bag and shoulders slumped in discouragement. It was back to junior high school in the Bronx. I had never failed at anything before; my confidence was badly shaken. And I was left with a blank space in my head where an optimistic vision of the future and my secure place in it had once shimmered brightly.

It was another half-dozen years before anything occupied that space. On graduating from high school, I had followed the expected route to college: City College of New York, which offered free educations to students with high school grade averages of 85 or better. But after a year of not knowing what I wanted to be or what I was doing there, I made plans to drop out, to work for a friend of my brother-in-law, Phil, in Connecticut.

That made my last carefree summer before taking a job in the real world even more appealing. I spent it working as a lifeguard at Grossinger's, a legendary Catskill mountain resort, and there, as July slid into August and thoughts turned toward September, a deceptively simple question put direction back into my life. It came early one morning while most of the guests at the resort still slept, as I was setting up chaise lounges around the Olympic swimming pool with my friend and fellow lifeguard Eddie Murphy.

"When are you going back to school?" Murph, a law student, asked.

"I'm not," I replied. "I've been talking to my brother-in-law in New Haven. He's arranged for a job for me with a buddy of his in the roofing supply business."

Murphy seemed genuinely upset. "How come?"

Unaccustomed to people outside of my family caring about what happened to me, I was surprised at the intensity of his reaction. "I don't know what I want to be," I explained, "and there's no point in going to college not knowing."

Murph looked thoughtful. "What," he asked after a short pause, "would you really like to be? I mean, if you could choose anything."

For a moment, my mind went blank. Murph had asked a question that, since Brooklyn Tech, I had been afraid to ask myself. But suddenly I blurted out an answer. And I was amazed when I heard it.

Amazed, because up until that moment I'd never consciously thought about being a doctor. Amazed that I would even think such a thought in 1949 when every Jewish boy from the Bronx knew that medical schools unashamedly employed quota systems. It helped if your father was a doctor or, it was rumored, if your family could make a large gift to the school. I had nothing going for me. But I needed a new dream. And this one sounded better than selling shingles in New Haven.

This dream had apparently been growing quietly somewhere deep within my brain. Its mother may have been a book I read in high school, a physician's autobiography that made medicine sound wonderful. ("This book had an appendix," I wisecracked in my book report, "but the author took it out.") Its father was probably a neighborhood GP, Dr. Anthony Susinno, whose what-seemed-like-magic pills cured me of a case of severe bronchitis, and who both charmed and awed me when he made a house call to see me. Its godfather, I suppose, was a copy of *The New England Journal of Medicine* I'd discovered and read raptly in a physician-guest's cabana that very morning.

"A doctor," I told Murph.

"Well, Hank," he asked, "why don't you become one?" I pondered that remarkable question for a moment and then echoed with a determination that surprised me: "Why don't I? That's just what I'm going to be!"

I started thinking, and the answers started coming. I couldn't go back to CCNY. I'd never get into medical school from there. Maybe a private school. Maybe Syracuse University, which I knew had a medical school because a friend's older brother had gone there. But that would cost money, and I'd never before thought about asking my parents to pay my college tuition. My bright and beautiful sister, Betty, had married at eighteen and hadn't gone to college at all; my older brother, Howard, got half his education at the tuition-free City College and the other half on the GI bill. I'd be the first to ask for parental help. But if I was serious, I had to. The moment of silence at the other end of the line when I called my parents from a pay phone at Grossinger's alarmed me. But when their shock wore off, they were enthusiastic. "Henry, that's wonderful," said my mother. "We'll manage somehow," my father assured me.

I wrote one letter to the admissions committee at Syracuse, posted another to City College requesting a transcript of freshman year grades, and in three weeks found myself accepted as a transfer student. Orange balloons and raucous songs from the orange-sweatered Goon Squad welcomed new students at the Syracuse train station that first day. But I suspected that I would have little to do with this exuberant side of college life. I would be a premed grind reaching for the stars and a straight A average. Between that and trying to build a credible extracurricular activities portfolio calculated to simultaneously offer me practical experience and impress a med school admissions committee, it would be all work and very little play.

But by senior year, my fate was no longer in my own hands. I had cast three medical school applications upon the waters, and they would either float or they wouldn't.

I could afford to relax my obsessive-compulsiveness a bit, and on Homecoming Weekend, I said to hell with self-discipline. Our football team had beaten its archrival, and my dorm celebrated. Alcohol was banned on campus, but the innocent-looking fruit punch in the tub on our festive table was powerfully fortified with 99 percent absolute alcohol, cunningly acquired at the lab by an enterprising science major. I had an attractive date, drank much too much punch, and for once was the life of the party.

But, like a steak fed to a starving man, the unfamiliar debauchery was a seismic shock to my system. The room began to spin, and I was overwhelmed by the need to choose between retiring to my room to be privately sick or staying where I was to publicly demonstrate the weakness of my stomach. Mumbling an apology, I reeled upstairs.

I hadn't been in my room all day. First there had been the football game, then setting up for the party and celebrating the victory. I collapsed onto my doubledecker's lower bunk, clutching the railing to keep from falling off. The bed rose and fell like a steamship in a storm. On the crest of a mighty wave, my eye caught the return address on an envelope on my desk beside the bed: Northwestern University College of Medicine. My brain, though numbed by alcohol, rose to the occasion. With a supreme effort, it coded an order to my hand. This, it announced, was the letter we'd been waiting for. The news was going to be great or it was going to be terrible, but it could not wait.

Unsteady but obedient, my hand stretched forth and captured the envelope. Ten thumbs fumbled with its flap, opened it, extracted the single sheet folded inside. I moaned. It was so ominously brief. I closed my eyes, said a little prayer, then tried focusing on the blurred message.

"Dear Mr. Eisenberg," it began. "We are pleased to announce that you have been accepted in the entering class of our college of medicine for 1952."

My wild whoop pierced the merry sounds of partying below. Alarmed friends pounded up the stairs. They came to rescue and stayed to congratulate. The letter was passed from hand to hand. I was slapped repeatedly on the back, increasing my discomfort. I don't remember their leaving. I didn't say goodnight to my date. My last thought before I passed out was: "If that admissions committee could see me now . . ."

Northwestern wasn't my first choice, but when my hangover cleared the next morning, it didn't matter. *Somebody* wanted me. Several weeks later, I learned that my first choice, Syracuse, wanted me, too.

But the euphoria died in September of the following year in anatomy lab. And when I went home for Thanksgiving vacation, I couldn't dispel the icy fog of depression that permeated my very being. My mother took one look at me and sat me down with a thick wedge of chocolate cake and a glass of milk. That had always worked when I came home from school with a long face when I was a kid; maybe it would work now. It didn't. I tried to be cheerful at dinner, but fooled no one. After the turkey had been considerably reduced in size and the company departed, my father asked sympathetically, "What's wrong, Henry?"

I broke down and cried. It was Brooklyn Tech all over again, I said. I didn't have the right stuff. I was sure I was going to flunk out. I didn't want to go back. It had all been a mistake. Instead of taking the New York Central to Syracuse on Sunday,

I would catch the New York, New Haven, & Hartford and talk to Phil about that roofing job.

My father was disappointed but understanding. My brother and his wife urged me to give it another try. My mother thought about it and suggested that I talk to our family doctor. "Wasn't he the inspiration for you to apply in the first place?" she asked. "Why not see what he thinks before you start changing trains?"

Dr. Susinno was wonderful. I sat across the desk from him, awed as usual by a physician in practice. Someone doing what I wanted to do, but now never would. When I explained that I was faring terribly in anatomy and expected to flunk the course, he looked neither surprised nor disappointed. "Ask three doctors how they did in their first semester," he said, "and two will tell you they had trouble with anatomy. I'm one of them." We talked for a long time. It was the encouragement I needed. "I know you can do it," he told me. "You're a bright young man, and you don't have to be an A student in anatomy. Just get through the course. Then you'll go on to other things, things you're more suited for. The thing to remember is that it isn't how you start that matters, it's how you finish."

I boarded the train to Syracuse determined to finish better than I'd started. Because I'd decided it was all over except for the painful breaking of the bad news to my family, I had taken neither textbooks nor notes home with me. With nothing to study, I leaned back in my reclining seat and reflected on the three months past and the crucial make-or-break weeks just ahead.

I could be tough. I would be tough. I had quit when I was having trouble with drafting at Brooklyn Tech, but I wouldn't now. I remembered another embarrassing incident when I was thirteen, just after I'd returned to my old junior high.

Rocky was the biggest, meanest guy in our gang on 171st Street. How I got into an argument with him I don't remember. I only know it ended in one of those primal nose-to-nose "Yeah?" "Yeah!" "Who says so?" "I say so!" confrontations from which there was no backing off. We were in an apartment building courtyard surrounded by ten other kids, exultantly encouraging us to settle it with a fight.

Rocky didn't disappoint his audience. First he bloodied my nose. Then he pulped my lips. For five minutes that seemed much longer, he used me as a punching bag. Finally, tiring of the sport, he left me beaten and blubbering. I had fought back and I refused to go down, but I felt totally humiliated.

The train swayed on, and I thought about what that afternoon in the courtyard had done to me. The physical damage healed quickly. But the psychic damage that told me that I wasn't part of the group, that I wasn't good enough for it, was permanently imprinted on my brain. I decided that since I was never going to be one of the boys, I'd have to manage on my own, learn to rely on no one but myself. Since I was unlikely ever to be the biggest and strongest kid on the block, I had to develop other strengths to carry me through: of mind, of purpose, of self-discipline and tenacity.

If I ever needed those strengths, it was now. I would persist. I would survive. I would even survive anatomy.

I attacked my studies with a new determination. One of my anatomy table partners, Larry Port, had often kidded me about the way I studied the subject from single-dimensional diagrams. Now I realized he had a point. Perhaps revulsion had interfered with concentration. The first time I walked into the anatomy lab and saw that aged shriveled man lying on a metal table submissively waiting for us to slice him up, vertigo danced dizzyingly with nausea in my head. I resolved to suppress this revulsion, to really look objectively at that three-dimensional cadaver, at how things were related and connected to one another, and what they were there for.

Another lab partner gave my spirits an additional boost. One morning, as I worked carefully on my piece of our cadaver, he remarked, "Hey, if you want to see what a real live patient looks like, go up to the obstetrical floor. If you tell them you're a medical student, they let you observe a delivery."

I went after class the same day—out of the basement, out of our morgue, up to the tenth floor of a real hospital, to see a real childbirth. It was like emerging from a smoke-filled room into a rose garden.

I watched enthralled as the attending physician and his assisting residents and nurses encouraged a straining, sweating mother-about-to-be. I marveled at their brisk self-assurance and at the birth itself: the baby's head crowning, its shoulders emerging, and finally its scrawny body skidding out, still attached to the mother by a long pulsing umbilicus.

I watched fascinated as a resident cut the cord and coaxed

out the placenta. I had seen one in a large bell jar in the lab. Now I slipped quietly to the table he'd slapped it down on and looked at it analytically, trying to place the anatomical details: where the network of blood vessels originated and terminated, how they related to the cord. This still warm mass of tissue that had for so many months nourished a growing unborn baby had far more meaning to me than the cadaver I'd fled from below.

But there was, I felt, something more to this moment than anatomic minutiae. I was caught up in the miracle and the joy of birth, understanding for the first time why it's called a blessed event. I had participated, however peripherally, in an experience that recharged my discouraged mind and body, that made me realize that the tenth floor was what I was really here for, what we were all here for. Medicine wasn't always going to be about being in the basement cutting up a corpse. It was going to be about real patients and marvels of birth and dramas of life, and it was all there waiting for me if I continued to persevere and took it, like my one-mile early morning training swims in Grossinger's swimming pool, one stroke at a time.

I wasn't first in my class at the end of the semester, but I made it through anatomy. And the following semester, in biochemistry and physiology, I began to perform as I had in premed. I still kept my professors at arm's length though. There was danger in their getting to know me too well: They could still decide they had the wrong man.

It took a long time for me to outgrow that. Every time a classmate dropped out, or the time when one buckled under the academic pressure and locked himself in a closet with a bag of oranges, I experienced renewed pangs of anxiety. It took repeated exposure to challenge and continued above-average response to convince me finally that the admissions committee hadn't made a mistake and that I was going to be a pretty good physician after all.

During my senior year, I got my first chance to prove it. I earned a year's externship at the small community hospital where many members of the medical school clinical faculty sent patients—a great opportunity to impress doctors who might one day be my mentors.

It fell to me every third night to evaluate patients who took a turn for the worse, and phone the appropriate attending physician to let him know what was happening. I handled people who went into heart failure, had pulmonary emboli after surgery, a patient so jaundiced he looked like a giant carrot. Sometimes the attendings hadn't yet seen the patient. Often they didn't want to get out of bed and would rely on my history and tentative diagnosis and tell me to do A and B and order X and Y. I enjoyed being able to make such a big difference, and was amazed that I had all this power and responsibility when it seemed to me that by any objective standard I wasn't ready for it.

But they must have known something I didn't. I quickly grew—and grew confident that I could handle things beyond those that my classmates were being exposed to in medical school clerkships. I assisted at deliveries, and even got to sew up emergency patients in the ER. I was taught by the extern who had the job before me, who was taught by the guy before him, who, we joked, was probably taught by the janitor.

I learned as much about doctors as I did about patients, not all of it good. We had a pair of physicians on the staff who were so bad that if the fifties had been as big on malpractice suits as the eighties, this paunchy Mutt and gangling Jeff of medicine would have spent more time in court than in the hospital.

They were GPs nearing the end of their careers who seemed never to glance at a textbook and who must have put aside their journals as soon as they'd read the medical society news. But thanks to ''grandfather clauses''—covenants in hospital by-laws allowing older doctors to retain their surgical privileges until retirement—they were free to perform any procedures they believed themselves capable of doing. Just about all their uncomplicated appendectomy and herniorrhaphy patients had complications. Yet their trusting patients loved them.

I had become an insider, and I was more than a little shaken by what I saw and heard. I came to understand that there were many kinds of doctors practicing medicine—that their degrees of skill, compassion, integrity, and commitment differed sharply. Making rounds with Dr. Mutt and Dr. Jeff, for example, was a lesson in creative medicine. I never heard them say, ''I'm not sure'' or ''I'll have to check on that.'' What they didn't know—which was considerable—they invented. But their bedside manner was so benevolent, so grandfatherly that their loyal patients would rather have died than doubt them. Some did.

I wasn't medically sophisticated enough to spot all the marginal practitioners. With everyone laughing, joking, and smoking cigars, the monthly ob/gyn department meetings I felt flattered and honored to attend reminded me of college fraternity meetings. I took it for granted, knowing as little as I did about obstetrics, that these men were all skillful and caring. Recently, at a chance reunion with a doctor, now retired, who was a resident at the time of my externship, I learned how inept several of these relaxed and jovial gentlemen actually were.

"A few of them," he said, "were just hanging on. They were still doing deliveries the way they'd learned them forty years earlier, but their patients, who thought they were great guys, loved them and didn't know any better." He shrugged. "Naturally, people then didn't expect the kind of perfect results they do now. So when there were complications because of poor obstetrical judgment or lousy technique —infants with cerebral palsy and worse—the doctor would say it was God's will. And people believed it."

But, of course, medical standards were much laxer then. Peer review didn't exist. Hospital administrators paid more attention to the number of paying patients you brought in than to the outcome obtained. Patients were far less sophisticated and media-educated. Magazines cleared everything about medicine with the AMA before publication. Lawsuits were so rare that some doctors didn't even carry malpractice insurance. And since there were no requirements for continuing education, a doctor who chose to do so could practice medicine well into the 1950s at the same level at which he'd learned it at the turn of the century. That sort of thing can't happen today. Thank heavens!

On the morning of my graduation, as I passed through the portals of Weiscotten Hall for the last time as a medical student, I looked up at the legend that spanned the columned entrance of the medical school's main building. I didn't need to read it; I had memorized it on my first day: "Dedicated to all those of scientific mind and investigative spirit who purpose to serve humanity."

I had started by very nearly flunking out. Now, near the top of my class, with my whole family watching, I was about to recite the Hippocratic oath and be awarded my M.D. That legend and that oath were what these tough four years had been about. During the next thirty years I would sometimes lose my way, but I would never entirely forget their message.

Leaves from an Ob/Gyn's Journal

It is Saturday night in the emergency room at Philadelphia General Hospital and action is nonstop. I've seen it all on TV: Sirens split the night air. A police ambulance stretchers in a gunshot victim. A short-skirted prostitute with a minor stab wound waits her turn, a bloody hotel towel pressed against her hand. A comatose accident victim is wheeled into an examination cubicle, shirt torn, hair and face painted crimson, frightened wife hovering over him.

Overworked interns, triaging the most critical needs first, shout orders to overworked nurses:

"Get an IV started here!" a voice calls from behind a curtain.

"Phone the OR," commands another intern. "Tell them a patient with a bullet in his chest is on the way up. Type and cross-match six units of blood stat."

"I *must* have your address," snaps an irritable admissions clerk.

It is the second night of my ER rotation and I'm getting the hang of it. "Give this drunk a Blockley cocktail and let him sleep it off," I tell a nurse. "Yes, doctor," she responds. Being called that still surprises me. I always think they mean someone else.

"Could you look in on the woman in the last cubicle?" she adds. "She's experiencing intense abdominal pain." Judging from the moaning and groaning at other end of the ER, it's a major experience. "Help me, doctor," she cries when I push aside the curtain. "It hurts real bad. Oh, do something . . . please!"

Her hair is damp and black on the white sheet, her round double-chinned face contorted with pain. I realize that I must make a rapid diagnosis. A lot of other people need help. But the Dx—diagnosis—for abdominal pain can be notoriously elusive. I hope I won't screw up in my haste.

I reach down to take my patient's pulse. It's a reasonably normal 85. "How long have you had this pain?" I ask. She is too distraught to answer. I pull down the sheet and see an expansive abdomen. Palpating it, I find a huge midline mass. What sort of tumor is this? I ask myself. To my patient, I say, "Relax —everything's going to be fine." But I am apprehensive.

I note the sheet beneath her hips is stained with a bloody discharge, and lift her legs to try to determine the source of the bleeding before calling for a surgical resident.

"Oh, Lord!" cries the patient. "Lord, help me!" She gives a mighty grunt and I see a mass of wet black hair protruding from her vagina. Even my untrained eyes recognize that this "tumor" is about to deliver. "Push," I order, as I position myself between her legs. "Push!"

2

Opening in Philadelphia

THERE IT WAS: "Henry M. Eisenberg, M.D.," embroidered on the breast pocket of each of the four heavily starched white uniforms. I riffled them like a winning poker hand and smiled gratefully at the lady behind the Philadelphia General Hospital laundry supply counter. She just nodded and went on to the next guy. Clearly it was just another set of white coats to her, but to me the uniforms proclaimed that I was a real M.D. at last. At the graduation ceremony in Syracuse a month before, the medical school dean had pumped my hand and congratulated me. But the rolled cylinder he handed me had been only a piece of ivory tower parchment. Now, clad in a white coat with my name on it, I *felt* like a doctor. And no one who passed me in PGH's endless corridors could have any doubt about it.

Those corridors seemed to go on for miles—thanks to the innumerable annexes and add-ons bricked onto the original Blockley building over the century or more of its existence. So that we and the patients who depended on us might survive, we quickly developed the fine art of walking at a run. But scurrying from point A to point Z, I often thought how sensible it would be for the administrator to issue interns not only well-starched uniforms but well-oiled roller skates as well.

PGH was almost as much a museum as it was a hospital.

Other hospitals had automated equipment for processing X-rays; at PGH, a direct descendant of the Philadelphia Alms House of 1731, technicians still processed them by hand. Obstetrical litters with crude wooden safety boards on their sides had not changed one whit from the time when the swollen women they transported had pulled up at the hospital entrance in horse-drawn buggies. Ancient chairs that would have looked at home in the city dump lined the corridors. Patients, dilapidated as the furniture, mostly poor and black, mostly elderly, shuffled or rolled slowly along in an endless two-way traffic stream. Nothing was new except each year's crop of interns.

It was certainly not state-of-the-art facilities that attracted medical school graduates from all over the country to PGH. I, like so many others, had made it my first choice because it had a unique reputation as "an interns' hospital." Residents supervised us, but interns enjoyed primary responsibility for patient care. That meant an opportunity to get right into the thick of the battle: immediate hands-on medicine. And that was something any medical school graduate would have gladly traded an arm for, if he didn't need it to take blood pressures. The other appealing thing about PGH was that it offered one of the best rotating internships in the country. Your year was divided so that you got a shot at playing doctor on practically every service in the hospital—internal medicine, infectious diseases, pathology, general surgery, gynecology, obstetrics, even the ER, where I delivered my first baby unassisted and unprepared.

The decaying surroundings, rather than depressing us, heightened the challenge and strengthened our resolve to serve. In an odd way, because the hospital was so much the same as when Sir William Osler strode through its wards in the 1880s making rounds even as we did now, the absence of change gave us a time-warped connection with that master nineteenth-century diagnostician that might otherwise not have existed. We identified with this George Washington cum stethoscope, whose penetrating eyes and dark Celtic features, softened by an underlying sense of mirth, stared down at us from walls everywhere. We saw, as he had seen, the sick, exhausted, impoverished, and fearful. They sat by the hundreds in vast dreary bus terminal-like waiting rooms, waiting, endlessly it seemed, for their turns in the free clinics. They were hopeless. We would give them hope.

Everywhere to inspire us there were memories of those who, like Osler, had preceded us. Every department had its ghosts and legends. In X-ray, we heard tales—true or not we didn't know—about the first chief, who had been exposed to so much radiation before it was known to be harmful that he wore bandages on every finger to hide the rotted flesh. We were assured that the antiquated cameras PGH technicians used weren't his original equipment, but they sure looked like it. Amazingly, they still turned out passably readable images. We could, at any rate, tell the patient who needed antibiotics for her congested lungs from the one who required a cast for his compound fracture.

Even the morgue had its share of historical romance. When we rotated there for our month of pathology service, it recalled the pathologists who had hunched over different cadavers but very possibly looked through the same microscopes to describe and publish early papers on the morbid anatomy of classic diseases, like cirrhosis of the liver or chronic kidney disease. So for us to be there a century later in the same rooms making the discoveries fresh for ourselves was amazing and enthralling.

Buoyed by the drama in our surroundings, we gave our all. Miracles of human spirit and medical valor were enacted daily, confounding the poverty that permeated both the place and its patients. There were 120 interns scattered through the huge hospital. Our working "days" were thirty-six hours long. When one group fell exhausted into its narrow beds, another phalanx took its place. It was grueling, straining our bodies and testing our endurance to the limit. But we were young and strong and resilient. For me, it was a year of intense sustained excitement of a kind I never experienced before or since.

We groused about the long hours on the wards that kept us from our beds. But we equally begrudged the time in bed that kept us from our patients. We were exhausted most of the time; but after all the years of studying diseases, to be able at last to diagnose and treat them in living people, to be able to hear—after working on a "hopeless" case with IVs and blood all night—a faint "Good morning, doctor," which meant we'd pulled it off, was intoxicating and wonderful. How could we ask for more?

In our rare off-duty hours, we lived well and were treated royally in a classic-columned granite building with the words

"Interns Home" over the entrance. Private rooms. Great meals. All we could eat. But this was training, education, apprenticeship—so minimum wage legislation could be studiously ignored. For eighty hours a week, we were paid fifty dollars a month. If we had actually worked only eighty hours, that princely sum would have amounted to something like fifteen cents an hour. In fact, any week in which we clocked less than a hundred hours on the wards felt as though we were on vacation. But that was okay. There wasn't one of us who wouldn't have contentedly worked without any pay at all.

In the exhilaration of it all, I didn't give much thought to how the patients felt about being at the mercy of unseasoned interns. Looking back, I doubt that they thought of themselves as our guinea pigs. Our embroidered shirt pockets, identifying us as M.D.s, eased any misgivings they may have felt. But it probably would not have been unfair to require us to wear labels reading, "The surgeon general has determined that this doctor may be hazardous to your health."

We were treating the lowest socioeconomic group in Philadelphia in pre-Medicare and Medicaid days, when there was a wide gap between the health care the poor received and that obtained by those who could afford to pay—an even wider gap than there is today. I suppose our patients knew this was the best they could get. And because it was service with sympathy and a smile (we appreciated having patients as much as they appreciated the free care), they seemed satisfied and pleased. Few ever questioned or complained.

There was much to complain about. The surgeons were generally residents. Some were excellent—well-qualified guys who'd been there five years, had handled stabbings, gunshot wounds, peritonitis and delayed treatment, poor tissue and poorer nutrition, the worst possible surgical risks, yet pulled the victims through with intense care and around-the-clock dedication. One of these was Dr. George Grimball, a Southerner with a thick drawl and droll sense of humor. No matter what the case, no matter how complicated the disease or how debilitated the patient, George could come up with a neat surgical solution. We beginners were impressed by this brash, improvisationally brilliant senior surgical resident whose big, competent hands seemed able to repair or rebuild anything—to redesign hopelessly diseased intestinal tracts as a skilled plumber would a failed waterpipe system. At PGH, Grimball was a man who inspired confidence: the Mister Goodwrench of the body business.

Other residents, however, were less experienced and didn't always know the best techniques or have the best supervision. We, the even less experienced interns, learned by assisting and, when something was clearly beyond us, by watching. When we pleaded for the opportunity to do more, Grimball cheerfully reminded us: "A chance to operate is a chance to mutilate."

I understood what he meant when I watched residents learning to do vaginal hysterectomies, a complex procedure that results in considerable blood loss if the surgeon's technique is imperfect. Among beginners, it usually was, and women often bled incessantly. Fortunately, the OR nurses were adroit veterans with more experience than the young doctors they served. They knew who was good, who was green, and when they needed to have plenty of extra blood on standby for transfusions. A pretty student X-ray tech confided that when called to shoot a film in an OR where a resident was doing a vaginal hysterectomy, she always donned hip boots first.

One resident, universally acknowledged to be the least likely to succeed, stubbornly attempted to develop a special expertise in doing infertility X-rays. As often as possible, whether they needed hysterosalpingograms or not, he had patients wheeled to the X-ray department for the procedure. Slipping a tiny cannula through the cervix into the uterus to introduce the contrast dye was a simple task only for an expert, and this resident easily qualified as inexpert. But he was not about to admit to the lissome young student X-ray techs who worked there that he didn't know what he was doing. So the scenario was always the same. He fumbled and swore. He groped and cursed. Then, with his patient writhing in agony on the table, he proclaimed aloud that this patient, too, had abnormal anatomy. "Gee-zus," he invariably declared, "no wonder I'm having so much trouble. This woman's cervix is obstructed!"

I had always been in awe of medical authority figures, but it was at PGH that the sharp distinctions within the medical hierarchy, in which the physician reigned supreme at the pinnacle, became clear. We interns were wide-eyed schoolboys in white coats, respected by patients as M.D.s, Nurses too, genuflected—at least to our faces. We, in turn, gave obeisance to the junior residents, who were subordinate to the senior residents, who were rungs below attending physicians.

A couple of times a week, as part of the teaching process, whichever local attending was serving as chief of service during that period led morning rounds. It always fascinated me to see that the residents listened as raptly to every word he said as we, in turn, did to theirs. Increasingly, I yearned to be at the top of this totem pole.

When my internship began, I was pretty sure how I would get there—by becoming an internist. Throughout medical school, the intellectual challenge of diagnosing someone's illness on the basis of his or her presenting complaints and symptoms—solving people puzzles—was where all the excitement was for me. I resolved to become an encyclopedia of arcane medical information: to know every syndrome that ever existed, all the signs and symptoms of every human illness. I spent a lot of time memorizing the pages of Cecil and Loeb's *Textbook of Medicine,* and it paid off. I was acknowledged as an astute diagnostician, and took pride in being able to spout on demand the signs and symptoms of whatever condition was under discussion.

But at Philadelphia General, diagnosis was almost irrelevant. So many patients came in on their last legs, with failing hearts, failing lungs, failing kidneys, that figuring out what was wrong wasn't enough to save them. This was before organ transplants, cardiac catheterizations, bypass surgery, and all the other wonders and dramatic developments of the last twenty-five years. We earnestly mixed pharmaceutical cocktails of diuretics and digitalis to relieve symptoms temporarily and keep our patients alive a few days or weeks longer. For a short time that was exciting and challenging, but it lost its fascination when I saw patient after patient whom I had diagnosed correctly wheeled down to the morgue with my sage chart notes taped to the sheets that covered them.

It all seemed so hopeless—much too grim a life for me to want to be a part of it. I saw that what I had done was not nearly so satisfying as the results that surgeons were getting. They saw the anatomical problem and repaired or excised it in a matter of hours. The patient was swiftly restored to health. After my early experiences in anatomy class, I had never thought of myself as a potential candidate for the American

College of Surgeons, but now I began to think it was time to reconsider.

I got some minor surgical experience—and a little bit of everything else—in my emergency room rotation. It was hectic and fascinating. But in those days, the ERs were staffed by interns and residents, and the specialty of "emergency medicine" didn't even exist, so this rotation didn't figure at all in my thinking about the future.

Meanwhile, there was the infectious diseases rotation: in the TB ward. It was, in theory, exciting to work in the very ward where Osler had treated tuberculosis patients. But there was constant anxiety over whether one of those tiny tubercle bacilli, coughed up in bloody sputum, was going to find its way into my lungs. I wondered if Osler had died of TB. I wore a mask a lot, washed my hands a lot, and every time I coughed I wanted to run for an X-ray.

My next service was pathology, where we did a lot of autopsies on the freshly cooled bodies of people I'd previously taken care of in medicine. It was interesting. It was educational. But it was also depressing. It was definitely not where I wanted to spend the rest of my professional life.

I thought briefly about research, about finding cures for the ills that had cut these people down. But I remembered my experiences in the lab as an undergrad. Things were constantly blowing up, apparatus collapsing, vapors and clouds of smoke filling the room. I was always burning myself on a hot flask or a Bunsen burner. An explosion in organic chemistry left a burn on ROTC trousers I could not afford to replace. (Fortunately it wasn't visible under the jacket.) With both pathology and investigative medicine ruled out, I looked forward with great anticipation to my next rotation: obstetrics and gynecology.

My first of two months was to be spent on the happy service: obstetrics. Its mysteries and miracles were not entirely new to me. There was that surprise package only a few weeks earlier on my emergency room rotation from the woman with "abdominal pains," and back in medical school, one of the requirements for graduation was the obligation of presiding over three or more deliveries during senior year. After three weeks, when my first baby had not yet presented itself, I had become concerned. I assiduously cultivated several maternity floor nurses, imploring them to call me first if anything came up.

I was on the tenth floor of Syracuse's Memorial Hospital when the phone call finally came. "Hank," my friend the ob nurse said, "there's an opportunity for a delivery at Crouse-Irving. It's a third child, so there isn't much time. If you hurry, you can do it."

Only a busy street separated the two downtown hospitals, but I knew Memorial's elevators took forever. So I grabbed my coat and ran down the ten flights of stairs two at a time. Dodging honking cars and trucks, I dashed across the street, raced up the stairwell to the labor and delivery area on the second floor, and arrived breathlessly in the delivery room just as a small dark patch of hair appeared, framed by the mother's vulva. "There's no time to scrub," called my nurse friend. "She's already crowning." I donned gown and gloves and eagerly took my place at the foot of the table in time to see the nurse easing a dark, squashed head streaked with blood out of the enlarging vagina.

"Ready to take over, doctor?" she asked. I nodded. My heart was pounding and my head light from a combination of exertion and excitement, but somehow I managed to maneuver first one shoulder, then the next through the opening of the birth canal. Then, suddenly, with one great contraction, the rest of the baby shot out into my unprepared hands. Somehow I held on to the slippery little thing and passed it on to the nurse for suctioning. Its bluish body took on a healthy pink color as it took its first breath. I took a deep breath myself. I'd delivered a baby! Well, part of it. But I got credit for a whole baby.

I didn't have to wait three weeks at busy PGH. The residents craved the challenges of complications. They didn't want to be bothered with normal deliveries, so these usually fell to the interns. Working thirty-six hours on and twelve off, we saw a lot of action. We enjoyed it. But that wasn't always true of our patients. PGH was a general dumping ground for the indigent —and these were the poorest of the poor. Most had had no prenatal care, and many had gone to the emergency room of the nearest hospital when they felt the first pains coming on. But those institutions rarely had beds for charity patients, so these frightened women were shipped across town to us by ambulance.

We heard a lot of screaming and carrying on from women coming in for their ninth or tenth babies—a lot of "Lordie, Lordie, help me. Can't you do something for me?" But like the

Hebrew women in the Bible, these women were "lively," and their babies would come out no matter how unskilled we were. If there were complications, we called on a resident to uncomplicate them.

Before we did our first episiotomies—the minor surgical procedure to widen the vaginal outlet, permit an easier birth, and avoid tearing—there was a brief demonstration by one of the residents. We watched respectfully as he made a neat incision when the baby crowned, then repaired the tissue after the birth of the placenta. It looked easy. But when we were on our own, I wished that I'd watched my mother more carefully when she sewed up the Thanksgiving turkey. The resident's stitching had been flawless, like the invisible mending of a fine tailor; mine was lumpy, uneven, overlapping. It would take a couple of dozen episiotomies before my stitching approached that smooth, professional look. But Mother Nature was on our side. No matter how unworkmanlike our sewing, by the six-week postpartum visit, the incisions had healed with no noticeable differences.

After I'd watched a few cesarean sections, a scalpel was placed in my hand by the resident. "Here, doctor," he said casually. "You open." The only time I'd ever taken a knife to a human being was in anatomy class. But that human being had been dead. For a moment, I thought the resident was crazy. But the scalpel felt right in my hand. I took a deep breath and applied knife to flesh. Nothing happened. "Press down," instructed the resident. I did, and the flesh parted smoothly, in a line as marvelously and surprisingly straight as if I'd used a ruler. Blood quickly filled the wound and I felt a momentary flash of queasiness. But it passed when I realized how easy it had been.

Sometimes I opened c-sections, sometimes I closed. Often I tied knots. They were good knots. They didn't slip. We all had plenty of practice. On nights off, or on ob duty waiting for babies to deliver, we sat around the doctors' lounge talking to friends and unconsciously—as our mothers unconsciously knitted mufflers and sweaters while talking to their friends —tied knots. Evidence of our industry was visible on every available chair arm, table leg, and doorknob. The lounge looked like the site of a Boy Scout convention and merit-badge competition, with knotted loops and ends of catgut and suture material everywhere. Nobody ever cut them off.

Assisting at D & Cs, hysterectomies, and c-sections, and surviving my initial alarm at the sight of blood flowing swiftly into our incisions, I began to realize that in time I could learn to be a more than competent surgeon. I resolved that I would be the best I could be—that I would not forget George Grimball's admonition, that my chances to operate would not be chances to mutilate.

The ob/gyn rotation gave me the opportunity, too, for my favorite challenge: diagnosis. None of my betters, the residents, had paid any heed to a woman in the prenatal clinic who complained of excessive belching and heartburn. Those were such common symptoms in pregnancy that they gave her antacids and sent her on her way. It occurred to me that she might have a hiatus hernia. I listened carefully with my stethoscope one morning and heard bowel sounds in the chest—an indication that the stomach might have been displaced up into the thorax, or chest cavity.

I called the resident. "I think this woman has a hiatus hernia," I said. His eyes widened as he listened. "You may be right," he said. "I'll get a film." No one worried about X-rays during pregnancy in those days, and the film confirmed my diagnosis. The whole department congratulated me. I began to see that the skill I had most enjoyed practicing in internal medicine had a place in ob/gyn as well. It helped me to make my decision.

So did the chief of service, a prominent Main Line specialist with a flourishing private ob/gyn practice in the community, who was serving his turn in this charity hospital. I was always struck by the way this man, handsomely attired in a different suit each day, came in from his affluent outside world of power and success to our environment of poverty, misery, and death.

Watching him make rounds was an awesome experience. He knew so much, seemed never to waver in his opinions, clearly expected no criticism or opposition. We rotating interns trailed after him in abject admiration. I began to see that I wanted to be this god in the three-piece suit.

I liked the specialty he had chosen. Even though there was a lot of screaming and crying in the maternity ward, there was a general atmosphere of happiness about the place. Mothers left in three or four days—walking out with babies in their arms, not carried out feet first. There was a sense of joy in obstetrics that appealed to me. There was a lot of talk among my fellow

interns about highly remunerative specialties with ophthalmol-
ogists' hours. That didn't interest me at all. But the challenge
and excitement of obstetrics and gynecology did. Now I knew
what kind of doctor I wanted to be.

That wasn't the only decision I was to make at PGH. If I was
unsure about my ability as a physician when I had arrived at its
hallowed halls, I was even more unsure about my prowess with
females. The interns of X-rated doctor movies, steamy medical
novels, and TV soap mythology who appeared to be 50 percent
healer and 50 percent lover were unknown to me. I experienced my first affair (though not my first "experience") in my
last year of medical school. At age twenty-four, some would
say it was about time. But, for the most part, after eight years
hunched over my textbooks, like most of my fellow doctors-in-
progress I was totally inept with any woman who didn't have a
thermometer in her mouth and a chart at the foot of her bed.

Philadelphia General Hospital may have been huge and
bewildering to a young intern, but its size had one advantage:
There was no shortage of attractive student nurses and other
young lovelies in training. One in particular caught my eye in
the hospital cafeteria, where, to compensate for our lack of
sleep, we did a lot of eating. She was petite, bright-eyed, and
dark-haired, with a dimpled smile and an animated way of
talking that appealed to me at first sight. Since I was privy to
the hospital dress code, the green apron over her white uniform
told me that she was a student X-ray technician. I decided to
ask her out. But she was always surrounded by a laughing
coterie of friends, and I shrank from risking the embarrassment
of public rejection.

My chance came the day she emerged from the radiation
clinic as I got off an elevator. I fell in step with her and,
eloquence failing, said only, "My name's Hank Eisenberg.
I've seen you around, and I'd love to take you out this Saturday
night." She smiled. There were those dimples again, only
close up this time. I smiled. She said, "Sure, okay. I'd like
that." My happy heart slowed down long enough for me to
note her name and phone number on a wooden tongue
depressor, the only convenient writing surface I could find in
my pockets. I walked away thinking, "Hmm, maybe pretty
girls do like doctors."

One acceptance and I thought I was Dr. Casanova. When,

the next day, I met Lynn, a dazzlingly blonde X-ray tech, I immediately asked her out, forgetting that I'd already promised that weekend night to another. She bounced cheerfully into the X-ray lab to report to her best friend, "I met this intern, Hank Eisenberg, and he asked me out this Saturday night."

I was a cad and a bounder. But all Madalyn said to her best friend was, "Oh, *that* jerk!"

Every day, I went down to X-ray, picked up Lynn and had lunch with her. When I had a spare moment, I stopped in at X-ray to talk to her, and I took her out every free evening. I didn't entirely forget Madalyn. Once she came into the X-ray clinic while I was doing a difficult procedure that inexperienced interns like me often bungled—a thoracentesis, an extraction of biopsy material from a patient with fluid in the sac covering the lungs, for analysis for possible chest cancer. Her presence inspired me to do my best, and I drew the fluid easily and with little pain for the patient. Everybody cheered, but the only applause I heard was Madalyn's.

New Year's Eve, I dated Lynn for the last time. She seemed less than enthusiastic about being taken to a midnight movie —which, at holiday prices was pushing the outer limits of my intern's stipend. And she was unsympathetic about the way I felt: listless and altogether awful. I resolved not to date her anymore—a decision she had probably already reached independently herself. Next day, a house officer identified my problem: a case of mono that put me in the infirmary.

After a lonely week in bed, I opened my eyes one afternoon to find Madalyn standing over me, smiling down like an angel. "I just came by to say hello," she said, "and to hope you get better soon." One of the first things I did when I did get back on my feet was to phone and ask for that long-delayed date. We bellywhopped downhill on a borrowed sled on a crisp cold January night in a park not far from her home. The evening ended in disaster, she thought, when we rolled over into a snowbank and her mascara ran all over her face. But I'd had a wonderful time and one date led to another. And another. When I asked her out to a nightclub (I wasn't about to repeat the mistake I'd made with Lynn), she insisted that a movie would do just fine. When I asked her out to dinner, she wouldn't hear of it, suggesting dinner at her house instead.

Dr. Armstrong's teas now seemed less daunting than dinner with Madalyn's parents. So I asked if my friend Larry could come, too. Halfway through the meal, I realized I'd made a terrible mistake. Outgoing and exuberant Larry dominated the dinner table conversation, and I sat there feeling like a flea on a dinosaur. Maybe, I thought with growing misery, he's the one who should be dating Madalyn. Her parents seem to really like him. But why shouldn't they? He's the life of the dinner party.

Mrs. Richman's roast beef was delicious, but I didn't have much appetite. Larry (who had a girlfriend of his own and really wasn't trying to take mine away) departed diplomatically shortly after dinner. On the living room couch, where the Richmans, also diplomatically, left us alone, I told Madalyn how badly I felt, sitting there at the table like a clam with laryngitis, and how her parents probably thought I was a big nothing.

"Hank," she said, "you don't have to talk to impress me. I'm already impressed. I know who you are, and you don't have to change for me to like you. And if I like you, my parents will, too." Other than my mother, I'd never met anybody who was willing to accept me totally the way I was and who could gently quell my concealed fears that maybe the way I was wasn't okay. That night I told Madalyn that I loved her. Not long afterward I had the chance to prove it.

During my month in internal medicine, a patient came into my ward all of whose vital signs pointed to the fact that he was slipping inexorably into heart failure. I tried everything I knew—which was not a lot—but my attempts to pull him out of it were in vain. When a repeat EKG late that night showed a disturbing downward trend, I panicked and paged the senior resident.

"Bring your chart to the switchboard room and I'll take a look at it," he said with what I felt was unseemly nonchalance. A patient could be dying. I hurried into the dim corridor, where dead light bulbs complemented the eerie silence. It was so different from the brightly illuminated, high energy pace by day. PGH after midnight seemed to me what the world might be like if all life was ending. There were muted sounds only. Here a nurse stealthily checked rooms with a flashlight. There a weary-eyed intern, stethoscope dangling, newly roused from slumber by yet another emergency, sleepwalked past in scuffed loafers. (White bucks looked better, but you had to lace them, and that cost you an extra moment's rest. A moment here. A moment there. It added up.)

But that night, as I rounded a corner, I imagined I heard raucous laughter ahead. I dismissed it; maybe it floated up from the street below. But when I turned into the switchboard room, I found a party going on. The senior resident waved a half-empty fifth of vodka at me, pointed to a stack of urine specimen cups, and yelled, "Have one, kid." I gulped and nodded No, visions of my patient turning blue waiting for help dancing in my head. The switchboard operator held out her cup for another round and gave me a lopsided smile. It was then that I realized Madalyn was there, whooping and laughing with them. I knew she wasn't a drinker and I was pretty sure she hadn't been imbibing. Though I wasn't happy to see her involved in this scene, that was the least of my worries at the moment. I could see in a flash that Ted was of no use at all, so I hurried back to do the best I could to keep my patient alive until morning rounds and the arrival of someone competent.

That afternoon, I learned that after I left the switchboard, Ted and the operator had played Airport and, imitating the control tower, they had somehow yanked the main plug, with the result that the hospital was isolated from the rest of the world for a period of five to ten minutes. That wasn't long, but long enough so that it was reported by incensed callers to the phone company, which dispatched an emergency crew to the scene.

When their report was brought to the attention of the hospital administrator the next day, it triggered an immediate investigation. At lunch in the cafeteria, Madalyn was distraught. "What am I going to do?" she asked despondently. "I'm supposed to testify at the hearing. I don't want to see Ted get hurt. If he's dropped from the program, that could finish his medical career. Should I lie to protect him? I could say the plug coming out was just an accident."

"Just tell the truth," I advised, "and whatever happens happens."

At the hearing, she told the truth and nothing but the truth. The switchboard operator was fired. The resident was censured. And Madalyn was commended for her honesty. Her dean told her later that it was a good thing she'd been forthcoming. If she hadn't, her connection with the episode would have resulted in her being dismissed from the program.

I felt good that I had given her the right advice. Given the honesty of my mother and the integrity of my father (who, when he lost his Cinderella Slipper factory during the Depression, chose to spend the next dozen years paying back every creditor 100 cents on the dollar), I didn't really have much choice.

After that, I spent every spare moment with Madalyn, something made easier when I needed an X-ray for a patient at night and she was on duty with no one else around. In the dark room, our relationship developed even faster than the film. But there were those who did not approve. Next day, a sign appeared: NO INTERNS ALLOWED IN DARK ROOM.

After we became engaged, I invited her to slip quietly into my room in the interns' quarters. Now it was the house mother who did not approve, and another sign appeared: X-RAY TECHNICIANS NOT PERMITTED IN INTERNS' ROOMS. When we persisted, Madalyn was reported to the head of her department and threatened with dismissal.

As the end of the year approached, I applied to several ob/gyn residency programs, with Yale my first choice. From anxious and uncertain, I had become cocky and confident. I had graduated near the top of my class at Syracuse, been initiated there into Alpha Omega Alpha, the honorary medical society, and I had done well at PGH. Why shouldn't Yale accept me? I knew what I was going to be. I knew whom I was going to marry. And I'd decided to go first class. Instead of going on the small stipend university medical center programs offered, I would enlist in the air force and continue my studies on a captain's pay. I could afford to get married, have a nice car, and maybe even start a family.

The acceptance letter from Yale completed my wall-to-wall mural of a bright and enviable future for Hank and Madalyn. When I finished my training at Yale, I'd serve whatever number of years the air force required in exchange for paying my way. The next six or seven years were going to be challenging and altogether wonderful.

Dr. Eisenberg had it all figured out.

Leaves from an Ob/Gyn's Journal

Mrs. Gordon has been in hard labor for more than ten hours. I've been at her side most of that time. Her baby is a breech, buttocks rather than head down, which makes for a riskier childbirth. She is the first obstetrical patient I've followed from her first visit. I have strong protective and proprietary feelings toward this young woman and for the baby in her uterus who will soon see the sunlight for the first time.

As my patient relaxes momentarily between contractions, I locate the strong, steady fetal heartbeat just above the navel, the usual location in a breech. It has moved down slightly, indicating progress. "Your baby's doing fine," I assure my patient. "How are you doing?"

She smiles weakly, then winces as another contraction begins. "They're barely a minute apart, doctor," reports the nurse, one eye on her watch, the other on our patient.

"Better take a look," I say, donning a rubber glove and inserting my hand into the birth canal. My hand gropes for the cervix. It is completely retracted and all five fingers fit into the opening.

"She's fully dilated," I tell the nurse. "Let's get her to the delivery room."

I scrub and tie a mask around my mouth and nose. The adrenaline is flowing. I've done very few breeches, and this one is special because she's "my" patient.

A nurse is strapping Mrs. Gordon's arms and placing her feet in stirrups when a third-year resident, a man who has made life miserable for me in many small ways, suddenly bounds through the swinging doors and takes his place at my side.

"Move over," he says crisply, "I'm delivering this patient."

For a moment I am stunned by the injustice of his claim. "Like hell you are," I snap, leaping to the defense of my turf. "I'm perfectly capable of handling this delivery. I've followed Mrs. Gordon for seven months and she's my patient. Out of my way—don't tell *me* you're going to deliver her!"

"As a senior resident, I can tell you anything I like."

Outrage envelops me. As a second-year resident, I've taken about all the pushing around I can handle. I pick up the first object that comes to hand and brandish it menacingly. Fortunately for both of us, it is not a scalpel.

"Get the hell out of here," I say tensely, "or I'll blow you away with this."

The threat of a forceps blow does not alarm him, but the armor-clad fury in my voice does. He retreats, but not before casting a you'll-be-sorry look in my direction. My heart pounds angrily against the wall of my chest. I breathe deeply, trying to regain my cool. The consequences be damned! I tell myself. This is my patient and I'm going to deliver her if it's the last thing I do at Yale-New Haven.

I position myself between Mrs. Gordon's feet and tell the nurse firmly, "We're ready to go." I notice the look of dismay on her face, as though she has concluded that ob/gyn residencies this year at Yale-New Haven have been parceled out to the local mafia. My patient, when I finally take notice of her, appears equally alarmed.

Without comment, I proceed with the delivery. What is important is a good outcome. The emotional reactions of mothers and nurses are irrelevant. They play no part in the resident training curriculum.

3

In Residence

To a young resident, making rounds with the formidable Dr. John Morris, Yale's (and perhaps the nation's) leading gynecological surgeon, was an honor and privilege akin to carrying George Washington's sword or Arnold Palmer's golf bag. He was meticulous in his surgery and insisted that follow-up care be rendered no less scrupulously. While other doctors' patients were rounded twice a day, we visited Dr. Morris's three or four times.

Morris had operated for cancer of the cervix on a patient he'd known for many years. Her surgery was long, complicated, and partly because of a puzzling and persistent anemia, resulted in an extended hospital stay of more than a month. Making rounds with Dr. Morris one morning in company with his usual honor guard of a half-dozen residents, I noticed that his patient's skin was pale and parchmentlike, that her eyes were puffy, and her reflexes sluggish. A bell rang.

"Dr. Morris," I ventured hesitantly, "I think the patient looks as though she's hypothyroid. Maybe that's why she's anemic."

Morris shot me a so-you-think-you-know-everything glance, then looked at his patient. "Hmm," he said after a moment, "she does look somewhat hypothyroid. Good obser-

37

vation, Eisenberg. Order some tests and let's find out.''

The tests came back showing extremely low thyroid function, and my diagnostic triumph was complete. I savored it to the fullest, and it's well that I did. It was to be one of my rare moments of glory at Yale.

The Yale experience began for me with that happy feeling that comes with knowing you are one of a chosen few. An acceptance letter signed by the chairman of the ob/gyn department, the internationally renowned Dr. C. Lee Buxton, reinforced my growing self-confidence. My high opinion of myself was further fortified by the manner in which I entered New Haven in triumph—in a spanking new white Ford convertible I could not possibly have acquired on a resident's stipend of $150 monthly, but which was eminently affordable on my captain's salary of $12,000 a year.

The welcome party for new residents at Dr. Buxton's country home at first heightened my high spirits. Outside of the movies, I had never seen anything like this great house surrounded by mighty oaks, vast lawns, and baronial gardens. Dr. Buxton indicated the pond. ''You'll have to come back in winter,'' he told us. ''When it's frozen, John and I and some of the staff play hockey here. It's great fun!'' I forbore from confessing that the only hockey I had ever played was on 171st Street, just off the Grand Concourse, with manhole covers serving as goals, and the puck constantly disappearing beneath parked cars.

I grew self-conscious. It was as though they, in their buttondown shirts, carefully accessorized rep ties, New Haven brogues, and tweed jackets from J. Press were grown-up preppies, and I, in my sale suit from Alexander's, wore the label, ''Kid from the Bronx.'' Trembling in the presence of the Yale-New Haven mighty, I felt my confidence draining slowly away. Who was I? Nobody. Who were they? American aristocrats. Nationally-known medical figures whose ancestors probably were ship's doctors on the *Mayflower* while mine came over in steerage two centuries later.

No Jivaro warrior ever did a more efficient job of shrinking heads than my chiefs at Yale. The ego-reduction process began the first day on the job. At PGH, we had been treated like physicians, capable of full-fledged patient care. In New Haven time didn't stand still, it retreated. We were students again, with our every move monitored. The scut work we were assigned—taking blood pressures, recording the orders of our supervisors on patient charts, checking IVs—was demoralizing. Instead of climbing new medical heights, I found myself bogged down in arid valleys long since explored. I understood that I was one of the lucky few to be at this illustrious institution, but I didn't feel lucky. Sometimes I wished I'd chosen a program less prestigious and more participatory.

In retrospect, my resentment was clearly just foolish youthful impatience—the young stag resenting the old bucks. Even then, I knew I was tail to the comet of some of the best people in my field, and that exposure to the way they did things would affect me positively all of my professional life. These were men so committed, so compulsive about doing things right, that it was ingrained in us not to overlook any single item, no matter how small it was or trivial it seemed, no matter how tired we were.

"Sports Shirt" Davis—there were two Dr. Davises, but informal Southerner and obstetrics department chief C.D. Davis stood out among all our professors as the only one who never wore a tie or jacket—had a tremendous impact on us, supervising daily rounds and making us aware of every tiny detail of patient care before, during, and after the labor room. We learned much, too, from Dr. Mastroianni, Yale's authority on infertility surgery. There were experts in every area from endocrinology to oncology, long before subspecialties in ob/gyn were officially created.

Yale was miles ahead in prepared childbirth. Perhaps it was the influence of its school of nurse-midwifery. In any case, in the mid-fifties, years before the long arm of Lamaze reached across the Atlantic from France, Yale-New Haven had begun to incorporate into its program some of the work of Dr. Grantly Dick-Read, author of *Childbirth Without Fear*. The idea was to take a new look at how labor could be assisted without medication or anesthesia, through greater patient education and participation and the support of midwives. It was my first inkling that the patient could have a greater role than that of an infant container with her arms and legs in restraints (so she couldn't thrash about, inadvertently damaging her obstetrician or interfering with his work).

But I wasn't ready for "childbirth without fear"—for my patients or for myself. I was too intent on learning the mechanics of my trade—accurate diagnosis, the use of forceps, doing c-sections and hysterectomies—to think about my patients' fears. And I had some fears of my own. I was afraid, I think, to open myself up to the uncertainties of the new and possibly faddish, and felt safer with the tried and true. I think I was even more afraid of the idea of giving patients a greater role in childbirth. I wasn't confident enough of my own role to be willing to share it. But somewhere in my subconscious I registered the information and the experience of a brand of humanism that I hadn't seen anywhere else and that I wasn't to see or experience again for a long long time.

What I was registering consciously was a rather different image of how a doctor treated others, modeled primarily after the way we ourselves were treated. As residents, ours was not to question orders but to execute them. Our chiefs were like college basketball coaches. You did it their way, or you were off the team. Or you were publicly tongue-lashed (there were always nurses to witness the humbling of the haughty) and humiliated.

Dr. Thompson was a champion at this. He had trained at Harvard under Joe Meggs, then the premier gyn surgeon in the country, and had himself developed techniques for radical surgery that were copied worldwide. Like a Marine drill sergeant, he was very likely only doing unto us what had been done to him, and with good reason. Charged with the responsibility for training residents properly, he wanted no one leaving Yale slipshod, imperfect, and telling the world, "I trained under Thompson." Probably a good part of it was an act, because underneath I think he was a pussycat, a man who really cared—about both his patients and his residents. But I was much too cowed to realize it then.

He had the stern handsome look of a movie star and the lean trim build and square jaw of a boxer. Drop your guard, and he hit hard. If, assisting in surgery, you handed him an instrument incorrectly—or, heaven forbid, the wrong instrument—he hurled it across the room. (The point was dramatically made, the impression deep. You were more careful next time.) The surgical knots you cut were either "Too long!" or "Too short!" If you tried helpfully to hold the end of his suture, he'd fume because your shaking fingers might pull it out of his needle. (And heaven help you if it pulled out more than once.) If you moved too quickly, he railed at you for being impetuous.

If you moved too slowly, he invoked all the curses of Hippocrates upon you for being tentative.

You had to subject yourself to this harrowing experience in order to learn from the master. But it was good for us. It was even better for our patients.

In my own case, that was not immediately noticeable. There have been enough tears shed by doctor-authors chronicling their sleepless residencies so that the condition of semicoma in which the resident patrols hospital floors is no news to anyone. That this state of extended insomnia does little to improve patient care or the young doctor's powers of observation no resident would dispute, least of all me.

Traditional therapy for uterine cancer in the late fifties, still common in many places, was to pack the diseased organ with a dozen radium applicator rods. The patient was then transported to X-ray, where the position of the applicators was checked, and the after-loaded devices activated to administer carefully measured dosages of radium. After the prescribed number of hours, the rods were withdrawn and placed in a lead container by the resident on duty.

It fell to me to tumble out of bed one 3 A.M. to perform this routine procedure. When my alarm sounded, I slipped wearily into my loafers (remember: quick off, quick on) and elevatored groggily to the postsurgical floor. The orders read, "Remove 12 rods." I did just that, counting and then carefully recounting, after which I staggered back to bed—fully dressed in anticipation of the next alarum.

That morning, the chief resident flogged me in front of the nursing staff, leaving them—and me—with the impression that young Dr. Eisenberg was a blithering, bumbling fool.

I only thought I'd taken out everything. I had removed the dozen applicator rods. But a radium pellet had detached from one of them, and I had failed to notice its absence. My feelings of guilt—that I had overexposed the unfortunate patient's uterus to six unnecessary hours of radiation—were the worst of it. As it turned out, my error didn't make a lot of difference. Six months later, her cancer killed her.

But to train is to learn, and—as I continually rediscovered —to learn is to make mistakes. In my second year, with the chief resident supervising, I was assigned to do a hysterectomy, one of my first. Things went splendidly. Or so I thought. On opening, I found a fibroid uterus, with one of the tumors located on the lower portion of the uterus, next to where the uterine artery connects to supply it with blood. Clamping the artery without injuring the ureter—which is in perilously close proximity at that point—is tricky business.

The experienced surgeon incises the tumor and shells it out, allowing it to collapse. Only then does he clamp the vessel. But this was a trick I had not yet learned. So I simply clamped the uterine artery, inadvertently clamping the ureter as well. When I sutured the blood vessel, my needle injured the ureter, but somehow neither I nor my supervisor realized that. In fact, when I closed, removed my mask, and toweled away the sweat, he congratulated me for a job well done. I sang euphorically in the shower afterward, delighted by the unexpected praise and extraordinarily pleased with myself for getting through a hysterectomy that would have been a difficult procedure for a skilled and far more experienced surgeon.

But I participated in my patient's daily post-op care, and its course was not smooth. Her abdomen was distended and her urinary output very low. Seeing that rapidly ballooning belly and reading the nurses' notes on diminished urine output, I experienced a sinking feeling. It was pretty clear that one of the most dreaded complications of gyn surgery had resulted from my inexperience. And worse: had injured my patient.

The nature of the injury quickly became apparent when diagnostic tests showed internal leakage of urine from the damaged ureter. In theory, though the ghost surgeon, I was not the responsible party. Officially, the chief resident and the staff men above him were the patient's doctors. I was only the apprentice learning his craft. But my hand had inflicted the injury. And, though our patient had not the faintest notion that while she was under the anesthesia I had performed her surgery, each time I made rounds I felt as though her eyes followed me accusingly from bed to bed.

I felt terrible every time I saw her and every time I thought about her for the remainder of my residency. To this day, it's one of a handful of painfully glaring mistakes in my training years that won't go away. It comes back not to haunt but to warn me every time I pick up a knife.

Then, I had not yet come to the more mature recognition that to participate in life means to risk losing, that to expect never to have a bad outcome in medicine is like expecting to be a major league pitcher who never loses a game or a basketball player who never misses the basket. Less than a month later, a senior attending gynecologist in our hospital inflicted the identical ureteral injury on a private patient during a hysterectomy. That didn't make me feel any better about the injury to my own patient, but it helped to know that even a man with thirty years' experience could make the same mistake. Still, when eventually my patient lost a kidney as a result of that slip of my needle, I lost for a time something absolutely essential to a young surgeon: self-confidence.

I got over it. I had to. And, as success followed surgical success, and I assisted at one flawless delivery after another, the flame of my self-esteem, like a candle that had guttered and almost flickered out, burned brightly once more. So brightly that it ended by fatally scorching my career at Yale-New Haven—in the delivery room with Mrs. Gordon.

Though the subsequent delivery went well and both mother and baby were fine, my less than meek response to the senior man's command did not go without reprisal. It figured, I'm sure, in the conspicuous omission of my name from the list of those residents chosen to stay for a third year in the prestigious Yale program. But there were undoubtedly other factors.

One of those looming largest, I suspect, was my effort to be—as much as my resident's schedule permitted—a family man. I had become one in my first September there, when I used my week's vacation to marry Madalyn and take her away from it all on a quick honeymoon. What followed was the development of a relationship between two people who loved one other, but who because of youth and inexperience were unable to empathize with each other's problems and provide urgently needed support.

My problems began almost immediately. Madalyn had taken a job as an X-ray technician at Yale-New Haven Hospital and, to my chagrin, immediately undertook to revamp the department. First, through a simple test (pinning an X-ray film on the inside wall of the adjacent room), she discovered that the wall separating the radiology department office from the adjoining X-ray room was not, as everyone had assumed, lead-lined and leak-free. In fact, doctors were being zapped with X-rays all day long. Perhaps Madalyn's supervisors should have been grateful, but they didn't take kindly to this recently certified snip of an X-ray tech pointing out the obvious to them.

Next, Madalyn targeted their technique for determining

radiation dosages. "It's silly," she told me. "They just look at someone and say, 'Well, he's fat, so we'll give him a little more.' Or, 'She's thin, so we'll give her a little less.' I think I'll make a chart like the ones they have at PGH. They should appreciate that." She did, but they didn't. Nor did they take kindly to her offer to rig a stirrup apparatus, similar to one used at Philadelphia General, to support patients' legs comfortably so they wouldn't move during the X-raying of hips.

Looking back, I can admire Madalyn's courage and initiative. At the time, it embarrassed me. I didn't have the nerve to speak up when I saw something I thought could be improved, and I wished Madalyn didn't either. Every time I had to go to X-ray or bumped into a radiologist, I flinched. But then —fortuitously, I thought—Madalyn became so fed up with the brick wall she was banging her pretty head against that she quit. "Henry," she declared, "I think it's time for us to have a baby."

Madalyn's transformation to full-time homemaker increased her problems, and mine. My bride's expectations were of a glamorous life as a doctor's wife. Reality swiftly altered them. She had a doctor for a husband, all right, but now that we didn't meet at the hospital, she hardly ever saw him. My resident's contract called for spending every other night on duty, so I was away for thirty-six hours straight three and four times a week. On alternating easy days, I'd leave our garden apartment at 6 A.M. for rounds and return at seven or eight that evening.

Madalyn soon realized these "nights off" were not something to look forward to. I've never seen medical documentation on someone drowning in a bowl of soup, but I risked that awful fate a time or two dozing off into my chicken noodle. My chief contributions to dinner conversation were "Yup," "Nope," or "Sorry, what did you say?" In response to the question that young wives used to ask, "What should I do?" (about a broken washing machine, a tire with a slow leak, a letter from the landlord), she heard only, "You take care of it. I'm too tired." Mostly I made it through the meal on automatic pilot, and then fell asleep in a living room easy-chair with the green journal *Obstetrics and Gynecology* in my lap while Madalyn disconsolately watched TV.

She was unhappy, and I could hardly blame her. While I paid the price of admission to the medical fraternity in unremitting work and long hours, she paid as young doctors' wives traditionally have: in frustration and loneliness. She was in a strange city, with a husband she didn't know all that well, separated from her parents for the first time in her life. Some wives found comfort in each other, but Madalyn was not admitted to their circle. "The first question they ask," she said wryly, "is, 'What college did you go to?' The second is, 'Do you play bridge?'" Madalyn hadn't gone to college, couldn't play bridge, and no one offered to teach her.

The only thing that seemed easy that year was conceiving. Madalyn became pregnant on the first try. But morning-and-afternoon sickness and the haywire hormones of pregnancy multiplied the heavy emotional load she carried. Marriage to an obstetrician, it's reasonable to assume, would be a godsend in such a situation. But I had little patience when Madalyn moaned about her nausea or wept about her hemorrhoids. My training was in the big things: life, death, acute hemorrhage, miscarriage. Those were what concerned me—with Madalyn as well as with my patients. Petty little pregnancy complaints (little to me, who'd never had to endure them) seemed just part of the price of motherhood. They weren't lifethreatening and I paid them little heed.

My approach to my pregnant wife (again, as with my patients) was clinical. I could remind her to take her nausea pills, but I couldn't deal with her emotional outbursts. Naturally, they became more frequent. "When I was little," she sobbed one particularly tearful night, "my parents worked and left me alone a lot. I thought getting married meant always having company. But you're always leaving me alone."

That hurt, because I loved Madalyn. But medicine and our future tugged me in the opposite direction. The program, I knew, preferred residents who remained coolly and clinically detached from their wives. What I was expected to do was firmly lay down the law: "Look, honey, the sooner you understand the system here the better. For the next four years, my first allegiance is to Yale-New Haven and my work; nothing else matters. Period."

I felt torn between my obligations to that work and my obligations to my wife. Madalyn was only nineteen and not mature enough to understand the demands training made on me; I was older, but not much more mature. Secretly, I resented her demands almost as much as she did my long absences. I remembered how I'd been able to give my all to Yale during the first three months of my residency, before we'd married. I had enjoyed that.

Still, Madalyn's tears made me feel like a heel. She was so young, so lonely, and so pregnant. There had to be a middle ground. Not realizing that this could cost me dearly, I tried to placate her. One way was to spend more time in her company. If Dr. Mohammed couldn't go to the mountain, why shouldn't his little mountain come to Dr. Mohammed?

Patients were supposed to be seen frequently. Mine were. But wives were not supposed to be seen. Mine wasn't—we hoped. But I'm sure she was smelled. A couple of nights a week, she slipped clandestinely into my little room at the hospital, a couple of minute steaks and an electric frying pan stowed with gown and bathrobe in her oversized shoulder bag. Soon the heady aroma of steak and onions wafted down the corridor and—if I wasn't suddenly called away on an emergency—our banquet began.

To avoid the necessity of crossing the hall to the ladies' room (and to maintain our naive illusion that no one knew she was there, which would have been possible only if a sudden olfactory epidemic had wiped out the sense of smell of everyone in the hospital), Madalyn brought along empty mayonnaise jars to dispose of liquid waste products considerably increased by her delicate condition. We laughed a lot, and in the morning, playing Medieval England, opened the window and poured the stuff out onto a flat roof below. Had they known, municipal health department officials would not have been pleased, but I was at the time more interested in not displeasing Dr. Buxton.

In this pre-ultrasound era, a reassuring peek at our baby was impossible. So every now and then, particularly when a Down's or hydrocephalic baby was born on the service, I found myself taking it personally. I said nothing to Madalyn. Instead I forced myself to recall how statistically rare such tragedies were, and pushed the fears from my mind.

When Madalyn went into labor, my concern switched to her. Progress seemed so interminably slow that I was afraid she wouldn't be able to deliver normally. When, toward evening, Dr. Buxton finally arrived in the labor room to check her out himself, he ordered Pitocin to strengthen the contractions. Finally, she was taken to the delivery room, and I was banished to the fathers' waiting room. I was accustomed to using spare moments gainfully, so I'd come armed with the latest ob journals. But now, at last, my Puritan ethic failed. All I could do was pace the floor.

About an hour later, Dr. Buxton came out to congratulate me and report that mother and baby were doing well. It was, when at last I saw them, not as well as I'd have liked. Madalyn had lost a lot of blood and her face, framed by a tangle of dark brown hair, seemed wan and worn. The baby boy she'd delivered looked terrible from the battering he'd taken during childbirth. His head was pointed, his face swollen and bruised. His Apgar* was only a 6 on a scale of 10, which told me his condition was merely so-so. Eventually, he would be a beautiful healthy baby and a fine young man.

But, both during and after the delivery, I resented my chief's treating me as a disinterested bystander, with no special consideration either as one of his residents or as the husband of his patient. I felt he didn't adequately inform me of what was happening during the labor and delivery, or of why he permitted Madalyn to suffer so long without deciding to do a cesarean section. But he was my role model, and I went on to do unto others as he had done to me: ignoring fathers, explaining little of the childbirth drama (or anything else) to either parent.

We named our son Jordan. I say "our" son, but at the time he was more Madalyn's child than mine. I had difficulty connecting to the squalling infant who arrived in one room while I waited in another. There seemed to be a certain symbolism there, because from that moment on, I was the jealous outsider. The one prop I had to lean on, the only person I could confide in, and brag and lament to, was busy feeding this other little person, singing and cooing to him when he cried, washing mountains of his diapers and clothing when he slept. Now I saw that there was a price to fatherhood as well.

Jordan changed Madalyn's life, too. She could no longer overnight at the hospital. A prisoner of our baby, she was lonelier than ever. And she was exhausted from her very difficult delivery and heavy loss of blood. I administered iron shots prescribed by Dr. Buxton, but they hurt so much that,

---

*The Apgar, developed by Dr. Virginia Apgar, is the test by which a newborn's appearance (color), pulse, grimace (reflex irritability), activity (muscle tone), and respiration are measured. The evaluation is made at one minute after birth and then again at five minutes. A 10 is a perfect score.

lonely as she was, there must have been times when she wished
I wouldn't come home—at least not with my hypodermic
needle.

Things were bound to get better. "Just hang in there a little
longer," I said, reassuringly. "Next year, I'll be home fifty
percent more. It'll be a picnic. I'll only have to work every
third night and weekend."

Wrong again. One of our residents resigned, and I was
informed that I would have to continue to work one night on
and one off for the second year as well. Madalyn held out as
long as she could and then, in tears, begged me to talk to Dr.
Buxton. "It's just not fair," she said. "Not when you have a
young wife and a new baby. He'll see that. And he'll do
something about it."

I wasn't at all sure he would. Nevertheless, I reluctantly
asked for an appointment with Dr. Buxton, and the following
afternoon entered his handsome oak-panelled office. I rever-
ently crossed the oriental rug and settled stiffly into an antique
chair opposite my chief, already regretting the request I was
about to make. I knew what his answer would be. Logistically,
it was too late to get a "Yale quality" replacement to fill in for
the unexpectedly departed resident. Or anyone else for that
matter. The status was quo. The rest of us would simply have
to work harder and keep a stiff upper lip.

Our conversation was brief. I knew that arguing that I
needed more time for my family wouldn't wash, so I put my
case in a businesslike way I reasoned he might find more
appropriate: that a contract was a solemn instrument and
obligation. I said that we residents had contracted to be on duty
every third night in the second year. Just because another
resident had dropped out didn't seem reason enough to breach
that contract. Filling the space was the program's problem, not
ours. I added that I was disappointed about not having enough
time to spend with my wife and child and hoped that something
could be done to ease that situation. But I didn't make that a
major issue.

I wasn't comfortable, and though I tried to hide it, indignation may have colored my voice. Dr. Buxton, as was his way,
showed no emotion at all. He was polite but unyielding. The
nature of the program, he said, was that you did what was
required. What was required in this emergency was to work
every other night. That was unfortunate, but it was the way it
was and had to be.

After that, I detected a certain coolness toward me on Dr. Buxton's part. I sensed that he saw me as someone who couldn't be counted on to be a 100 percent team player. It was as though, if you're not willing to work every other night, what kind of doctor are you? And beyond that, I had complained. If you complain to the coach, you don't stay on the team very long. More than a little (though I tried to hide that, too), I was irritated by Madalyn's pushing me to act in a way that was much more her style than mine. She tended to damn the torpedoes and plunge full speed ahead. I preferred to avoid confrontation. Now, sidestepping it again, I avoided revealing my feelings to her.

I didn't dwell on the incident. The year progressed, and so did my skills. I worked hard—every other night and weekend —and complained no more. I was always tired, but it was a good feeling. I learned something new every day or got better at doing something I'd learned the day before. I felt I'd earned my place in the program and expected to continue in it for a third year.

Near the end of my second year, I entered Dr. Buxton's office again, this time at his request. I wasn't worried. Undoubtedly he wanted to discuss my teaching responsibilities for the following year. In my third year, for the first time, I would do more than just learn. I would supervise new residents as well.

Dr. Buxton invited me to be seated, then got right to the point. "As you have been aware from the beginning," he said, "not everyone who starts the program here at Yale remains for the full four years."

I swallowed hard. My mind raced ahead. There could be only one reason for a department chairman to begin a conversation this way. Despair and rage welled up in me. He couldn't do this. I wanted to stay on at Yale. I deserved to stay. The benefits won by hard work, the increased responsibility and the opportunity to be a star in the system that were so long in coming, were about to be mine.

"It's not that we don't think you're a good resident or a good doctor," he said. "It's just that we have a system, and not everyone can stay on. I'm sorry to tell you that we're going to have to find another position for you elsewhere, because we're not going to have a place available for you here next year."

"Who are you going to put in my slot?" I asked, attempting

unsuccessfully to be a good loser, to keep the sharp edge of resentment out of my voice. "Four of us started two years ago. Taylor dropped out. Johnson's decided to go into research. That leaves only one other guy and myself. Who's going to do all the work?"

"We're bringing in a man who's had three years of a surgical residency here, but wants to transfer to our program. He's coming in as a third-year resident."

This is a terrible injustice, I thought. I've worked hard for the right to stay. How can you bring in a ringer to usurp my rightful place? But at that stage in my life, I hadn't courage or maturity enough to be able to express my feelings honestly to an authority figure like Dr. Buxton. It would have been like correcting the spelling on the Ten Commandments.

"We can get you a good position," he continued. "I have friends in excellent hospital programs. I'll make some calls." He mentioned the chairman of an ob/gyn department in the Bronx, and I grew angrier still. A nowhere program in a nowhere hospital. No thanks, I said to myself. You don't want me? I don't need you. I'll find my own job. Aloud I said only, "Thank you, Dr. Buxton. I'll look for a position elsewhere and let you know what happens." I wasn't smiling as I left. He wasn't either.

Much later, I realized how difficult it must have been for him to break that kind of news. I hadn't had any really close contact with him, but he'd known me for two years, and undoubtedly sensed what a crushing blow he'd dealt my ego. What he couldn't know was that it was one of those episodes that reawoke the Lone Ranger in me. I didn't need to be patronized. I would survive.

Nor could he know that the not so subtle message he—and the entire Yale-New Haven system—had been trying to get across to me during the past two years, that work comes first, family second, had finally sunk in. My conflict with The System was one reason for my dismissal, and deep in my subconscious a core of resentment was building up. My family wouldn't interfere with my work again for a long time. I was totally unaware of it, and I know it wasn't Dr. Buxton's intention, but the dehumanizing process intrinsic in doctor training now had young Dr. Eisenberg firmly in its grip.

The crack in my ego healed quickly. It took me about ten minutes to rationalize my premature separation from Yale as a good thing after all. Certainly if I planned to teach, to go into academic medicine, more time there would be valuable. But two years around these top-notch people was long enough to pick up the essentials necessary for private ob/gyn practice. And there was something else. Even as I walked down the corridor to phone Madalyn, I realized that if I stayed on at Yale two more years, I'd have to put in an extra two years in the service to repay the air force. Now, with only one more year of residency, instead of five years before I could go into private practice after residency, it would be only four.

Madalyn wasn't delighted about being uprooted again so soon, but the hope of getting into practice a year earlier made the change in plans easier to accept. "Anyway," she said, laughing, "with a wife like me and a little luck, you could be the next surgeon general." I mailed a letter to the office of the U.S. Air Force Surgeon General reporting that I would not be staying on at Yale and wondering what, if any, opportunities existed to complete my residency in the military. My answer came back promptly. Suitably impressed with my Yale credentials, a staff officer asked if I would accept an assignment as chief ob/gyn resident at the William Beaumont Army Hospital in El Paso.

I sent my Yes by return mail, and orders were cut for me to go to Texas. I went to one of New Haven's snappiest tailors, had myself measured for a splendid air force dress uniform, threw back my shoulders, lifted my chin, had my Ford convertible simonized, said goodbye all around, and, wife and son beside me, proudly left Yale. Chief resident of an army hospital, I thought. Not bad. I'd been pushed around long enough. Now it was my turn to push.

But I still felt bruised. And before we drove off into the sunset, I confided my hurt and anger to Walter Hermann, an attending physician who'd been particularly kind to me. I thanked him for his friendship, something I said I'd felt had been in short supply there. He congratulated me on my chief residency. Then, placing his hand around my shoulder, he added (and if I learned nothing else at Yale, this advice would have been worth the price of admission): "Hank, don't keep searching for a place with perfect people in it—in this world, it doesn't exist. Wherever you go, you're going to find the same people with different names. Just learn to live with them."

PART TWO

BECOMING GOD

Leaves from an Ob/Gyn's Journal

Operating room silence envelops me as I make the abdominal incision on the airman's wife before me on the table. This is not my first hysterectomy, but I am neither so experienced nor so jaded that I consider it routine. I know that, as in most surgical procedures, the odds are with the patient and the operating team. But I know, too, that there is always an element of risk: that this could be the patient for whom the odds turn and the bells toll.

I go about my work, aided by an assistant across the table who sponges away the blood that suddenly floods the length of my scalpel's fine incision. I slice through the fascia, my assistant blotting and sponging as more blood seeps into the wound. Blood vessels beneath the skin are clamped and tied off. When the peritoneal cavity is exposed, I push the bladder and intestines out of the way. Having the patient enter the OR clean—fasting and after an enema—makes that easier. Effective anesthesia helps, too. It relaxes muscles and prevents organs from rebounding to crowd my fingers as I work in the limited peritoneal space.

I reach for the uterus, the object of this exploration. It is swollen, filled with large fibroid tumors, most likely benign but causing my patient bleeding and discomfort. The anesthesiologist reports an uneven heart rate pattern. I am concerned, but not alarmed. Though this is unusual, it's not necessarily an ominous sign. It may be only an eccentric reaction to one of the drugs or agents being administered. The anesthesiologist is trained to correct the problem.

But a few moments later, I hear panic in his voice. "My God!" he exclaims. "Her heart's stopped. We've got a cardiac arrest!"

Momentarily, it is as though my heart, too, has stopped.

An experienced surgeon is at my side observing. Wasting not a moment, the hospital's assistant chief of ob/gyn slices open my patient's rib cage and, up to our wrists in blood, we take turns massaging her heart. We work feverishly with increasing despair for almost an hour. My arms ache. Sweat soaks through my scrub suit. I feel depressed, frustrated, sad. What went wrong? Why did this have to happen to her? To me? I am haunted by the knowledge that even if we succeed in the resuscitation, there is a strong possibility that this terribly invasive open-chest procedure will subject her to the complications of severe and perhaps fatal infection.

Finally, my colleague, breathing hard, wipes his hands on his gown and says quietly, "It's no good. She's gone."

I look numbly down at the bloody cavity and the heart that will never throb again, and up at the pale face too soon at peace. I continue to stare as the nurse pulls a sheet over the body. This shrouded motionless figure is the first patient I've lost on the operating table. I pray she will be the last. I am devastated by feelings of helplessness and loss. Logically, I know it isn't my fault, not anybody's fault, that it was probably an unexpected reaction to the anesthesia. Still there is a part of me that feels guilty. I know she needed the surgery. But if I hadn't recommended it in the first place, she might be out somewhere playing tennis.

This, I realize as I slip off my mask, is the part of being a doctor you don't think about when you dream of training to be one. But, my surgical greens stained with her blood, it now falls to me to go out and tell a waiting husband that the operating team I led has let his wife die. I turn to the senior attending. "I've never done this before," I say lamely. "Would you . . .?"

"Go with you? Of course."

The sergeant listens quietly to what I say. His face whitens as I speak. He has been in the air force since World War II and death is not new to him, but this is his wife. Still, he does not forget he is a career non-com and I wear the silver bars of a captain. He does not interrupt.

When I finish, he looks momentarily confused, unbelieving. "How is that possible?" he asks pleadingly, as though I can change the bad news to good. "You told us a few weeks ago that it was a simple operation."

"It is," I say helplessly. "Most of the time."

4

Doing It Air Force Style

I LEARNED A lot about obstetrics and gynecology at Yale. I would learn a lot about patients—much of it misleading—in the air force.

My sudden enthusiasm for doing my third year as a military residency was more than smiling through while supping on sour grapes. There are no snapshots of fierce ancestors crossing the Rubicon with Caesar or the Alps with Hannibal in the Eisenberg family album. But buried somewhere deep within me throbbed a patriotic/military vein. I had thoroughly enjoyed ROTC in college, worked my way up to cadet major, and without firing a shot in anger, was named a Distinguished Military Graduate. My backup plan if I didn't make it into medical school had been simple. I would accept a regular commission, sign on for flight school, and enjoy a career of high adventure as an air force jet pilot.

Now I could experience the excitement of both worlds, in a colorful part of the country I'd seen only in westerns. And a military residency offered another unusual experience for a powerless youngest child: I found myself with a captain's disciplinary power over subordinates, and the power of a chief resident over doctors junior to me. I discovered something that surprised me: I liked being the boss. Power was exhilarating.

Giving orders instead of taking them was intoxicating. The uniform and being saluted at every turn added to the aura.

If you think of God as having awesome power—the omnipotent and unchallengeable kind that Drs. Buxton and Morris and their associates had wielded at Yale, controlling everything and everybody and having the last word about how it's going to be—then suddenly I had acquired the lightning. It was a great feeling.

I'd coveted their omnipotence. And, as part of the process of surviving as a resident, I'd borrowed their style, their way of getting things done. Gradually, as this mentor modeling process progressed, I became their personality clone. Dealing firmly with junior residents, nurses, and assistants who were caring for patients of mine and didn't measure up could be justified in the name of quality patient care. I saw myself as carrying the torch of meticulous modern medicine, of passing on the tradition. But I was only a partial clone. What I didn't realize was that those doctors I admired most had another quality vital to a good physician and teacher: compassion. I now understand that Dr. Thompson and many of the others had exercised ruthless compassion—something even a parent often finds necessary. There were, I'm sure in retrospect, times when, like the doctors I admired least, I displayed the ruthlessness without the compassion.

Part of the authoritarian wall I surrounded myself with was defensive. At Yale-New Haven, as the kid from the Bronx, I had been socially on the fringe. Here in Texas, I was totally outside the pale, a stranger in a strange land—a presumably liberal and effete Ivy Leaguer, different culturally and religiously. I'd appeared out of nowhere (very much, it occurs to me now, like the third-year surgical resident who took my place in New Haven) to usurp the coveted leadership position so patiently and eagerly anticipated by the senior residents who'd preceded me. I was an outsider who hadn't come up through the ranks, and I acted—in their view—as though I knew it all.

Well, I certainly knew more than they did. And I didn't like the way they did some things. I expected them to stay with patients and listen to fetal heartbeats with more regularity; to take blood pressures more often than they did. I wanted them to call me if they had any kind of complication, so I'd be aware of it immediately. That must have hurt. These were things they'd done without supervision in the past. I'd already forgotten how resentful I'd been when "demoted" to scut work at Yale after running my own show at PGH. Or maybe I remembered and deep down felt that what was good for the goose would be even better for the goslings.

I learned one morning how much I was disliked by at least one of my residents when I opened my locker and found a box with a bright red ribbon tied around it. I was puzzled. Hmm, I thought, someone whose baby I delivered must have given it to one of the nurses for me. But inside I found a bottle of Pitocin with a crude skull and crossbones painted on it, along with an unsigned note suggesting that I take the first train north. The meaning of the note and the skull was obvious, but why the Pitocin? I concluded that it was because, unlike previous chief residents, I'd ordered it used when warranted to augment labor, as I had been taught at Yale.

I was stunned. If anyone had asked me how I ran the department, I'd have replied that I was reasonable, prudent, and sensitive. But it's never easy to evaluate yourself. Clearly, I came off to at least one staff member as an arrogant sonovabitch.

In retrospect, I can see that my military experience—and a random look at any page of the current *Directory of Medical Specialties* indicates that probably one out of every two or three doctors has been in the military—was probably important in shaping the way I reacted to patients, too. Typically, they were like the sergeant who, when I told him his wife had died on my operating table, listened politely instead of reacting with anger, as though his wife had died in the line of duty. In the presence of officers, and particularly doctors, military personnel were compliant, even submissive. Eager to please, they were prepared to accept orders or recommendations without question. Doctors could do no wrong no matter what wrong they did. The military wives I treated were, like their military husbands, obedient and accepting.

Military people and their dependents are no longer as passive as once they were—which accounts in part, I'm sure, for the recent indictment of the chief vascular surgeon at a U.S. military hospital on charges of incompetent heart surgery. Service families, like everybody else, are demanding quality medical care and accountability on the part of those who dispense it. But at Beaumont Army Hospital and in the four years at my next military post, they didn't demand, they were commanded.

True, civilian patients were also passive in those days, but not so uniformly. My military patients inadvertently trained me to see all patients as accepting and docile, as objects rather than subjects of my medical ministrations. It was at that point, I suspect, that I began to think of myself as, if not God, then his special ambassador to womankind on earth. It was here that I learned to play His omnipotent surrogate, creator of life around whom the sun, the stars, and ailing and pregnant women revolved.

Not to mention Madalyn and my family. I worked all day in an atmosphere of military precision. I expected a similar level of efficiency at home. Dinner on the table, the house clean, and Jordan ready for bed (I felt I needed *some* peace and quiet) when I returned home from the hospital.

I didn't need a bugler blowing reveille to get me out of bed every morning. I rose and donned my uniform, eager for the day ahead, with visions of making the Beaumont Army Hospital ob unit every bit as good as Yale-New Haven's. That meant putting in long hours reorganizing the system, improving my skills and those of my subordinates. It didn't occur to me that the longer my days and nights away from home, the lonelier Madalyn's task of fending for herself and our family —no easy task in yet another strange city, thousands of miles from the support of family and friends. If I had thought about it, I'd probably have concluded that, well, she was an air force wife now, and that's what air force wives did.

Base housing was roomy and comfortable. But it wasn't air conditioned, and every time the sand blew down the hillock behind our quarters, it ended up *in* them. The first sandstorm, with our windows left optimistically open to catch any stray cooling night breeze, we awoke with dunes in the living room and grit in our teeth. "Oh," Madalyn moaned when she looked around us, "what did you join: the French Foreign Legion?" She was not amused by my suggestion that a wall-to-wall sand box would keep Jordan occupied. And after that, hot or not, we kept the windows permanently shut and Madalyn stuffed tissues in the cracks, which limited the damage to a dusting of sand rather than the entire Sahara.

Madalyn battled unaccustomed sand and heat, single-handedly unpacked all our worldly furniture and goods, and had to cope with housework, diapers, an active toddler, her second pregnancy, and finally a newborn, our second son,

Bruce—all with neither significant help nor sympathy from me. One night, which she, not surprisingly, remembers better than I do, she came down with a case of food poisoning. She sat on the bathroom floor with her head in the bowl all night—and I slept soundly through the entire event, impervious to her cries for aid and comfort. I didn't think I was being unkind, just pragmatic. I had early surgery, for which a steady hand was required. I knew that, other than hand-holding, there was nothing I could do to help. And what good would that do her deranged digestive tract? A lot, I realize now, but didn't understand then.

Madalyn was slowly building up a full head of steam, but it would be years before she blew up, in a ski lodge in Vermont. Meanwhile, she sealed off her resentments as I had bottled up mine. Perhaps guiltily aware that releasing them in New Haven had led to my early retirement from the residency program, she was determined to be the good soldier, the stoic air force wife now. If she had broached her bruised feelings, would it have changed me at that point? I don't know. I do know that I would never intentionally have hurt her. But I saw and heard no evil, only glorious days and nights of deliveries and surgery ahead.

When our year in Texas ended and my next assignment began, I was no longer an ob/gyn resident. I was, at last, an ob/gyn. My only disappointment at Dover (Delaware) Air Force Base was the absence of opportunity to soar into the high blue yonder. I might as well have been an infantryman. The command dispatched flights daily to Europe, Asia, and Africa, but I was too busy to go.

I didn't have to be. We delivered about seventy-five babies a month on the base, but the first thing the officer I relieved as chief of ob/gyn told me was that if we were ever overworked, the thing to do was give a bunch of the wives coupons and send them into town to be delivered by local physicians. No way, I thought. Why should the government incur that extra cost? We—myself and sometimes one, sometimes two other base ob/gyns—were being paid to deliver those babies. I was bound and determined that we would.

The hospital commander was pleased that women no longer had to go off base to deliver. And I was fortunate during most of my years at Dover to have eager young ob/gyns on my staff who were as determined as I to take on every case we could get, and, like me, counted every baby we didn't deliver as experience lost. Some, of course, felt otherwise; they hated to work at night. Perversely, the more they hated it, the more I loved it. They were infuriated by my fanaticism: God sayeth, "Thou shalt deliver all babies at the base hospital." End of discussion.

My ascetic philosophy was equally unpopular with the base doctors' wives—my own included—who would have liked to enjoy their husbands' company more often. Madalyn could never figure out why I wanted to work that hard, but neither, in those docile early days, did she dare to openly raise questions like, "Why can't a few wives be delivered in town, so I can see you once in a while?" If, in a weak moment, she hinted at her misery, I didn't hear it. At Yale, I'd learned my lesson the hard way: The dedicated doctor does not let his wife's discontent control his professional decisions.

Nor was I beloved of the obs in town, whose incomes had traditionally been fattened by an overflow of dependents' deliveries from the base. All in all, I was the scourge of Dover. But I *was* loved by airmen's wives, who appreciated not having to bus or drive into town to see their doctors or have their babies.

Birthing that many infants, we handled quite a few complications and an uninterrupted night's sleep was rare. But it was the first solo test of my ob wings, and I loved every minute of it, no matter when, night or day, that minute came. Once, in a rare quiet moment, with the children out for the day with her visiting parents, Madalyn and I, building dream houses in the sky, figured out what our income would have been if this had been my own private practice. At $500 per delivery, plus surgery, it came to a gross of something like $350,000 a year. Of course, working at that intensity would probably have killed me before I could spend it.

Though I was chief of ob/gyn, with several apprentices under me, I still had a lot to learn—a fact I did not care to announce publicly. Sometimes my patients and I were just plain lucky. I did things that, rather than risk a bad result and a malpractice suit, I would now refer to a subspecialist. I managed complex urethral surgery effortlessly. And I performed a successful uterine reunification for a patient who was experiencing repeated late miscarriages.

But not everything came out right. There was, for example, Mrs. Craig. When you do a vaginal hysterectomy, a bladder repair is part of the process. Often the traumatized bladder doesn't empty for a period of time after the surgery. Usually it's functioning again after a week or so, and almost always after three weeks. Mrs. Craig was an alarming exception.

When I checked her out after a week's hospitalization, her bladder still wasn't emptying on its own, so I left in a catheter—a tube in the bladder draining into a collection bag strapped to the inside of the thigh—and told her to come back in a week to have it removed. "After that," I said heartily, "you should be fine."

Mrs. Craig returned in a week. I removed the catheter and said, "I'm sure you'll be okay now. Why don't you go home, relax with a pitcher of lemonade, and come back in three or four hours so I can check you out?"

When Mrs. Craig was ushered into my examining room, it was clear that she was not "fine." Her abdomen bulged as though in midpregnancy. The pitcher of lemonade had entered her bladder, but found no convenient exit. It was up to me to provide it, and, reluctantly, I catheterized Mrs. Craig once again. Patient, sweet, understanding, she submitted without a murmur. "Another week should do it," I said hopefully, and she trundled cheerfully off.

At the appointed time, I removed the catheter. This time my directions were different. "When you go home," I suggested, "drink a bottle of beer. The alcohol will make your bladder contract. Then squat in the shower and let the water run."

She returned in midafternoon, her face noncommittal. "How'd you make out?" I asked apprehensively.

"Not a drop," she replied.

"Not one drop?"

"Nary a one."

I smothered a sigh. "Well," I said, stoically recatheterizing her, "I guess we'll have to go for another week."

That week stretched into another. And another. And still another. My anxiety increased. She, remaining cheerfully optimistic, continued against all odds and good sense to believe in me. The problem had to be her body's fault. After all, I was the doctor, and a captain to boot. How could I not know what I was doing?

As death reminds us of our mortality, seeing Mrs. Craig

continually reminded me of my fallibility. Madalyn and I often encountered her shopping in the post commissary. On the first occasion, summoning reserves of affability and congeniality I did not feel, I greeted her warmly and then asked, "Well, and how are you doing, Mrs. Craig?"

"Just fine, doctor," she replied amiably. She paused thoughtfully, then as my eyes bulged in surprise, hiked up her skirt and pointed at the catheter bag. "The only thing is I get a little chafed down here from the strap." After a few such encounters, whenever my wife and I saw her coming down the aisle, we quickly wheeled our cart about and hurried off in the opposite direction.

Time passed, but water didn't. As I was the chief, I had no one to consult with. Finally, I called the senior gyn surgeon at Andrews Air Force Base and summarized the case, concluding with the question that had troubled me for more than a month: "What do you think I ought to do?"

"Well," he said, "she probably has a borderline problem with the nervous system's control of the bladder, and the surgery changed the angle enough so she's having a hard time urinating. If she doesn't have a severe neurological impairment, she'll probably get over it eventually." There was a long pause before he continued. I could imagine him puffing his pipe speculatively. "Come to think of it, I recall one exceptional case at Walter Reed where the patient never did urinate normally again after the bladder repair. They had to put in a permanent suprapubic cystotomy tube."

"I hope," I said dejectedly, "that this isn't the second case."

"Just stick it out," he said. "No use worrying. It'll probably turn out okay. And—" long pause for pipe puffing "—short of that permanent tube I mentioned, there's nothing else you can do."

Time turned out to be the best healer, and to my relief, Mrs. Craig proved not to be that second case after all. It was another six weeks before I could navigate my cart down a commissary aisle without having to do an abrupt about face. But finally, I removed the catheter for the last time, and Mrs. Craig was able to exuberantly report by phone an hour later, "You did it, doctor! Or rather . . . I did it."

But time was an ally I could not count on to solve all my problems. I was scheduled to operate on an air force wife for a prolapsed uterus and correction of a bladder dysfunction—a difficulty which, since I'd recently been well sensitized by Mrs. Craig, I planned to handle with extreme care. In the examining room, my patient awkwardly blurted out the opinion that her vagina was too large and that she feared she wasn't satisfying her husband during intercourse. "While you're in there," Mrs. Wilson asked shyly, "could you maybe do something about that? Like take a few stitches and sort of tighten everything up?"

I told her that, although most women were too embarrassed to talk about it, the problem of stretching was not uncommon in mothers who, like her, had had several children. I assured her that Old Doc could handle the matter easily. And, when I completed the uterine surgery, I proceeded to carefully cut and snugly suture the mouth of her vagina. When Mrs. Wilson healed, her ardent husband—he'd been a long time between performances—blissfully attempted to enter her. Next morning, I took a furious phone call from him.

"Captain Eisenberg, sir," he said, "what did you use on my wife—some kind of crazy glue? Sir, she is more of a virgin now than she was when we went on our honeymoon. I tried to make love to her for a half hour last night, and in the end I had to give it up as a bad job. Sir, I believe a midget would have a tough time screwing her now. I don't know what you did, sir, but for heaven's sake, can you undo it?" It was clear that, though trying hard to keep in mind that he was talking to a superior officer, the sergeant was not having an easy time saluting my incompetence.

Ordinarily, in our busy shop, appointments were made a week or more in advance, but I saw his wife that afternoon. I noted that her vaginal area was painful. "You seem to have formed a lot of scar tissue," I said. "I think if I cut that away, your problem will go away, too."

I hoped it would, but I was far from certain. I feared that in my zeal to give her a snugger vagina, I had cut off a bit more tissue than necessary. I operated again, removed the scar tissue, made the opening smoother, and waited nervously for the phone to ring. It still looked tight to me, but I hoped for the best.

No such luck. If I'd been a civilian doctor, a malpractice suit would have put me on front pages around the world. Military doctors couldn't be sued, but I hoped the angry non-com wouldn't mug me in the parking lot behind the Officers' Club. Embarrassed and apologetic, I referred my patient to the chief of gyn at Walter Reed. He saw her, did some skillful vaginal skin grafts, and enlarged her vagina. He gave her a dildolike cylinder to wear at night—to stretch the walls and hold them apart so they wouldn't close down or form new scar tissue. Six weeks later, she was happily back in bed with her husband. I was more relieved than disappointed that she never came back to me.

One patient more or less wasn't missed. Running a high volume operation, I was almost always overbooked. With so many unscheduled deliveries at night, so many patients scheduled by day, so few doctors, office hours were like a Willow Run assembly line.

I became accustomed to rushing, to trying to get to the end of that long daily list of names, so that even when I had time, I behaved as though I didn't. With our biomechanisms speeded up, interaction with patients was routinely impatient. We all hurried, sometimes pounding round people into square holes. For the most part, we had to observe with half an eye and listen with half an ear, knowing that another patient, like another streetcar, would be along in another few minutes, and this one, the one to whom we were even now giving our divided attention, would have to be out of the way.

More than my attitude toward patients was being shaped. I was developing a concept of what a doctor is, of who I was. When you have the power and skill to ward off impending death or, as an obstetrician, the special opportunity to bring forth life, it's not hard to see how you could come to consider the man shaving in your mirror a special person deserving of special admiration and respect. The more that grateful patients communicate it, the more this feeling is validated, and the more likely it is that a certain arrogance and self-righteousness will develop. It's possible to lose touch with who you really are and where your power is coming from.

In surgery, you are the center of the operating room universe. You have only to quietly command "Kocher!" and a Kocher clamp is dutifully placed in your right hand. Call for a Heaney, a Kelly, a Metz—and hysterectomy clamp, Kelly clamp, and Metzenbaum scissors obediently appear. (You'll only need ten or twelve, but a tray of dozens of sterilized instruments awaits your pleasure.) Use one briefly, flip it casually aside, and your nurse retrieves it and returns it to her tray. The once meek medical student is suddenly the star of the show. And after a while, he may begin to act the part.

Nurses contributed to this kind of thinking. Not too many years ago, they were taught in training to stand up when a doctor came into a room, to say "sir," to bring him coffee with the right amount of cream and the correct number of sugars. With that kind of veneration, it's no wonder that young physicians would begin to think of themselves as God the King and of hospital protocol as part of the religion. We don't get as much respect from nurses as we once did. Today's nurses are more independent and less worshipful. They don't stand up and click their heels when you enter. But the doctor still gets a goodly measure of deference from them, and even more from his office staff, whose jobs and futures are directly dependent upon him.

Does the royal carpet treatment doctors become accustomed to make them self-confident and self-assured? Frequently, yes. But many of us are notoriously insecure. If you're afraid of people—as all people are to some extent—then the safest way to deal with them is to put on your white coat so that ("shh!) you don't give away your secret. The more insecure you are, the more likely you are to be impatient and intolerant, to use authority as a tool to strip those around you of their dignity, trying to build your own. That white coat becomes a suit of armor—our Superman cape. We put it on and, immediately, we are less vulnerable.

Despite the fact that it was in eastern Delaware, not South Korea, the Dover AFB hospital was not unlike M.A.S.H. Many of the doctors I worked with had been drafted into what they perceived as involuntary servitude. They considered themselves—and were—hot stuff. One had trained at Yale, another at Harvard. They saw the air force command structure as Mickey Mouse and had no desire to be part of it. So they never saluted anyone, whether higher or lower in rank, when they thought they could get away with it. They were nonconformist, too, in matters of uniform, wearing their officers' hats only infrequently, for example, and as a result constantly being stopped by military police.

One doctor occasionally replaced the silver air force medical insignia he was required to wear with something that resembled a pilot's wings from afar. Upon closer examination, it proved to be a woman's legs spread wide in the lithotomy birth position. He and the other officers enjoyed practicing medicine, and that's what they did, ignoring as much as possible the fact that they were practicing in a military setting. Their spirit of anti-establishment levity was so pervasive around the hospital that after a while it enveloped even sober-sided, quasi-militaristic me.

How else can I explain my decision to break every regulation in the book by bringing my dog to the hospital for emergency surgery? It all began when somehow—memory fails me on this point—Prince cut his tail. Maybe he caught it in the screen door. Maybe there was an open dog food can standing around and he wagged too hard welcoming me home from a delivery. In any case, the more he wagged, the more he bled. And since he followed me from room to room as I went in search of a gauze bandage, our little house soon threatened to resemble the killing floor of the Chicago stockyards.

There was a veterinarian on the base, but it was a little late at night to call him. I thought, "Hey, I'm a doctor. I did canine surgery in the medical school physiology lab. Why do I need to bother a vet? I'll just drive Prince down to the hospital and sew him up myself."

I spent so much of my time at the hospital—far more hours there than at home—that I had, in fact, begun to think of it less as government property than as my own. And who was going to be there at midnight anyway? Only a couple of corpsmen, and nothing would suit them more than to participate in a little change-of-pace madness with me.

I led Prince into a little sterile operating room and gave him a calming shot of Nembutal. Five minutes later, he still hadn't relaxed. But I was afraid if I injected any more he'd O.D. Never had a tail wagged a dog quite so vigorously. Anesthetized or not, Prince's wouldn't stop, and with every orbit the walls of the room were spattered with more blood. I called for reinforcements. Finally, with one corpsman holding the dog and a second holding the tail, I managed to put in a few stitches, bandage it, and get the hell out of there. Not, however, before I spent ten minutes wiping the evidence off the walls and ceiling because I was too embarrassed to order the corpsmen to do it.

But it was not a perfect crime. Next day, word of my unscheduled surgery reached the ears of the hospital commander, and I was summoned to his office. "Captain Eisenberg," he demanded peremptorily, "is there any possible way you can explain your suturing your dog's tail in the emergency room? And your splashing blood all over the walls and ceiling? This is not the K-9 Corps, doctor; it is the air force. In this hospital we treat human beings, not our four-footed friends. I would hope that an officer would set a better example." He paused for my reply, but I could think of nothing to say in my defense. My CO was not at all at a loss for words. Picking up where he had left off, he said everything but, "You're a disgrace to the service, and I'm going to see to it that you're court-martialed."

If that was the end of the beginning of my yen for an adventure-packed military career, Madalyn's air force misadventures could be considered the beginning of the end. They began with her first invitation to a tea of the Air Force Hospital Officers' Wives Club—which, it turned out, was a special meeting called by its president, the hospital commander's wife to disband the group. In a fit of pique over what she quite sensibly interpreted as a lack of interest—poor attendance and failure of a majority of the members to pay their dues—she informed the assembled white-gloved ladies that she no longer wished to lead the group and that, in her considered opinion, it should forthwith pass out of existence.

Instead of understanding the colonel's wife's statement as a political grenade lobbed in their midst to awaken the ladies to their sinful behavior (after which they would surely beg her to change her mind and return to their ranks), my naive young wife took the president at her word. Madalyn, who considered the Wives Club a splendid medium for meeting and establishing friendships with other medical families, was disappointed. Innocent of protocol and unaware that the rules of rank and military seniority applied to officers' ladies as well as to the gentlemen themselves, she piped up earnestly after the colonel's wife swept haughtily out of the room: "Why don't we meet without her? I'll call her up tomorrow and tell her that we're going to—unless she wants to change her mind. There's no law that says doctors' wives can't get together if they want to, is there?" There was, of course. An unwritten law. And it wasn't long before Madalyn was made aware of it.

My wife phoned the colonel's wife next morning and gave her, the evidence suggests, instant apoplexy. "I thought our talk went very well," Madalyn told me that night at dinner. "I told her we had this discussion after she left. That we decided we really wanted to continue meeting because the group had been meeting for such a long time and it was such a good way for us to get to know one another. I didn't want to hurt her feelings, so I told her she was welcome back any time." Madalyn looked at me for approval. "Wasn't that brilliant of me?" she asked. "All the wives are really happy about the way I saved the club. We elected new officers and I'm the secretary. I think if I weren't so new I might have been elected president."

I approved. But my boss didn't. When first I met him, the hospital commander had impressed me as friendly, amiable, and mild-mannered—the kind of man who, when you step on his foot, says, "Excuse me." But it was his wife's feet that had been stepped on, and if he was my commanding officer, she was his.

I don't know what she told him. Maybe: "When I'm humiliated, so are you." But I know what he sternly told me: "Captain Eisenberg, you're not the only one in your family who is in the air force. Your wife is, too. She should be told in no uncertain terms that disrespect to a superior officer's wife is no different from disrespect to a superior officer. If you should decide to make the service your career, captain, I've got news for you: Wives can have an important effect on their husbands' careers. You will get absolutely nowhere in this man's air force until your wife understands it and learns to toe the line." The following week, there were new elections. Madalyn was not reelected.

My wife never did learn to toe that line. She never understood the air force, and the air force brass never understood her. The next battle in what became a four-year war came over water rights. There was a shortage that summer, and the base commander issued an order that lawns would be watered only on even days of the week. Madalyn stepped out our front door one day after I'd gone off to work and noticed that our grass was dying. "My," she thought, "I'd better do something about that before I get Henry in trouble again."

She connected the garden hose and began to water the lawn. Of course, the base commander chose that moment to drive by. Offended by this open breach of discipline, he ordered his driver to stop, and stepped out. Their conversation, as Madalyn later reported it to me, went something like this:

GENERAL: Young lady, what are you doing?

MADALYN: I'm watering the lawn.

GENERAL: This is an odd day. You're not supposed to water today.

MADALYN: I know, but I forgot to water the lawn on the even day, and our grass is dying.

GENERAL: Don't you realize that you are living on a military post and that your actions are governed by base regulations? Are you aware that there is a published regulation against what you are doing, and that by doing it, you are committing a major offense?

MADALYN: Well, general, if the regulation says you're only allowed to water every other day and I forgot to water yesterday, what's wrong with my watering today?

The general was not known for unconditional surrenders. Though unpersuaded by my wife's logic, he was probably confounded by it and apparently decided that this was the wrong battle in the wrong war. After gruffly commanding her to stick to even days, he undertook a strategic retreat.

When summer turned to fall, Madalyn once again found herself in violation of air force rules and regs. Again I was away in the delivery room. Again the general's staff car pulled up in front of our house. Again she faced him alone.

GENERAL: Ma'am, your lawn looks abominable. It needs policing badly.

MADALYN (innocently): Policing? What's that?

GENERAL (angrily): It means that every other house on the block has raked up its leaves, and you have not. Your lawn is a disgrace. This is no way for a captain's quarters to look. I want this lawn policed.

MADALYN (grudgingly): All right.

GENERAL (nudgingly): Are you going to do it today?

MADALYN (stubbornly): No, I'll do it soon, but not today. I

have to go out to the commissary now to shop for supper. I have two hungry little boys to feed.

The general was not amused. If the regulations had allowed court-martials for wives, I'm certain he would have convened one immediately. He contented himself with sending me a grim warning letter.

But Madalyn continued to offend. She greeted me one evening incensed by the news that hats, gloves, and calling cards were now required at Wives Club luncheons. "Me wear a hat and leave a calling card? What do they think this is? Jane Austen's England?"

Now Madalyn was as upset as the general. "They're writing it down in their heads," she continued. "Madalyn Eisenberg: She doesn't wear a hat, doesn't wear gloves, doesn't carry calling cards, talks back to the colonel's wife, waters the grass on the wrong days, and her lawn needs policing. The question is, will this woman make a military wife? And the answer is absolutely No!"

I had to agree. But things were happening that made me wonder if I wanted her to remain one. The most important had occurred in the first year at Dover. I learned shortly after my arrival at the post that for the past several years air force wives had been afraid to give birth to their babies at our hospital. It had developed a reputation as an unsafe place to deliver because, within a few days of their arrival home, so many newborns broke out in the ugly yellow pustules of staph infection.

Perturbed, I talked to the hospital commander about it. "Well," he told me, "unfortunately, it's an old story. Your predecessor's efforts to solve the mystery were fruitless; you're welcome to try, but I doubt you'll have much luck."

I wasn't satisfied with that view. Healthy Dover AFB babies were now my responsibility, and I took it as a personal insult that any department that I headed could produce such an epidemic.

Did we have a modern version of Typhoid Mary—a Staph Stanley among us? I began a strict surveillance. All personnel were cultured every month. Anyone whose throat showed staph colonization was masked, transferred to another area of the hospital, and treated with antibiotics and lozenges until his or her throat tested negative again. The epidemic continued.

We instituted new policies in the nursery: gowning and masking, special handwashing procedures, increased distance between cribs. The epidemic would not go away.

Captain Sterns, a young pediatrician, and I read every article we could find on the treatment of infant staph epidemics in hospital nurseries. We seemed to have touched every base. So what was wrong? Could there be some unknown source of impure air, like an operating room. "Of course!" It hit us both at the same time: "The air ducts . . . it could be the air ducts."

It was a good theory, but hospital blueprints from the engineer's office showed clearly that the newborn nursery had a totally independent system of ducts. "Look," the engineering officer explained, spreading the sketches out on a table in his office, "this nursery was designed to be infection-free. Like an operating room. There's no way contaminated air from anywhere else in the hospital can get in. The system sucks in only fresh air—from outside the hospital."

Another dead end. Yet we had no place else to go. "I know it's a long shot," I said, "but what if there was some kind of screwup during construction? Sure, the drawings show air intake from outside the hospital. But what if a contractor got lazy or goofed or took a construction shortcut while the hospital was being built?"

"You're wasting your time," said the engineering officer. But he agreed to help us run an experiment with an innocuous but odiferous chemical. One by one, we checked out possible sources of infection, placing chemical smoke dispensers at exhaust ducts in each suspected area, and sniffing for the smoke in the nursery.

The first several tries were discouraging. The nursery remained smoke-free, and we were beginning to think the engineer was right. Then, suddenly, Eureka! An orderly we'd stationed at the nursery air shaft smelled smoke. A duct servicing an outpatient surgical clinic where boils and abcesses were drained had been venting that contaminated air and recirculating it. It was being introduced directly into the newborn nursery—staph and all.

"Well, do you believe us now?" we asked the engineer. "There has to be a connection."

"There can't be," he said, with considerably less conviction than before.

There was. We reinforced the evidence by phage-typing the staph present in the outpatient department and comparing it with the phage type of the infections the babies were contracting. They were identical. And once the offending duct was closed off, the epidemic ended.

Sterns and I wrote a report, signed it proudly, and dispatched it to the Chief of Professional Services, to be forwarded to the hospital commander and on through channels to the area commanding general. We'd played detective purely for the satisfaction of solving a serious health problem. But at the bar of the Officers' Club, where we went to celebrate our success, we couldn't help speculating.

"Do you think we'll get some kind of air force commendation letter?" I wondered aloud.

"Letter, hell!" said Sterns. "It ought to be good for a medal."

It was. But not for us. The Chief of Professional Services had put his name on our report. The base commander had endorsed it and passed it along upstream to air force headquarters. Several months later, I read a notice posted on the bulletin board announcing a special parade to be held the following week at which our chief, who had had nothing whatsoever to do with the experiments, was to be awarded a Commendation Medal for solving the problem of recurrent staph infections. We never even got a "thank you."

I was getting tremendous experience. I valued the work that I did. I was greatly improving my medical skills. But I was beginning to think that an organization that rewarded you not for excellence but for political manipulation was no place to spend a life. (I hadn't yet learned that politicking is the norm in virtually every kind of organization, civilian as well as military.) When I finally decided that I had to get away from the tension and take a week's furlough—TDY, or temporary duty, on one of those wonderful flights to London or Paris that so many base docs had gone on—I was told officiously that I couldn't go. Because of abuse of the privilege generally, the base commander had just ordered that only officers on official business could hitch rides on overseas flights. That wasn't much of a reason to de-enlist, but piled on top of the others, it was the straw that broke the back of any intention that remained in me to spend my medical career in the armed forces. Madalyn, who had concluded much earlier that the petty tyrannies in the life of an officer's wife were not for her, was delighted.

I found it was easier to get in than out. I knew that when all our household goods were out of the house, it was necessary to "clear base housing." This meant passing inspection by a housing officer. I'd heard it was more than a mere formality, but there were guys on the base who'd been running exit-expediting house-cleaning businesses for years. For a fee, they guaranteed that you passed inspection or your money back. I was about to call one when Smitty, the corpsman in charge of the ob floor of the hospital, asked if he could do the job for me. He said that he needed the money—he had some family problems—and had been thinking that going into this business might be just what he needed to balance the family budget. I sympathized, and agreed to be his first client for a fee of fifty dollars.

Friday at 4:45 P.M., *I* had the family problem. "I'm mighty glad you got here on time," I told the white-gloved second lieutenant from base housing. "My family and I are expected at my wife's parents for dinner this evening. In Philadelphia."

He seemed unimpressed. I noticed with horror that he was opening the back of the refrigerator and examining the coils. Had Smitty thought of cleaning there? In a moment, I had my answer. "Hmm," said the lieutenant coolly, "missed some dust."

He crossed the kitchen floor to the stove, opened the oven door, and—could I believe what I was seeing?—slowly rubbed the tips of his white gloves across the oven's interior. "Hmm," he said, "missed some grease."

He removed a dime from his pocket, kneeled, and inserted it deftly into a crack between the floorboards. "Hmm," he said, "missed some wax." He rose. "Sir," he said, sounding pleased, "I'm sorry to say that your family is going to have to go to Philadelphia without you. There's no way this house passes inspection."

"How can you say that?" Madalyn cried indignantly. "This floor is clean enough for my husband to operate on."

In my head, I could hear myself saying things that would only make matters worse: "I've just finished four years of faithful and dedicated service at this base. I've delivered more than 1,000 babies. I've worked overtime to save the government money. I earned a medal and someone else got to wear it. And this is the appreciation I get? To end up at the mercy of an arrogant second lieutenant who is having the time of his life humiliating me?" I said nothing. "Sir," he said, so politely that it would have taken a micrometer to measure the sarcasm in his voice, "I'll be back tomorrow morning to inspect this house again."

Madalyn and the boys drove off. I would have cheerfully paid a cleaning service's $100 weekend rate, but no one was available. After vainly trying to locate Smitty, who had already left the base for the weekend, I settled down to work. I scrubbed and scraped, rescrubbed and rescraped until it was too dark to see. Then, my bed long gone, I laid me down to sleep on the hard wood floor. At dawn's early light, I began cleaning again. True to his word, the lieutenant showed up at 9 A.M. once more—but only to have the pleasure of failing me a second time. "Sir," he said, "the refrigerator is fine now, but you've got a way to go to get that wax buildup off the floor and the grease out of the stove. I'll be back again this afternoon, sir." I thought I could hear him chuckling to himself as the screen door banged behind him.

Drenched in sweat, I went back to my scrubbing and scraping. How fortunate for the lieutenant, I reflected, bitterly, that air force doctors don't wear side arms. In midafternoon, smiling toothily, my tormentor returned. "Okay, sir," he said, with only a cursory glance about, "you're cleared for take-off." I could only assume he'd learned that another family would be moving in that evening, and that time was running out for him to play cat to my mouse.

As I toweled my wet and weary brow, he saluted smartly and departed. I didn't return his salute.

Leaves from an Ob/Gyn's Journal

I review the sparse patient files in my cramped office. Then I reread the latest ob/gyn journal. If it's happening in my field these days, I know about it. I have little more to do than keep up. It is 11 A.M. and I don't have a patient scheduled until late in the afternoon. The empty waiting room, after the nonstop stream of patients I was accustomed to in the air force, is unnerving. The phone rings and I jump. My hand reaches for it eagerly.

A patient! Not a gyn patient, unfortunately. But a patient, nevertheless. A house-call referral from the Onondaga County Medical Society—a service both to the community and to young doctors like myself just getting started in practice and hungry for work.

I lock my empty office and head for the address I've jotted down. It's the drab apartment of a widow in her late sixties with a respiratory infection. I examine her carefully, give her a prescription, and, doing my best to repress the eagerness in my voice, say, "That will be ten dollars, please." She, perhaps under the impression that house calls are a free service of the medical society, seems surprised. "I'm sorry," she tells me, "but I don't have that much in the house."

"Oh," I say, "I was really counting on that money."

"Well," she replies, "I have it in the bank."

Desperation roughly shoulders aside professionalism. "Would you like me to drive you there?" I ask quickly. "After you withdraw the money, I'll be happy to drive you home." As an afterthought, to assuage my lingering sense of guilt at having to charge this grandmotherly lady anything at all, I add, "That is, if you can spare the money."

"Oh, that's all right, doctor," she says, obviously a little surprised at my offer. "I just have to get my bankbook."

I park in the lot behind the bank and help my patient out. "Only be a moment," she assures me, and disappears around the front of the building. I wait five minutes. Ten. I tap my foot nervously, anxiously crush an empty paper cup on the front seat. Suspicion floods over me. She looked so sweet and caring. Could she have given me the slip? Maybe she took ill in the bank. Maybe I should go in and look for her.

It is time for decisive action. I start rolling up the car windows. Just as I take the key out of the ignition, I see her in my side-view mirror, hurrying to the car.

"I'm so sorry," she says as she climbs in beside me.

I resign myself to hearing that she is out of funds. Not only did I not make my ten-dollar fee, but I wasted an extra hour trying to collect it.

"I'm sorry," she repeats as she unsnaps her large old-fashioned handbag. "The lines were so long I thought I'd never get to a teller."

She doesn't miss my sigh of relief as I watch her pull a crisp new bill from her purse. She hands it to me and smiles sympathetically.

The odd looks she occasionally casts in my direction as I drive her home lead me to think maybe she believes I am not really a doctor, but only an imposter trying to con her out of ten bucks. Who can imagine a doctor so hard up for money? Who indeed?

5

Practice Makes Imperfect

OKAY, NOW WHAT? (In the air force, there was never a thought of where the rent or my next patient was coming from.)

And where to? (Should I start a practice of my own or become someone else's junior associate? If the first, where will I get the money to open an office? If the second, how will I make the connection?)

My father-in-law made it for me. "Henry," Madalyn said jubilantly when I walked in the door about three months before my air force tour of duty ended, "my father called. One of his customers is one of the biggest ob/gyns in Philadelphia, and he's looking for an associate." She hugged me enthusiastically. "Henry, this is so wonderful! And if we can get an apartment near my parents, we'll have built-in babysitters."

My father-in-law owned a service station, and when I called back, the linkage was quickly made clear: "His name is Dr. Ripley. I wouldn't say we're buddies, but he's been coming to me for years for gas and repairs. Yesterday, I mentioned my son-in-law was an obstetrician, too."

"What did you say?" I asked. The palm holding the phone was starting to sweat.

"Only the truth. That you're getting out of the service in a few months. And, of course, that you're brilliant, well-trained, and would be an asset to his practice."

I cleared my throat nervously. "And what did he say?"

"He said it was a fortunate coincidence. He and his associate are looking for a young doctor to come in with them. He said he'd like to speak to you."

Not immediately, I hoped. I was speechless. What a great guy my father-in-law was—risking his relationship with a good customer to help me get started. My own father had always said how important it was to be in the right place at the right time. This could be one of those times. "Wow!" I exclaimed when I hung up. "A big-city practice, Madalyn. Near your parents, and only an hour and a half from mine. Boy, are they going to be happy about this!" I fell asleep flipping mental photographs of a spacious home on the Main Line, the country club, the whole avocado. The best part was no more air force politics. Just taking care of women and delivering their babies.

A couple of Saturdays later, we drove from Dover to Philadelphia, deposited Jordan and Bruce with their grandparents (a preview, we envisioned, of many mutually pleasurable babysitting engagements to come) and continued on to beautiful Bala Cynwyd (another rosy-futured omen). Madalyn and I rang Dr. Ripley's doorbell, and were cordially invited to sit down, enjoy predinner hors d'oeuvres politely served by a uniformed maid, and make ourselves at home.

"Gee," Madalyn whispered when we were alone for a moment, "he must have some practice! What a beautiful home—and his wife can even afford a maid."

After dinner, the taste of which I could not attest to, so busy was I listening to Dr. Ripley hold forth about himself and his flourishing practice, the doctor invited me into the living room to conduct the evening's principal business. He glanced at my resume, dropped it carelessly on a cocktail table, and returned to his favorite subject.

He waxed eloquent about his own credentials, but asked no questions about me or mine. When he had finished making it clear beyond a doubt that he was one of the best and busiest obstetricians and gynecologists in the city, a professor at the medical school, a valued teacher of ob/gyn residents, and much in demand as a lecturer on the medical school circuit, he paused for a moment.

"Son," he said solemnly, "I want you to know that if you come in with me, it's going to be a very slow process for you to be accepted around here—by my patients, by my associate, and by the people in the medical school." He paused for maximum impact. "After all, I'm Dr. Ripley. And you're Brand X."

My discomfort level, which had been rising all evening as it became increasingly clear that I was in the presence of a pompous self-important ass, took another great leap upward. I knew I would have to make sacrifices to get started in practice. But could I stand working day in and day out for a man like this?

I never had to find out. Dr. Ripley had finally gotten around to "the offer." He cleared his throat like a basso about to deliver an aria. "I think," he said grandly, "I could give you a salary of $7,500 for the first year."

My response popped out of my mouth almost involuntarily: "Dr. Ripley, you must be kidding. I earn almost twice that much in the air force!"

But he wasn't. And when that was clear, I thanked him for the excellent dinner and said that I guessed there wasn't too much more to say because, with a wife and two children, there was no way I could entertain that kind of offer. There were a few other things I wanted to say, but I decided to keep them to myself.

I had briefly dreamt I'd dwell in marble halls. Now it was back to reality. We'd never saved any money in the air force, and unless I changed my mind and reenlisted, I was going to need a job, and soon. A quick swing the following month to interviews with multi-specialty groups in drab New England towns that had once been thriving shoe manufacturing centers proved unproductive. So I called my old medical school buddy, Larry Port, to ask what the picture looked like in Syracuse, where he, with no armed forces obligation to pay off, had already been in the private practice of internal medicine for several years.

"Hank, you can't go wrong here," he urged. "Tell you what. I've got a couple of patients who just found out they're pregnant and haven't lined up obstetricians yet. I'll handle their obstetrical care temporarily and I'll tell them I've got a friend moving into town who's the greatest ob since Semmelweis. Get here by the end of their first trimesters, and they're yours."

Two guaranteed deliveries. It was an offer no penniless
young ob/gyn could refuse, and I didn't. I felt a momentary
twinge of doubt when, visiting town to try to find a place to
live and practice, I paid a courtesy call on one of the
community's most prominent ob partnerships. "Go see
them," Larry had urged. "You never know. With a practice as
busy as theirs, they might be able to use you for weekend or
vacation coverage. Or maybe even throw their overflow your
way."

I introduced myself to the senior partner, a man in his early
fifties, and told him that I was an S.U. grad thinking of settling
in Syracuse to practice ob/gyn. He asked me a few questions
about my background, at which point his associate came in.
"This young man is on the verge of opening an ob practice
here in town," said the first doctor. "What do you think?"

"I think it's a mistake," said the partner coldly. "The
community's got too many obs already. Why don't you try
Rochester or Buffalo?"

"Good suggestion," said the senior man, and pleading the
press of patient care, he asked his nurse to show me out.

I was young, vulnerable, and badly needed to feel some
warmth and cordiality from older colleagues. That unfriendly
reception, clearly calculated to bar the door against potential
competitors, still upsets me when I recall it thirty years later.

But I had another appointment that afternoon, this one with
Dr. Nesbitt, a professor and chief of the department of ob/gyn
at the university hospital. From him, I got an entirely different
feeling: that I would be a welcome addition to the community,
and welcome as well in his department as a clinical instructor
of medical students and residents. If it were up to the first two
doctors, I might well have decided against Syracuse and left
with a bitter taste on my tongue. But the warmth of Dr. Nesbitt
rebalanced the equation.

On the long drive back to Dover, I entertained Madalyn with
a rosy rainbow of memories of undergraduate days at Syracuse. She really wanted to live in Philadelphia. Any other
choice, she said, would break her parents' heart—"though, of
course, they'll survive it." But if this was what I really
wanted, if I felt it was the right move for me
professionally . . .

For the first year, it didn't look as though it was. We left the
air force with thirty cans of tuna fish and a dozen boxes of

cereal purchased on special at the post commissary, an aging car, and about $200 in savings. Almost half of that went for the first month's rent of the office of Dr. Gilmore, a benign and amiable semiretired eighty-five-year-old GP to whom I'd been introduced by his son, a prominent gynecologist and former professor of mine. Much of the rest went for rent on a small apartment in a two-family house owned by a general practitioner (I hoped he would refer patients, if only to be sure we could pay the rent regularly; he didn't) and on such necessities as milk and babysitters for the kids during office hours.

I couldn't afford a nurse, but neither could I practice without a chaperone in the office. Madalyn's protests ("But how am I going to find the time?" and "Who'll take care of the children?") were overwhelmed by financial and professional concerns ("Where am I going to get the money to pay a nurse?" and "How can I do a pelvic without a third party standing by?") So we agreed that I would attempt to schedule my few patients in clusters, and Madalyn would arrange for a reliable babysitter to guard our family jewels during her absences. Of course, not all patients were that easily wrestled into a time spot of our choice. And we could hardly afford to automatically reject all patients who declared the days and hours convenient to our babysitter inconvenient for them. That's where our new friend and neighbor Shirley Hornstein came in.

"If Henry gets a last-minute patient," she offered, "just drop the boys off at my apartment. With my noisy kids, I won't even notice the difference." So Madalyn was my minuteman and Shirley was hers, and often at a moment's notice, she apologetically dumped Jordan and Bruce at our good samaritan neighbor's and headed hurriedly for the office.

Walking into it—and seventy-five dollars a month gave us that privilege three days a week—was like reentering the nineteenth century. I had the use of the original museum-quality instruments and examining table, a set of overstuffed, mohair waiting-room easy-chairs, and a consulting room so narrow that it had to have been built *around* the massive old oak desk that was its centerpiece.

When I was conferring with a patient in the consulting room, Madalyn, my combination nurse, office assistant, and receptionist, couldn't very well sit in the waiting room, so she slipped into our single examining room. When I moved in there, she readied my patient and, because the little room was so crowded, hastily retreated to the consultation room.

Between patients, we argued over such matters as whose turn it was to clean the speculums. She, resenting my lolling about with my feet on the desk between patients, would say, "Clean them yourself. I'm not getting paid for this job." I, on the other hand, wasn't used to having the nurse tell me to clean the instruments. (In those days, I didn't even wash dishes. I certainly wasn't going to wash speculums.) Threatening to fire her was no good. That was just what she wanted to hear.

It quickly became apparent that it would be a while before I earned enough in the office to pay my rent, so I offered my services to the Onondaga County Medical Society for emergency house calls at ten dollars per visit. I wasn't the only starving young doctor on their list, and it was like winning the lottery when my name came up. No matter how late the hour, I gratefully grabbed my little black bag and went.

Patients with arthritis. Patients with colds and fevers. Patients with anxiety and patients with vertigo.

I used to dream about a house call where I'd see a gyn patient. Finally, one day, the medical society answering service lady called with news of a woman alarmed about heavy pelvic bleeding—and in a respectable part of town at that. It wasn't nice, but I rejoiced. I did a pelvic exam to see if anything was grossly wrong, palpating carefully, then probing internally. An enlarged fibroid uterus! A candidate for a hysterectomy! I tried to keep the euphoria out of my voice as I soberly suggested a more intensive examination under optimum conditions in my office next day.

I reexamined her there, confirmed my findings, told her that she needed surgery, and then called the hospital to schedule my first major case in private practice. I was thrilled not only because, for the first time in months, I had an opportunity to improve a gyn patient's lot and to perform surgery —something I had come to really enjoy—but also, I freely confess, because of the fee. It would, if we continued to live prudently and enjoy tuna fish, take care of both office expenses and feeding all the big and little Eisenbergs for a whole month.

The surgery was routine and successful. Madalyn mailed a bill, and we waited for the check to arrive in the mail. Patiently but in vain. Madalyn phoned to prod politely a half-dozen times, but my patient had more excuses than she had lately had fibroids. Our offer to allow her to pay it out over a year's time was gratefully accepted, but when three months passed without our receiving so much as a token ten-dollar bill, I began to suspect that I had operated on a professional deadbeat. When I turned over her name and address to a collection agency, that suspicion was quickly confirmed. "You should see the list of physicians she owes money to," I was told. "That's probably why she called the medical society." So, the only reason I'd gotten the case was because no other doctor in town would touch her with a ten-foot scalpel. Well, I had picked up some experience. About people as well as hysterectomies.

After seven years of modest expectations but a certain amount of security while I was training, Madalyn found it scary to have a bankbook with a balance of only $9.12 recorded in it. Still, asking for money was as embarrassing for her as it was for me, and after years of not receiving a fee from patients for my services, I felt uncomfortably like an amateur turning pro. Given the fee-for-service system I was now practicing in, I decided I had to strive to be the best physician I could be, give people the kind of service they deserved, charge a fair price, and put the profit motive way at the end.

In fact, that's where it was for me. There was joy in practicing medicine, joy in taking care of people, joy in seeing good results, joy in becoming more and more accomplished as a physician and surgeon.

The joy of putting money in the bank came later, but it did come. In the meantime, there was dire need. So one day, when it seemed that it would be necessary to borrow weekend grocery money, I asked Madalyn if she had been paid by a patient I had just seen.

"No," she said, embarrassed to have been too embarrassed to ask.

"Well," I said, "ask her for money before she leaves."

"She's already left."

"Then, for heaven's sake, go after her!"

Obediently, Madalyn dashed out the door, sprinted down the street, overtook our patient and, feeling like a complete fool, said breathlessly, "Oh, by the way, I forgot to ask you, would you like to make a payment today?"

She came back triumphantly waving two five-dollar bills. "Mrs. Caruso looked at me as though I was crazy," she reported, "but I got it!" There was food in our refrigerator that weekend. And I knew we'd both turned pro.

I asked a lot of Madalyn that year. Our babysitter/
housekeeper quit because the bathtub ring had rings after
Madalyn gave our dog a bath. (''Great!'' said Madalyn. ''She
wants a clean apartment to clean!'') After that, Madalyn had to
worry not only about the office, but about the apartment, the
laundry, and the kids, too. With no babysitter, the chaos that
two little boys can wreak was frequently transferred to the
garden behind the office and—after Mrs. Gilmore complained
that they were trampling her pansies—to the driveway. There,
where Madalyn could keep an eye on them, Jordan and Bruce
were urged to ''play quietly'' together. Of course, they played
noisily, and periodically, when the sound level exceeded Mrs.
Gilmore's tolerance threshold, she would totter down the
stairs, burst into my office, and declare, ''You've got to do
something about those kids of yours.'' In midpelvic, Madalyn
would have to run out and chloroform the children.

The fact that our children were unwelcome wasn't the only
thing wrong with my office. The tiny superannuated space was
not the kind to inspire patients with confidence. If I didn't bet
on my future, who would? When I learned that a new medical
office building was nearing completion downtown, I decided it
was time to go for it. Wearing my best suit and a freshly ironed
white shirt (Madalyn had ironed the parts that showed), I paid
a call on the Merchants Bank of Syracuse and signed for a
$20,000 loan—enough to furnish and equip an office that
would not scare patients away and to pay a full-time nurse/
receptionist.

Having little confidence that I was immediately going to
become the busiest ob/gyn in Syracuse, I rented the smallest
office available. But that was a distinct step up the ladder.
Now, though it was only slightly more than bridge-table size, I
had a business area. Instead of one tiny examining room, I had
two. And the waiting room was big enough to seat six people,
if they were good friends. The receptionist I hired was so
sultry-voiced that the first day Madalyn (now happily returned
to home and hearth) called and heard her response, she hurried
to the office to see if she looked as sexy as she sounded.

''Henry,'' she told me that night, ''she is so beautiful and
has such a great body, she worries me.'' She worried me even
more, but I survived. Unfortunately, she didn't. The Marilyn
Monroesque beauty that other women envied as a blessing,

she, like Monroe, apparently found a curse. She resigned before the end of that first year because of severe emotional problems.

I had a new office, a new receptionist, but not a lot of new patients. Once a month, I sat down with a pile of bills and said, well, I can't pay them all. I'll pay some and ignore some. I had been accustomed to hustle nonstop from patient to patient in residency and the air force. To not rush—just to sit and read journals, talk to my receptionist, daydream about the future —was difficult for me. But it's not easy to rush when you're doing nothing.

My thumbs didn't twitch, but once again I was full of self-doubt. What I'd done up to that point didn't matter: my Philadelphia successes, my training at Yale, my accomplishments in the service. All that mattered for me at the moment was succeeding in private practice in Syracuse. And quickly, because that's what my ego needed. I had to make it, and that would be "it" for me. (Until it was "it." Then I'd need a new "it"—but I didn't realize that at the time.)

I was not good at playing The Game. The Game was something young doctors were introduced to early. Every once in a while, we were invited to a spectacular party at which everyone was either a physician or a physician's spouse. You knew why you were there. Pediatricians invited golden-armed obstetricians. Anesthesiologists and their mates smothered surgeons and theirs with love and attention as with halothane. Radiologists invited just about everyone. Obstetricians invited family doctors who didn't do maternities. And if you played The Game, it worked. If a guest wasn't dazzled into channeling an occasional referral to the gala-giver, he frequently found himself among the uninvited the next time around.

But, I thought, I'll be damned if I'll refer my newborns to the pediatrician who mixes the best martini. Granted, a referral isn't necessarily a matter of life and death. It's ordinarily a choice between two doctors of relatively equal skills. But I wanted the freedom to remain totally objective. And in my heart, I rejected the idea that I had to be some kind of medical politician currying favor with people so patients would be referred to me. I wanted to earn referrals for competence as an ob/gyn, not charm as a host.

So at a time when I should have reached out—to other doctors who might have helped me get a running start—I withdrew into myself. Instead of working hard at building a referral network by entertaining internists and GPs, or at least by paying courtesy calls on them, I followed the longer and less certain route of waiting for patients to refer their friends. I told myself, and Madalyn, that the reason was that this sort of thing was repugnant to me. But there were other reasons, too.

No one had taught me in medical school or in residency how the system worked; I had no mentor to guide me in its mysterious ways. Even when an occasional doctor I met at a staff meeting referred a patient to me, I didn't know enough to send a thank you note, and often it was the last referral he sent me. In the military, patients had just come to me; I didn't have to seek them out. I liked it that way; I was very uncomfortable as a salesperson for my own work. (What could I say? "Hi, doctor. I'm Henry Eisenberg, the best darned ob/gyn this town's ever seen. Your patients will be eternally grateful for your wisdom in referring them to me.") And I admit, I still smarted from the rejection of those first two obstetricians. My antipathy toward them had soured me on the medical community as a whole—an immature, illogical reaction, but one it took some time for me to outgrow.

There was, I suppose, another factor as well. We were, it must be said, plain folks. Aside from our wedding—which my in-laws had choreographed—we had never had a catered party. Madalyn was afraid at that point in her life to undertake one, and even if she hadn't been, we couldn't afford to cater anything anywhere near the crystal-and-silver elegance of those we'd been invited to attend. The house we moved into after four years in Syracuse was small and shabby compared to the homes of the established doctors in town.

Our chronic lack of money was a nagging toothache. My old PGH buddy Larry Port was always inviting us to join him on exotic vacations to faraway places far beyond our means. I made a lot of excuses having to do with lack of coverage and care of children and dogs. It was too hard to admit flat out, "Look, you're established and successful and I'm neither. If you want to get together at your house or our house, okay. But Bermuda is out of our league."

Finally, when Larry and another doctor asked us to join them at the Persian Terrace of the Hotel Syracuse for New

Year's Eve, I told the truth: "Larry, we can't afford it. I had more money in my pocket when they paid us fifty dollars a month at PGH than I do now."

"Well, why didn't you say so?" he exclaimed. "Your shiny new office fooled me. But listen, how about coming as our guests? And don't say No, or I'll take back those two *prima gravidas* I gave you."

In the air force, I'd been too busy. Now I was too broke. I'd taken Madalyn out so little in the past several years that I felt that this time I had to say Yes. But it was an uncomfortable evening, even though, when the whopping check came and they split it, I insisted, with a confidence I didn't feel, "Next year, I'll pick up the tab."

Meanwhile, in self-defense, we began to avoid doctors and make friends with people of lesser means. Later, I fear, I fell into the we've-got-it-so-let's-spend-it pattern myself. But now, still the outsider, the kid without the ice cream cone staring enviously at the kids ostentatiously licking theirs, I was immensely put off by high-living big-spending colleagues.

As I virtuously parked my battered Ford convertible in the hospital parking lot next to fellow physicians' Caddies and Corvettes, I thought that, okay, maybe requiring young medical school graduates to take vows of poverty with their Hippocratic oath might be going too far. But, on the other hand (the one wearing that ultrathin, $2,500 gold Rolex watch), too much money in the bank was bound to distract from doctoring. There'd be entirely too much time spent trying to avoid taxes and probate and making sure your money made money. And wouldn't daily reading of the *Wall Street Journal* lead to neglect of medical journals?

And what about the Mansion-of-the-Month contest that seemed to be going on in medical circles? Every doctor appeared determined to build the biggest showplace in town, with "his" and "hers" saunas, and country kitchens so vast that the islands in the middle seemed to require palm trees.

When a doctor's home is a castle, I sermonized smugly to myself as I walked from car to hospital, the danger arises that the art of healing that physician practices will become a means to the end of ever-expanding income. I recalled the surgeon only a few years my senior who'd recently grumbled to me about being called away by a resident from a Saturday night party at his home. I diplomatically refrained from reminding him of something I was certain was true: that during his first few years in practice he would cheerfully have gone out at 2 A.M. in a blizzard just to change a dressing.

Then there were the doctors who collected yachts and yawls like seven-year-olds collect baseball cards. "Come on out to the lake this weekend for a cruise on my new boat," Dr. Horatio Hornblower urges. "No thanks, Horatio," you reply. "You took us out on your new boat just last month." "Oh, no," he corrects, "that was my *old* boat!" Horace seems blithely unaware that his wife is about to jump ship. She confides to friends that when summer vacation approaches she prays for a typhoon to sink their latest flagship at its moorings.

It was years before I had sufficient success and self-esteem to enable me to be comfortable with my colleagues—although many of them were good people and fine physicians. It was almost Yale all over again: I was the newcomer, the outsider. Most doctors establishing practices had trained in Syracuse, knew other physicians in the system and were known. I hadn't been in Syracuse in eight years, and then, only as a medical student. I didn't know the ropes, and had less money, status, and polish than the doctors I passed in the corridors—or so I felt. The highly politicized medical school atmosphere was unpleasantly reminiscent of Yale. I later moved to, and was happier at, the brand new and less academic Community General Hospital. While at the medical center, I never quite felt I belonged, although I didn't go so far as to consider reenlisting or moving elsewhere. Here I was and here I'd have to make it. But after the security of a military salary, having to scrounge for the money to feed and clothe my family roughed up my ego still more.

My discomfort came out as hostility. Madalyn has not-very-fond memories of some of our early entertaining when, as we sat in the living room chatting after dinner, I'd suddenly get up and start collecting ashtrays and turning lights out. If those rude hints weren't taken, my next move would be to remove my shoes, stretch, and yawn. She was horrified but didn't know what to do but smile sweetly, distract our company by passing the pretzels, and hope that someday my manners would improve.

Although I shunned successful doctors, I was perfectly comfortable with those less experienced than I. I volunteered as a mentor for a medical school program that would acquaint students with my specialty. A bright young man in the program came to me as a freshman. Jack Yoffa was gregarious and easygoing. I liked him immediately—maybe because we were so different. We became friends, and saw each other socially. When he was a senior, he decided on an ob/gyn residency in Syracuse. Later, his residency in ob/gyn completed, he was to become my partner.

Shortly after we moved to Syracuse, a young obstetrician who'd been in practice for four years but still remembered the difficulties and uneasiness of his first few years, thoughtfully invited us to dinner. I thought he, too, could be a friend. But I saw his handsomely landscaped home, the two new cars parked in the circular driveway, the tasteful interior reflecting long hours of designer consultations, and realized we weren't in the same league.

Dr. Friendly meant only to empathize and put me at ease when, during dinner, he discussed the problems of the young doctor just starting practice. But, defensive as usual, I felt patronized. And when at one point I remarked on the wide experience I'd gained in the air force ("You know," I said proudly, "I averaged a hysterectomy a week"), he told me he was averaging two. It was hard to believe that he was so busy after such a short time in practice when, here I was six months into mine, and I could still count the number of patients I saw each day on the fingers of one hand—and generally have a thumb and pinky left over. I should have taken heart from his rapid progress. Instead I decided he'd succeeded because of his outgoing personality, and worried that my reserve would hold me back.

The following week, when I spotted Friendly and another physician coming toward us on a downtown street, I turned my head away, took Madalyn firmly by the arm and steered her across the street. I would never have admitted it then, but it was all about envy. In those early years, I had a lot of trouble with that. So it was back to the way it had always been for me. Either do it yourself or perish.

Relating to my patients on a human level wasn't any easier. In some ways, preparing to become a doctor ill-equipped me to become one. I had attended one school after another —studying, repeating like a parrot, performing like a trained chimp, leading a structured, tightly disciplined, narrowly channeled existence with little time for exploration of self or of life. I'd had very little contact with anyone other than those academics directly responsible for my education. I'd learned little or nothing about communication, compassion, under-standing, the need for sharing and interacting with my col-leagues. Indeed, my colleagues were rivals, competitors for "head of the class."

What I increasingly learned to do was to become stronger, ever more disciplined, more able to go it alone—to fight off feelings of panic, to overcome whatever needed overcoming. Without help. That was the prescription I had written for myself after my childhood run-in with Rocky, and I had lived with it ever since: The way to get through is to rely on your own muscle, to tap your own inner strength and resilience. My best friends were my books. They were nonjudgmental. And they were always there waiting to be opened, ready to share their secrets, to help me get through.

That process went on through all those years of study, so that when, finally, I reached what I saw then as my ultimate goal—the completion of my education, the awarding of an M.D.—I was a whiz with books and the facts in them. But unlike a salesman who meets the public every day, or someone with a lot of close friends to talk with and listen to, I was totally unequipped to sally forth and deal with people, particu-larly patients.

I had never learned what to say next after, "Hello. How are you?" And I didn't really want or expect an answer other than the bare medical details. If a patient answered, "Terrible. I have this pain, doctor," I could handle that. A good diagnostic challenge raced the blood and tingled the cerebrum. If, on the other hand, she responded, "Terrible. Things haven't been going well at home lately," I would freeze momentarily, then quickly return to *materia medica*, ignoring the potentially significant comment she'd made. Conversation was easiest when limited to, "Here's the treatment plan I want you to follow . . ."

It's not fair to put the entire blame on medical education. Many doctors certainly manage to rise above it. They are outgoing, warm, compassionate when they enter medical school, and they stay that way. Some develop sensitivity by being exposed to a particularly humane role model. But our training (thank goodness, it's changing)—like that, I suspect, of police, clergy, and other authority figures—did tend to create people who were afraid of people, who used their authority images as shields.

Of course, nobody knew that. We learned to hold our shields high enough so that few, if any, of those around us ever got close enough to find out.

That's why I was so comfortable with my fast-moving air force assembly line—the kind of practice sometimes referred to as "veterinary," because the doctor can stroke his patients instead of talking to them. And why I was so uncomfortable with my slow-moving civilian practice, where, with only a handful of patients, I had more time than I knew how to spend with them. My bedside-deskside manner was midway between those of a supermarket checkout clerk and a motor vehicle bureaucrat. I wasn't relaxed enough to just enjoy passing the time of day with people; I didn't know how. It was a skill I needed to develop in order to be a complete physician, one who can really make a difference in people's lives. But it wasn't taught in medical school. I hadn't learned it during adolescence. And it was a quality that definitely didn't come naturally to me.

I was blithely oblivious to this deficiency. I firmly believed that if I became a superior craftsman, a superior technician, a superior surgeon, that was all I needed to be the best possible ob/gyn. I didn't recognize the flaw in this theory until many years later.

I believe most of my patients were equally unaware that I was flawed. Ralph Nader had begun to challenge the assembly lines of Detroit, whose products he declared were "unsafe at any speed." But consumerism had not yet touched assembly-line medical practices. When a new patient came in, the scenario was simple: I talked and she listened. The kind of patient who asked more than a couple of questions in the first visit—particularly, challenging questions—was one who immediately pushed the button called "This patient is a pain in the ass and is making me angry."

Twenty-five years ago, that kind of patient was blessedly rare. Subconsciously, I had adopted the prevailing medical attitude: "Nobody questions God. What I say goes because I know best. Today it will rain; tomorrow it will snow. You will take this and you will do that because I know more than you do and I say so. That's the way it is." The implied message: If you don't like the way God does things, find yourself another religion.

A few years later, when I didn't want extra night work if I could avoid it, I would (in the days before elective induction came to be considered poor practice) recommend inducing labor, if I had a patient who was at term and whose cervix was ripe. If the patient was reluctant, I didn't throw a tantrum, but my stern mien made my feelings clear. Like the seasoned farmer scanning his orchard for ripe fruit, I knew best when baby was ready for harvest.

The patient who expressed reservations about my decision upset me, because that meant she didn't trust me. I turned on the heat to get what I wanted. First came the red warning light: "You're really very ripe, so ripe I think you should be admitted immediately. If we put it off, there's a possibility you might not make it to the hospital in time." Then the appeal to reason: "Induction is very safe. I'll just rupture your membranes and you'll deliver in a few hours. It's something I've done many times. If I didn't think you were ready, I wouldn't suggest it."

Finally came the salesman's closing pitch: "So why don't you reconsider and just go on up to the hospital? I'll be there in a few hours. We'll get you going and you'll be delivered by five this afternoon." After nine long months, the idea of getting the ordeal over with quickly was appealing. It was very seldom that anyone refused.

Because those were the rules of the game, it was seldom that anyone took umbrage. What good would it do to feel offended or that one's dignity had been violated? Everyone else's obstetrician played by the same rules. What was seething inside my patient, I never knew, but what showed on the outside was respect for educational credentials, submission to authority, the feeling that I knew better than she did.

The concrete evidence that I was okay with my patients was the steady growth of my practice after those first slow months. Women I treated when covering hospital emergency rooms later became my private patients; they told their friends and my empty waiting room began to fill up. When you're in a business that keeps growing without any advertising, without any effort on your part but being there, you begin to believe that you must be doing a good job. Your feelings are supported when appreciative thank you notes and letters and sometimes

—even when I'd already been well paid for my services—gifts begin to arrive in the mail. You don't feel the need to try particularly hard to have a pleasing personality or do anything but what comes easily to you.

But in spite of the fact that on the outside I was beginning to act more and more the role of the venerated medical deity, there remained inside a soft core of weak self-esteem. I really didn't believe I deserved these patient accolades any more than I'd believed I deserved to be in medical school. This time I was right, but for the wrong reasons. Technically, I was a very good physician, rendering excellent care to my patients. As a human being, offering understanding, comfort, and sensitivity, I'm afraid I was a failure.

Leaves from an Ob/Gyn's Journal

The woman in my examining room is petite, blonde, and attractive, and I haven't seen her in eight or nine years. She is a pilot's wife, and I delivered her baby in El Paso. Our relationship then was that of doctor and patient, nothing more. Still the surprise is a pleasant one when I find her gowned and waiting. It is gratifying to learn that she has sought me out for care here in Syracuse.

"Cathy Everett," I exclaim. "I thought the name on the chart sounded familiar! What are you doing in town? Did your husband resign from the air force?"

"No," she says with a shrug, "I resigned from him. Three years ago." She gives me a sunny smile. "I'm a lot happier since we broke up."

"I'm sorry it had to happen. But what are you doing in Syracuse? And what brings you to my office?"

"I'm visiting my sister, and it's been a couple of years since my last checkup. When I saw your name in the yellow pages, I thought, why not?" She smiles again. I return the smile and get on with the examination. She trembles perceptibly as my hands traverse and explore her.

"Cold?" I ask. "I can turn up the thermostat."

"No," she replies, her voice subdued. "Just a little nervous."

She has no apparent problems, and I tell her we'll send her a card with the results of the Pap smear. I say goodbye and wish her well.

This is my last appointment for the day. I return to my desk, dictate some notes, then pick up my coat and walk to the front desk to say goodnight to my office staff. Cathy is standing there, her coat on, studying a magazine article that seems to have captured her interest. I assume she started it before being called in and wants to finish it. "Take that with you, if you like," I say. She thanks me, slips it into her handbag, and we exchange smiles again. Then, thinking about the surgery I've scheduled for the next morning at Community General, I walk out into the corridor.

Rather than wait for the elevator, I decide to walk down to the lobby. As I open the door to the stairwell, Cathy catches up and falls in step with me. I step aside and hold the heavy door for her. As it closes behind us, she spins suddenly, tilts her head upward, and kisses me. I am baffled and amazed. This is something that happens in steamy novels, not in real life.

But this *is* real life. "I've been wanting to do that for a long time," she says softly. "Let's go someplace where we can be alone."

6

Intimate Explorations

A SPECIAL RELATIONSHIP, an intimate bond, exists between a woman and her ob/gyn. He may share her brightest moments or be privy to her darkest secrets. Only a husband or a lover is permitted such intimate explorations. Not surprisingly, the motives of the male "women's doctor" have been suspect almost from the first moment that the first man invaded what had been, for centuries, exclusively midwife territory.

In 1542, a pioneering German named Wertt had tried it, and his career went up in smoke. Literally. After posing as a woman in order to attend a patient in labor, Herr Wertt was burned at the stake. When herdsmen and shepherds, experienced in delivering calves and lambs, began to attend women, a 1580 German edict summarily prohibited them from delivering babies. But things went better in France, where male midwifery actually became fashionable. For delivering the grand dames of the French court in the late seventeenth century, Julien Clement was appointed royal *accoucheur.**

In England and America, self-appointed defenders of public morals stubbornly continued to object to male midwifery.

---

*from *Obstetrics and Gynecology in America: A History* by Harold Speert, M.D.

Perhaps suspicious of anything imported from France, John Blunt warned in seventeenth-century London that "women . . . ought not to provoke [their spouses] . . . by a wanton and unnecessary exposure of the most sacred parts of their persons to men-midwives." He added sternly, "Man-midwifery is a personal, a domestic, and a national evil." And in mid-nineteenth-century Boston, it was Samuel Gregory's published opinion that male obstetricians "undermine the foundations of public virtue." When men were permitted to deliver babies, it was with a sheet covering the woman's body.

Gregory argued that young men took up obstetrics out of lewd curiosity, that they subtly persuaded women to take up prostitution, and that their alien presence in the birthing chamber was so shocking to pregnant women that birth complications inevitably followed. "Husbands have told me," he concluded ringingly, "that they had no children, and wished to have none, if they must have a doctor to bring them into the world."

Public opinion has changed, but more than a century later private opinion tends to remain skeptical. When I'm introduced as a gynecologist at parties, the wags start wagging: "You mean you get paid for what you do? Hey, anytime you need help, give me a call!" Even bachelors with brimming little black books offer to trade places with me. And after a drink or two, more than one woman has confided that, no matter how crisp her ob/gyn's manner when he examines her, she still wonders if his thoughts are as sterile as his disposable gloves.

From the very beginning, a thread of ambivalence runs through the life of the male ob/gyn. We enter medical school barely out of adolescence, with its keen interest in sex. By training's end, we are expected to be pristinely professional, suppressing any undisciplined thoughts and feelings. Early on, we are programmed to understand that our patients are not to be considered sexual objects.

It isn't anything our professors say in so many words. It's the lessons we pick up in observing their interactions with unclad women and with each other. I never heard, in a doctor's locker room or in a hospital coffee shop, a joke, off-color or otherwise, about women or their bodies. By example, they taught us that our white coats are a medical version of the

clerical collar, that what we see in the examining room is akin
to what the priest hears in the confessional booth. As students,
we got the message. To be different from our role models was
unthinkable.

The need to program ourselves to remain ever cool and
clinical may be responsible for many ob/gyns seeming just that:
cool, curt, clinical. Some of us undoubtedly overcompensate.
In rejecting temptation, even the very idea that it exists, we
may appear brusque, disinterested, detached.

The sensitive patient may wince and wonder: "Lord, why do
I have to submit myself to humiliation by this ice-cold
stranger?" The seductive patient—and every gynecologist
encounters a few—may speculate as her ob/gyn palpates her
breasts or his gloved fingers carefully probe her vagina, "I
wonder what he thinks of my body. Do I excite him? Or am I
just cervix No. 19,458?"

The fact that we appear withdrawn doesn't mean that
inappropriate thoughts never stir within us—particularly when
we are still relatively new at the game. Sometimes it means we
have them and are trying hard to overcome them. One pilot's
voluptuous wife remains golden in the memory of my early air
force days. Blonde and beautiful, she could, I'm sure, have
been a movie starlet, a model, a Playboy centerfold. I
discreetly admired her from afar when I saw her around the
base or at the Officers' Club. My wife, no fool, noticed my
wide-eyed admiration and had the good sense to laugh, not
fume. "Henry," she said, poking me in the ribs one day,
"you're staring!"

When I saw the woman's name on my patient appointment
book one morning, a thrill of anticipation coursed through me.
I knew that my reaction was unprofessional and mentally
chided myself. I recognize now that it was human, too—that
this was one appointment that only a twenty-seven-year-old
doctor carved from a block of ice and with chloroform flowing
through his veins would not have looked forward to.

When I walked into the examining room and saw her,
appearing even better put together under a gown than fully
clothed, it took a great deal of willpower to thrust a not
sufficiently fleeting fantasy from my mind. She seemed totally
oblivious to my plight. The fact that I barely said two civil
words to her during her physical, and buried my head in my
notes during the follow-up consultation, probably convinced
her that I was not only not interested in her as a woman, but

that I wasn't even interested in her as a patient. I breathed a sigh of relief when she left, and my next patient turned out to be a dowdy civilian secretary in her early sixties.

The first pelvic I ever did was in my third year of medical school. It was at the Syracuse Free Dispensary, where indigent women from all over the city waited in line for hours for gyn exams. There was no fee, but they paid a price. They had to submit to not one but three pelvics—one by the medical school professor and two by students like me.

I knew in advance that I was going to the gyn clinic and that was where pelvics were done. I was excited. Everything was exciting to me. Putting a mirror in back of an elderly man's throat to see the larynx was exciting. Listening to heart murmurs was exciting. Not long before, there would have been an added excitement—that of exploring the most intimate part of a woman's body. But we'd already learned that in medical school emotions are reined in. The important things were: "Did you feel the uterus? Could you feel the ovaries?" And if I didn't, "Dammit, why didn't I?" Not, "Oh boy, I'm going to get to touch a woman's vagina!"

In fact, my most vivid memory of that morning is of science, not sex. Not the intimate experience of doing a pelvic—which with three of us and a nurse hovering over the worried middle-aged woman on the table was anything but intimate—but the formula Dr. Gilmore taught us to summarize what gynecologists look for. It seemed so simple, so much less to worry about than what we did in taking the hour-long survey of every body system that was required for an internal medicine history. Here we had to consider only five areas: pain, bleeding, discharge, urinary tract, and gastrointestinal problems. Though it was some time before I decided that ob/gyn would be my specialty, I found the limited focus very attractive.

The ob/gyn's educated hands quickly become an examining instrument. Fingers are sensitive. They connect directly to the brain. (In an experienced hand, medical instruments can be almost as sensitive. The curette that suctions and the curette that scrapes eventually become metallic extensions of your fingers. It's remarkable how much feedback you can get from that razor edge while gently scraping the lining of a uterus during a D & C. It almost seems to become part of you, informing you finally, "Okay, all done—clean as a whistle.")

As impersonal as instruments, our gloved fingers tell us a great deal during a pelvic. In the classic bimanual examination, only one finger is used for a virgin or a woman not sexually active. Inserting the finger or fingers in the vagina, we push the uterus up against our other hand, which rests on the abdomen. The uterus is now plainly palpable, and so we palpate, probing for tenderness that could flag infection: pelvic inflammatory disease (PID), for example, or the endometritis (inflammation of the lining of the uterus) that occasionally follows childbirth. Next our fingers check the ovaries on either side of the uterus, scouting for tenderness, enlargement, masses or other thickening that could signal infection or the presence of a tumor or cyst. Feeling behind the uterus can tip us off to possible endometriosis, a common condition in which bits of endometrial tissue grow outside the uterus and may cause not only pelvic discomfort and pain, but sterility, too.

Inspection is as important a part of the pelvic examination as palpation. When we insert the speculum to dilate the vaginal canal and peer in to view the cervix and vagina, we're playing detective, not voyeur. Is vaginal mucosa normally corrugated, as in healthy young women? Or pale and thin, as when not enough estrogen is being manufactured by the body in prematurely menopausal or postmenopausal women? Does it show the telltale signs of DES prescribed for the patient's mother during pregnancy? Are there any of the little strawberry-red patches characteristic of trichomonas? Any discharge? Color, character, and odor all contribute to a diagnosis even before we look at a sample under the microscope. A heavy malodorous, greenish-yellow discharge signals the parasitic infection trichomonas vaginitis, commonly called trich. When it's thick and white, it points to candida, a yeast infection. Gray warns of the Gardnerella organism, a common form of bacterial vaginosis, while a greenish discharge indicates the possibility of gonorrhea.

Even the shape of the cervix can be revealing. It's small and round in a woman who's never had a child or never been instrumented for a D & C or an abortion. In a pregnant woman or one who has had children, the cervical opening is larger and, instead of round, it becomes slitlike. And, of course, we don't neglect to carefully inspect exposed portions of the body: skin, breasts, and vulvar areas in search of lumps, retractions in the breasts, lesions on the skin, redness, sores, scaliness, cracks, warts, or vesicles that might be herpes lesions. The ob/gyn has about as much time for sexual thoughts during a gynecological exam as a traffic cop at Times Square during rush hour. The body is an ob/gyn textbook and we're rapidly turning the pages.

It was a few years ago that I did a vaginal hysterectomy on Mrs. Falk, but the embarrassment is still fresh. The procedure had gone smoothly. I dutifully phoned in my surgical report to a recorder-robot in the hospital records room. Then, at the recovery room nurses' station, I slid my patient's chart out of the rack and sat down to write my orders.

Returning the chart to the rack, I stepped to the foot of Mrs. Falk's bed to examine the perineal incision, assure myself that there was no bleeding, and give her the "all's well" reassurance, as important to her recovery as the IV dripping into a vein from the stand beside her bed.

I lifted the sheet, spread her legs, and looked between them. Everything looked normal. Too normal. My face turned the color of the antiseptic solution that should have covered her shaved pubic area. There was no sign of Betadine. The perineum was not shaved.

I dropped the sheets and looked up. The woman in the bed stared at me aghast. Her lips moved but no sound issued forth. "Who the hell are you?" the unspoken words seemed to demand. "And what are you doing inspecting my private parts?"

It wasn't Mrs. Falk. It was a woman I'd never seen before in my life, either above the belt line or below it, and she didn't know me from the janitor. "Oh!" I said eloquently. "Excuse me." Crimson-faced, I slunk away, hoping she wouldn't scream for Security. Later I learned (from the nurse, since I was not eager to go head-on with Mrs. Mistaken Identity again) the reason for her stunned expression. Since the operation she'd just had was a tonsillectomy, she'd had no reason to anticipate an examination from the opposite end.

If I were an ENT surgeon and asked the wrong patient to open her mouth and say, "Ahhh," the mistaken patient would have been surprised, but not aghast. The difference: how women feel about examinations of their vaginas as opposed to their throats.

I wish it were not, but I'm afraid it is true that many women dread visits to my office the way I flinch at the thought of a visit to the dentist. That's the closest analogy that I, as a male, can make. I imagine that lying vulnerably nude on the examining table in the presence of a man you don't know all that well triggers the gynecological equivalent of dental chair panic. But there is, of course, more to it than that.

Our culture has handed the female patient a set of attitudes she brings with her when she walks through the examining room door. Usually she has grown up believing that a woman's body is something she exposes only to her mirror, her husband, or her lover. Because of taboos ("Don't touch yourself *there!*" "Don't let anyone touch you *there!*" "Big girls don't walk around with no clothes on!") accumulated en route to adulthood, she's often uncomfortable with her body.

Our concept of the Ideal Woman adds to her discomfort. Rare is the woman, even among the most shapely, who doesn't find a flaw that keeps her from considering herself a perfect 10. When she disrobes in my examining room, the typical patient is ashamed that she's too fat or too thin; secretly believes her breasts are too small, too big, or too pendulous; worries that her vagina may smell less fragrant than a rose garden. That she has tried to overcome this last possibility by showering, douching, and applying cologne or baby powder is often clear when I examine her. (Fortunately, most women coming in for a Pap smear or the diagnosis of a vaginal discharge are sophisticated enough to know that they shouldn't douche for a couple of days prior to their visit. That would be like hosing down the scene of the crime to wash away the evidence.)

The most common reaction from patients, particularly young patients who haven't experienced a pelvic exam before, is a tense, "I really don't like this!" (One middle-aged woman confessed that at her first exam she had the urge to withdraw her foot from the stirrup and kick her gynecologist in the face.) I try to make it easier. Before we begin, I tell my patient what's going to happen and why.

I apologize in advance for my cold hands. (Should I, I wonder, have been barred from the practice of ob/gyn because of them?) When I'm relaxed my hands are warm, but when I'm stressed they ice up. The office is unfortunately a stressful place—phone calls interrupting me, women going into labor, the ever-present possibility of a sudden emergency, the need to tell a patient something she doesn't want to hear. So my hands are cold even in July, but they're at their chilling worst during a Syracuse winter, when I've just come in from fifteen minutes at a cold steering wheel. I pity my first few patients then.

During the exam I do a running commentary for young first-timers or anyone who is clearly anxious: "Now I'm going to examine your neck, your breasts, and your abdomen . . . I'm feeling for lumps or irregularities . . . Next I'm going to put one or two fingers in your vagina and my other hand on your abdomen . . . You may feel some minor discomfort . . . If you concentrate on your breathing, that should help to relax you . . . This is a speculum . . . I'm going to insert it in your vagina in a moment." (Before we started warming our speculums, patients used to jump out of their skins when cold steel made contact with warm tissue.) With most women, I keep conversation—with them, or with my nurse—to a minimum during the examination. They seem more comfortable and feel I'm focusing all my attention on the exam.

Gentle manner or no, even patients who've been having pelvics for years still tell me, "No matter how often you do it, I feel the same way. Nothing personal, Henry, but I really hate this damn exam!" Many of those who come do so because they're more afraid of cancer than they are of the gynecologist. Only during childbirth do women seem to lose this inhibition about exposing their intimate parts to the doctor's sight and touch.

Probably that's because the last thing in the world most women feel like when they are delivering a baby is a sex object. At other times, I suspect, no matter how the medical profession tried to convince them otherwise, many women worry that a gynecological exam may be stimulating to the examiner. A few, I've discovered, worry that it may not be, particularly if they find the exam stimulating themselves.

But for the jaded author of Ecclesiastes, there was nothing new under the sun; and for the experienced ob/gyn, there is nothing new under the examining room drape. Whether his practice is in Beverly Hills or Boston, after thousands and thousands of bodies, there are no surprises. Doing an internal exam is no more arousing to an ob/gyn than counting packets of hundred-dollar bills is to an experienced bank teller —though either may occasionally fantasize about running away to Tahiti: the teller with the cash, the doctor with the patient. If, indeed, a doctor did allow each patient who walked into his office to stimulate him sensually, he would never be able to get through the day. For all our God complex, we are only human.

Partly in self-defense, partly because of our professional training, and partly because anything you do day in and day out, year in and year out, loses its aura of mystery and excitement, we see just another body under that drape. It doesn't matter whether we're examining a mommy or a movie star.

I can understand how the typical male might doubt that a gynecologist can examine twenty pairs of breasts a day and not be turned on. Unlike cultures in which the breast is accepted for its primary function—as a mammary gland—and naked breasts are largely ignored as they swing freely in public, our society has made the breast a primary sex symbol.

But to an ob/gyn breasts, like eyes or noses or anything else, fall into categories. Some are fatty and therefore soft and yielding. Some are mostly glandular and therefore firmer to the touch. (Occasionally, I encounter breasts with a subtly different feel. A breast that's been surgically augmented with an implant, though firm, stays soft and feels much like the real thing. Sometimes a patient elects to keep a mammoplasty her secret when I take her medical history. But to practiced fingers, such an implant feels a bit *too* firm. The surgical scar, carefully hidden by her plastic surgeon in the crease underneath the breast, is equally subtle. But if a breast doesn't feel quite normal, I look for a scar, and then—not because I want to show my patient how smart I am but because it's an important piece of her history—I ask if she's had implants done. Often she says Yes sheepishly. She may be able to fool her husband or her lover, but she can't fool her ob/gyn.)

The breasts of young women who've never had children tend to be firm and upright, with the areola surrounding the nipples shaded tan. Pregnancy pigments and darkens the areola, and in the occasional woman unusually responsive to the hormones of pregnancy, increases breast volume and weight to the point of irreversible sagging. Too much weight gain during pregnancy can compound postpartum droop. Genes often play a commanding role in how breasts respond to pregnancy and weight gain. When firm breasts run in the family, I may see a patient whose breasts, even after nursing four or five babies, appear almost "as good as new." Usually, though not always, they finally succumb to the aging process. After menopause, when mammary glands are no longer needed for milk, glandular tissue is replaced by fat, and breasts become softer and more pendulous.

Most important, breast examination is serious business. We're not looking for kicks. We're looking for suspicious lumps or skin or nipple retraction—a kind of dimpling that may be an exterior clue to life-threatening interior activity. Just as the internist still listens to hearts and lungs even though he has cardiograms and X-rays, the ob/gyn checks breasts manually even though we have mammograms capable of detecting tiny needle-point lesions long before we can. Many women either don't get those important mammograms, or, procrastinating on the theory that no news is good news, don't get them often enough.

Women may be reassured to know that a draped female lying on an examining table is less likely to fatally attract her ob/gyn than the same patient in a sexily slit dress in his consulting room. (It's the *Penguin Island* principle—from the wonderful Anatole France satire about the wandering monk on an island of shamelessly naked penguins who dresses the female penguins to improve the state of their morals, and causes the males to go mad with lust.) It would be dishonest, or naive, however, to say that an ob/gyn is *never* attracted to the woman he is examining. Like anyone else, a doctor is a sexual being. If he's having family problems, is single and looking for a woman, or—and medicine has its share of these—is always trying to prove his masculinity, he may very well be looking at the patient with a personal as well as a professional eye. Not because he's a doctor and she's a patient, but because he's a man and she's a woman. A doctor who acts on such an attraction is, of course, courting big trouble. Very few do.

Most patients are too focused on what brought them to the doctor in the first place to think of him as anything more than a vaginal service manager. But occasionally, the patient is the one who's attracted. Maybe it's the intimate setting, maybe it's because she feels very vulnerable in the presence of the physician, maybe she's just lonely and unhappy and reaching out toward anyone who might be kind and loving to her. Most of the time, I imagine, she, like the doctor, keeps her feelings to herself. But once in a while, she makes it clear by conspicuously flirtatious behavior that she's interested in more than an exam.

In a random survey of 300 physicians by *Medical Economics* magazine, one out of three doctors reported having blocked at least one patient pass. The invitations may manifest themselves in body language, in provocative eye contact, in a murmured remark: "Umm! That feels good . . ." None of the doctors, anonymously surveyed though they were, admitted yielding to such advances. They reported a wide range of rejections—from studiously ignoring repeated hints to (perhaps something of an overreaction) threatening the patient with a chair. Some doctors brushed the matter off lightly, while others, sensitive to the hurt they might inflict, made the No a gentle one. One ob/gyn reported reasoning calmly: "There are many good lovers in the world, but few good doctors. You need a good doctor."

It's important for ob/gyns to remember that there are women (as there are men) who behave in ways that may be misinterpreted as seductive when they are meant simply to be coquettish. So an overt rejection can turn out to be embarrassing to both parties. When I think a woman is being more than mildly flirtatious, I take it as my cue to be very professional, very polite, reduce body contact to an absolute minimum, and act as though the only signals I'm getting are from my nurse to hurry because I'm falling behind schedule.

Doctor-patient passion is, of course, no genie come lately. It's been around since the first doctor prescribed the first potion, and the first jealous husband feared it was a love potion. The temptation factor for doctors was recognized by Hippocrates himself, who required his interns to make this statement part of their solemn medical-ethical oath: "Whatsoever house I enter . . . I shall go for the benefit of the sick, refraining from all wrongdoing or corruption, and *especially from any act of seduction.*" The oath's intent, as I read it, is to inhibit physicians from being aggressive, opportunistic seducers. Mostly it works.

But even priests have been known to slip and fall. Doctors, who take no oath of celibacy, are no better—but neither, I think, considering the daily opportunities, are we much worse. A dozen years ago, another *Medical Economics* study found only one out of four surveyed physicians admitting to extramarital affairs, a rate lower than that of the general population. It's probably up—it appears to be for almost everybody—but I still have the feeling that doctors are less, rather than more, promiscuous than most.

When doctors do have affairs, that study indicated, they are likelier to have them with employees, friends, or "others," than with patients. I know a number of doctors who divorced their wives to marry their secretaries or nurses, but I can think of only a few who divorced their wives to marry patients. But doctor-patient affairs do happen. A vulnerable doctor—one whose marriage is on the rocks, for example—may drive to the nearest motel with a Cathy Everett whether her invitation is issued at his office or at a cocktail party.

Affairs with patients are not bragged about. Intimate relations with a patient can wreck a doctor's family, his practice, society's trust. To avoid the appearance of misconduct or an unjust accusation of rape, the male ob/gyn routinely insists on doing pelvics (particularly on patients he doesn't know well) only with a nurse present. But sometimes routines break down—in flu season, at vacation times, on busy days.

Even a nurse's presence during the actual pelvic doesn't always guarantee safety, as I discovered on a summer afternoon a few years after I'd opened my own practice. At the conclusion of the examination, my nurse walked out to attend to some pressing, unfinished business, leaving me alone with my still demurely draped patient.

"Why do I need this silly thing covering me?" she asked, suddenly sitting erect and dramatically ripping off her paper drape. "It's just the two of us in here, and I don't want to wear this anymore."

Staring in spite of myself at her tanned and shapely body, I stammered a response to her comment: "We generally suggest drapes because most women feel more comfortable wearing one." She smiled invitingly. "Doctor," she challenged, "do you feel uncomfortable when I *don't* wear one?"

Here was big trouble wearing the garb of naked opportunity. I cleared my throat nervously. "Um, yes," I said, "as a matter of fact, I do." And muttering something about having to see a patient and that I would see her in the consulting room after she dressed, I hurriedly left the room.

When I, not without some difficulty in concentrating on her problem, had finished seeing my next patient, I adjourned to the consulting room. It was empty. My seductive patient, apparently offended by my rejection of her advances, had paid her bill and left. If feelings of 99 percent "Go!" and 1 percent "Stay!" can be considered mixed, I must confess to mixed feelings about her departure.

Leaves from an Ob/Gyn's Journal

Bryan Henrie, a kind-faced, white-haired, small-town physician with the look of a clean-shaven Santa Claus, is an ex-convict. Once a Grove, Oklahoma, town councilman and civic association father-of-the-year, he has been stripped of his license to practice medicine. His crime, he explains to his audience, was performing hundreds of illegal abortions before the U.S. Supreme Court legalized the procedure.

"But surely you knew the risk you were taking," someone says. "Why did you do it?"

"The first dozen years in practice," Henrie replies, "I didn't. Like most doctors, I refused to do abortions." Physicians in the crowd nod. They, too, have refused to do abortions.

"Then one afternoon," he continues, "a lady from a nearby community came into my office. She was unmarried, socially prominent, and in a family way. She pleaded with me to save her good name. We talked a long time, but I turned her down on legal and ethical grounds—as I'd had to turn down so many others before her."

Again there are nods. The story is familiar.

"She was sad and upset," he goes on, "but I didn't know how sad and upset until I read about it in the newspaper. After leaving my office, she took her car onto a lonely side road, floored the accelerator, and plowed into a telephone pole at eighty miles per hour." Dr. Henrie sighs as though the accident is still fresh in his mind. "After that," he continues, "when a woman asked me to do an abortion, I found it pretty hard to say No."

7

A Question
of Conscience

I WAS STILL an ob/gyn resident when Bryan Henrie went to
prison to serve his two-year sentence. A state prosecutor had
called him an abortion butcher, but before the deputies
handcuffed him for the train ride to the penitentiary, half the
town—grateful patients, friends, and neighbors—turned out
to wish him well, obviously unconvinced that he was a
criminal. They couldn't compensate him for the shame and
humiliation he was suffering, but they threw him the biggest
farewell party Grove had ever seen.

My own jarring introduction to unwanted pregnancy came
on ob/gyn service in Philadelphia General Hospital during
internship. There, in a drab open ward with forty cots lined up
in melancholy rows, I witnessed the tragic consequences of
criminal abortion. Hemorrhaging women and young girls were
stretchered in and lowered onto the sheets in overwhelming
sepsis or renal shutdown. Knitting needles and twisted metal
coat hangers caked with blood often jutted from their painfully
perforated uteruses.

Some came in wailing and screaming. Some were beyond
pain: comatose or in shock. Those responsible, unlike the
skilled and compassionate Dr. Henrie, were often genuine
butchers: backstreet abortionists, or friends or relatives trying

to help, who had clumsily inserted potassium permanganate tablets into vaginas or administered douches of lye or other savagely toxic chemicals, assuring, "This may hurt, but it'll get rid of the baby." It seemed to. Bleeding followed, and the victim rejoiced through clenched teeth at what she interpreted as a sign of successful miscarriage. In fact, the harsh solutions were causing ulceration and hemorrhaging. Some died. We interns and residents did what we could.

Some of the worst wounds were self-inflicted. I thought about the level of desperation required for an otherwise healthy woman to grasp a sharp steel shaft and blindly stab deep within her in an attempt to end life even as that life began to quicken. It violated every law of nature. But despair and social pressures proved stronger than either mother love or the fear of death.

When the long night in the ward was over, a prominent Main Line specialist with a flourishing private practice in the community, serving his turn as chief of service for a few months, would bustle in. We'd trail after him as he moved quickly from one bloodstained cot to the next on morning rounds. I was always struck by the way this man, wearing a different suit or tweed sports jacket each day, came in from his affluent outside world of power and success to our little island of poverty, misery, and death. The residents recited their litanies of peritonitis, acute abdomens, raging fevers, and hematocrits of 20 that should have been 40, and the attending crisply issued orders to start our patients on huge doses of penicillin and to pump them full of blood.

Standing at the foot of the beds, we rotating interns watched this high drama unfold. We listened in awe to this skillful veteran who knew so much more than we mere apprentices and could bring our patients back from the brink—though some, defying his magic, would be wheeled on a final journey down to the basement morgue.

I began to see that I wanted to be this self-confident ob/gyn attending. And a half-dozen years later, perhaps in part because of those early dramatic imprints, I became him.

When I opened an obstetrics practice of my own, I saw women with different faces but the same fears. Teens with tear-reddened eyes who wanted to finish high school, not commence motherhood. Desperate coeds whose college careers were about to end, not because they'd failed their courses but because their contraceptives had failed them. "My boy-

friend told me it couldn't happen the first time," they'd say
with eyes downcast. Or bitterly, "He told me he loved me.
Now he won't even come to the phone." And they would
implore: "Just this once. Please make an exception just this
once!"

I couldn't help them. The law said No. Nor could I help the
mother with six children who couldn't emotionally or finan-
cially handle a seventh. Or the bride-to-be stunned to find
herself pregnant with a previous boyfriend's child. Or the
dozens of others who came to my obstetrics office to ask not for
help in bringing a life into the world but for help in snuffing it
out.

I understood that many of those I refused would keep trying
until they got a Yes for an answer—more than likely from
someone with a set of knitting needles and a supply of
potassium permanganate. And occasionally I'd find myself at
the hospital in the role of my former mentor, tending to a
hemorrhage, recognizing an ashen young face. Maybe God
was punishing them. But there was something terribly wrong
with the system.

Sure, abortion was illegal. Sure, I'd had it drummed into me
that it was also unprofessional. For centuries, respectable
physicians had hewed unfalteringly to the Hippocratic oath:
". . . I will give no deadly medicine to anyone if asked, nor
suggest any such counsel; furthermore, I will not give to a
woman an instrument to produce abortion." That position was
perfectly proper, perfectly understandable. The thought of
ever having to perform an abortion, of instantly becoming a
certified baby killer in a white coat, deeply disturbed me. But
there was the other side: Women who urgently needed medical
help weren't getting it. Wasn't that part of our oath and our
responsibility, too?

Was saying No just taking the easy way out—a societally
sanctioned way for physicians to turn their backs on someone
in trouble? Taking an ethical position to duck an embarrassing
one? Was Bryan Henrie a murderer or a man of courage? There
were a lot of unanswerable questions. The more I thought
about it and the more desperate coeds and separated wives I
saw at the office, the more ambivalent my attitude toward
patients who wanted to terminate their pregnancies became. I
began to believe that the choice should be theirs, not mine.

I started to refer patients to a clergymen's group in town

with underground railroad links to doctors specializing in abortion in Mexico and Puerto Rico. That helped to quiet my increasingly troubled conscience. But foreign abortion packages were costly—$1,000 or more for fees, fare, and hotel. And care, I found, was sometimes less than ideal. Some women returned with septic or incomplete abortions, with high fevers and infected and ultimately useless reproductive organs. So now I had another question: Shouldn't a woman have as much right to a safe abortion as to a safe pregnancy?

I pondered that one—a moral dilemma with only illegal solutions. I wasn't about to break the law. My father had taught me too much respect for it for that. But the law in New York State did permit hospital abortions when a mother's life was at risk physically or emotionally. A psychiatrist had to certify urgent need, and such certification was ordinarily reserved for the victims of incest or rape. But my associate, Jack Yoffa, and I decided that if such cases came to us, we would accept them.

Even legal abortions weren't easy to arrange in the atmosphere that prevailed in New York hospitals. Doctors who were "soft on abortion" were not particularly popular with their colleagues. For every procedure the hospital abortion committee approved, it turned down two or three. One of the two attending psychiatrists on the staff had at first been willing to certify our cases, but now, he, too, turned reluctant. He confided his fear that acquiring a reputation for being an easy okay would cost him patient referrals from other physicians. He admitted, too, that, although as a psychiatrist he was supposed to be free of hang-ups, he still felt squeamish about "taking life."

By June 1970, we had performed fewer than a half-dozen hospital abortions. The others—and there were many once the word got around—we were forced to refer to the clergymen's network. But though the doctors of New York State were not ready for abortion, the people, through its legislature, apparently were. Suddenly, to almost everyone's surprise, a bill legalizing abortion was approved by that body, and the governor signed it into law.

About a month later, as the effective date approached with no indication that our hospital would do anything about it, Jack and I attended the medical staff's bimonthly meeting hoping to prod it into doing its part to carry out the provisions of Section I, Subdivision 3 of Section 125.05 of the New York State Penal

Code: "an Act to amend the penal law in relation to justifiable abortional acts by physicians in the course of their practice of medicine." We failed—at a meeting in which the room temperature was just about right for quick-freezing whole sides of beef.

"Doctor," the chief of staff told me icily, "we have a committee studying this matter. Its chair will report to this body in due time." Further discussion was tabled.

When I checked with the head of the abortion reform committee, it turned out that the chief had mentioned to him the possibility of forming an ad hoc group to discuss the implications of the new legislation for the hospital. But the suggestion had been so vague that the physician, one of the community's busiest gynecologists, had not felt impelled to call a meeting.

At the next medical staff meeting, Jack and I waited patiently until it was clear that the chief did not plan to raise the abortion issue. Jack requested a report from the abortion reform committee. Told politely that it had not yet completed its deliberations, he then asked for permission to propose an interim emergency plan—which we'd worked on together for several nights. We had optimistically had twenty-five copies made to be passed out, but the chief accepted only one. "I am," he said, "referring your memorandum to committee."

"Doctor," I said, my pulse accelerating, "that committee has not even held an organizational meeting. I respectfully suggest that abortion is not only our office problem. It is a community problem, a hospital problem, and I move that —agenda or no agenda—an emergency discussion of how to respond to the new legislation be held here and now."

They argued that as doctors we were pledged to save lives, not take them. We argued that times and even religious ethics change, and that a lot of women died unnecessarily every year because of greedy, incompetent back-alley abortionists who could now be put out of business once and for all. And so it went—until Jack declared that if the hospital would not serve the needs of the community, then perhaps we, and any interested physicians willing to join us, should open a private clinic to do the job.

On that defiant note, the meeting ended. Jack is not thin-skinned, nor am I, but both of us were made uncomfortable by formerly friendly doctors who passed by empty seats at our table in the hospital coffee shop to squeeze into places considerably more crowded. Colleagues who used to greet me amiably in the corridors now passed by with brusque nods.

In the end, the abortion committee's labors brought forth a barely animate mouse. The committee recommended, and a staff vote approved, what amounted to token abortion—no outpatient abortions, and a grand total of four inpatient D & C procedures a week.

One day, when our office hours were over and our assistants had gone home, Jack and I sat down for a long talk. We discussed the fact that the ob/gyn practice we'd worked so hard to build might fly right out the office window if we developed a reputation as ''the town abortionists.'' But we felt we had to put our skills where our big mouths were.

I had trained with a doctor who was now health commissioner of an upstate county, and I phoned him for an informal opinion. He told me that our hospital staff was not unique in dragging its feet on abortion, that even ob/gyn chiefs at supposedly enlightened university medical centers were doing the same, being outdone only by conservative boards of trustees at community hospitals. His recommendations matched our private thinking. We might, he said, join with interested colleagues and a group such as Planned Parenthood to set up a public clinic. Failing that, since state law carried a good deal more legal weight than medical society voluntary guidelines, there was no overwhelming reason why a competent practitioner could not simply make abortion an office procedure—if his office was close enough to a hospital to obtain prompt emergency care.

The first course seemed much the more attractive to us. Several other ob/gyn men had either openly or covertly sympathized with us and responded favorably to a preliminary sounding. We met several times and tentatively decided to incorporate, in order to dilute any personal stigma that the practice of abortion might entail. By a fortunate coincidence, a new medical office building had recently been completed. One of my assistants told me: ''The builder has problems. Either someone misled him about the location or this town is overbuilt on medical office space. He's having such a hard time filling his suites that he's offering rent-free concessions of three months.''

The arrangement seemed ideal. The renting agent greeted us

like visiting royalty. But when I reached my office feeling good about our progress, a phone message awaited me. It was the renting agent, very apologetic and unhappy. He'd phoned the builder with the good news, only to be testily rebuffed. "I'd rather keep the building empty," the owner had told him, "than give it a reputation as an abortion mill." The builder had a change of heart when our attorney threatened him with legal action, but by then Jack and I had decided to go it alone. We asked our receptionist to start accepting appointments for early terminations of pregnancy as of July 1.

But as that date and my first solo legal abortion drew closer, my conviction that I was doing the right thing faltered. An occasional abortion certified by a hospital committee was one thing. Doing a dozen a week—with the possibility that this could rise to twenty or more, for an awesome annual total approaching 1,000—clearly took on aspects of what abortion opponents at that stormy hospital meeting had labeled "playing God." And it wasn't easy to forget what one doctor, in a hospital corridor, had angrily suggested we rename our partnership: Murder, Inc.

On the night of June 30, I had trouble falling asleep. Tomorrow abortion would no longer be a criminal act, but it went against all the moral teachings I'd ever been exposed to at home. It made a joke of the essay I could remember writing for my medical school application—about my wish to help save lives in a world where life was cheap. Abortion might be legal, but it felt criminal.

I decided, finally, that the mother-to-be must make the decision and live with its consequences. My role was to be patient and understanding, and to make my skills available to those who needed them. Many women who'd come to my office in the past two weeks had told me their hopes had been buoyed by the law's passage but dashed wherever they turned. One told me her own doctor had referred her to Planned Parenthood, which referred her to another doctor, who said his hospital had no abortion beds available for another four weeks. That would push her into the second trimester, and add an embarrassing two-day hospital stay while quintupling her expense. The gratitude on her face when I said that, Yes, I could help her, reinforced my belief that Jack and I had chosen the right path.

But next morning, when my nurse brought in the woman

who was to be my first abortee under the new law, I was as nervous as she was. Paracervical block administered, I dilated her. As the curved surgical steel contacted softly yielding tissue, my ears suddenly exploded with a heart-chilling, "Murderer!" I almost dropped my curette.

Hollywood has no productions like the theater of the mind. This wasn't my first abortion. But the half-dozen I'd done at the hospital had been performed in righteous indignation, thinking not about the rights of the fetus but about the wrong done to a young victim of incest. This abortion was different. This was the start of what opponents called "abortion on demand." Hesitating, I glanced at my patient's determined face. Only the whitened knuckles that gripped the table revealed her anxiety. I took a deep breath, ordered myself to relax, and resumed scraping. Like this young woman, I had made my decision. Like her, I would have to learn to live with it.

Sixteen years have come and gone since that day, and abortions have become routine, but they've never gotten any easier. As the Right to Life movement became increasingly active, I'd stop for a red light and see a bumper sticker on the car in front of me accusing: ABORTION IS MURDER. And I'd sit there, knowing how many I'd performed, entertaining the painful thought that, M.D., white coat, and good intentions notwithstanding, how different was I, after all, from Hitler's gas chamber technicians who took millions of lives in the routine performance of their jobs? It's not pleasant to think that you may have terminated more lives than you've helped bring into the world.

So when some people say that doctors who perform abortions are killers, a part of me agrees with that. But—and this would have to be true or I couldn't live with myself—I've chosen to do what I do because my internal "majority view" is that I'm doing something that, all things considered, has to be done. That I'm "saving" the lives of women who might be crushed were their pregnancies continued.

People who want abortions are there because they don't want to have the child, and any woman who carries a child in that frame of mind is starting motherhood with a lot of hostility and resentment. It's difficult enough to be responsible for being the parent of a child today when you really want the child and are willing to give it as much love as you know how. Sure, there are some parents who, once they see the baby, will fall in love with it. But many will be child abusers. Most won't get that far. They'll have their pregnancies terminated, no matter what I do.

I don't see the world as perfect the way it is. And the way it is, there are women who are pregnant but don't want to be, and I'm trained to terminate their pregnancies, and that's a fact. For me to say I'd prefer it to be another way is like saying I'd prefer it to be warm and sunny 365 days a year.

So one or two afternoons a week are set aside for "terminations" at the office. Some days I do the procedures, some days Jack does. We see girls of thirteen and women of forty-eight, married and unmarried, victims of rape and of incest. Children of police officers and of diplomats—like the daughter of a high-ranking Canadian dignitary who was brought to my office because abortion is still as illegal in Canada as it once was in the U.S.

There was Marilyn, a retarded fifteen-year-old raped by a retarded young man at an institution where they both lived, whose physician father brought her to my office. In terminating her pregnancy, I was able to prevent what was already a traumatic episode from turning into a potential long-term catastrophe.

Behind every abortion I perform, there's a broad range of human emotions. There's frequently disappointment, often anger and resentment, always guilt and grief. Sometimes abortion is the final act of a relationship that has failed. A husband who walks out, leaving his wife with a pregnancy she didn't want and a financial burden she can't carry. Or a boyfriend who professes undying love that suddenly dies when a pregnancy test comes back positive.

I see tearful married women in their late thirties and early forties who discover to their dismay that they've missed a period. "Well," I comfort, "of course, there are added risks at your age. But you seem to be in excellent health. If we monitor you carefully, it's certainly not too late in life for you to have a baby."

"But you don't understand," Mrs. Smith murmurs. "It isn't my husband's baby."

"Are you sure?"

"Five years ago he had a vasectomy."

But women with perfectly wonderful marriages come in to

ask for abortions. They've had X-rays without knowing that they were pregnant or taken drugs for ulcerative colitis or some other medical problem. They say they've read—or been advised by the family doctor—that the baby may be affected. I discuss the odds and explain that the chances the fetus will be harmed are slim. Still, their fears, rational or not, tend to rule them. Sometimes with good reason. I remember a patient in her forties who had been delivered several years earlier of a monstrous congenital anomaly that lingered in her nursery for three agonizing, emotionally exhausting months. She came to me distraught and said, "Doctor, I've missed two periods."

I went through all the appropriate motions. "I can do an amniocentesis at sixteen weeks," I said, "and order a chromosome study. If it's another defective fetus, I can refer you for a saline abortion."

"I'm forty-three," she said, "and too old to be a good mother. I couldn't go through another disappointment like that. I just don't want to be pregnant." The next day, she no longer was.

On a recent afternoon, there were three failures of birth control, or of their users. A sad-eyed thirty-nine-year-old working mother with three children had been using a contraceptive sponge. "I work," she said simply, "and I have to keep on working. My husband and I agreed that this is the best way."

A twenty-one-year-old nurse's aid—single, on the pill, with a steady boyfriend—was next. "I don't understand," she said. "I took it faithfully. I never missed a day."

"You're positive of that?"

"Well, pretty positive."

She and her boyfriend plan to get married in a year or so. In the meantime, she'll return to the pill. So will the twenty-two-year-old who missed two days because she forgot to renew her prescription when it ran out. "Would you believe it? Two days!" I believed it.

A chestnut-haired twenty-five-year-old Ph.D. candidate greeted me cheerfully. During the pelvic, she talked about school, skiing, anything but what was about to happen. "I guess I'm not as smart as I thought I was," she said wryly. She'd been working on her thesis, reflecting on whether it was really worth the effort, thinking about how hard it was to find a job in her field, wondering if she'd be better off trying to find a husband. She was lonely, and when a young man who sat down next to her in the grad school library ("he looked like Christopher Reeves") suggested that they take the rest of the night off, she was ready. A half bottle of California wine simultaneously stole away the good sense to insert her diaphragm and the ability to control her life. "At first," she said with a sigh, "I was angry. Not at him. At me. But I decided it could happen to anyone. So I've forgiven myself." Not entirely. When it was over, the feelings of guilt and regret that she'd managed to suppress finally escaped. She clutched my hand and wept.

My next patient was twenty-six, divorced, attractive. Her marriage of three years had ended partly because of her inability to have children. Now, unexpectedly, she found herself pregnant. "I just broke up with my boyfriend," she said ruefully. "I can't face being a single parent. Not on what a receptionist makes. And I can't raise a child with a guy I know would make a rotten father." Clearly, she would have preferred motherhood. Afterward, her lips compressed, she said tearfully, "I felt connected to it. But it's still for the best."

When a young rape victim is referred to the office by an agency requesting a termination of her pregnancy, she is often terrified of the encounter and by the whole procedure. It takes a lot of support to see her through it. We try to make certain there's sufficient psychological follow-up by the agency, so the memory doesn't linger on and cripple her sexually later on.

Sometimes it isn't rape, but the blind leading the blind in a society that, in too many communities, no longer places cultural restraints on kids. In the forties and fifties, a teen attraction usually led no further than the heavy necking depicted in movies of that era. Now it leads to what kids see suggested or explicitly performed in musical-beds series like "Dallas" or "Dynasty," in films with misguided PG seals of Hollywood approval, and in the moral wilderness of cable TV daytime soaps.

I sit too often at the feet of a frightened fourteen- or fifteen-year-old girl in stirrups who should be at the kitchen table doing her homework. After an unchaperoned Friday night beer party, she has her first sexual experience with a boy a year or two older. He assumes she is on the pill. (Actually, she is in her fertile midcycle.) She assumes he is experienced and

knows what he is doing. (In fact, it's his first time, too.)
Perhaps her boyfriend knows one of my sons and worries
enough about the consequences of his act to ask my advice. I
suggest the pill twice a day for three or four days. Sometimes it
brings on her period. If she has any sense, it also brings on a
resolution to steer clear of beer busts, drive-in movies where
the action isn't all on the screen, and after-school visitors of the
opposite sex when her parents aren't home.

When a pill blitz doesn't work, there is only one way out for
fifteen-year-olds. They don't understand the ramifications of
abortion, but they understand the ramifications of pregnancy.
So somehow or other they get the money. The problem comes
for indigent kids without parents or Medicaid to bail them out.
Many of them go to Planned Parenthood, and sometimes
counselors call to ask if we'll do the procedure but forego or
reduce the fee. We seldom refuse.

For young patients, nothing is more important than an
atmosphere of understanding and consideration. Most have
mothers with them. If they don't, we ask if their parents know,
and suggest it would be better if they did and could be present.
When a girl's reaction makes it clear that her family would go
to pieces, we don't insist. Our first responsibility is to the
patient.

Though some women saunter in for an abortion as noncha-
lantly as they would into a department store to buy a skirt and a
couple of blouses, most wear frozen smiles beneath sorrowful
eyes. They are easy to distinguish from the expectant women
with glowing faces who come in for prenatal care. Abortion is
no blessed event.

Some cry during the procedure, but when it's over, almost
everyone looks relieved. They've already endured weeks of
agonizing over their options. They've wept. They've stared
unseeing out the window. They've been counseled. They've
debated and disputed with boyfriends, husbands, parents. So in
many ways, the worst is over before they face the vacuum and
curette.

Abortions are accomplished in one appointment. A nurse
takes a history and does minor blood work, checking hematocrit and hemoglobin to be sure the patient isn't anemic.
Borderline cases are handled with care. The procedure can be
done with very little blood loss, but an abortion on someone
markedly anemic is just not a sensible office procedure.

If the patient doesn't know her blood type or have a Red Cross blood donor card or other documentation, we send her down the hall to the lab. If she's Rh-negative, she gets a protective injection of Rhogam so she won't develop antibodies that might be harmful in a future pregnancy. Next comes a film that explains the procedure step by step, after which it's into the examining room for me to do a pelvic, to confirm that the fetus is under twelve weeks. If the examination is equivocal, the patient undergoes a more exact ultrasound dating.

Question time follows: "Will it hurt? How badly?" If a woman has had children, she asks, "Is it like labor pains?" If she hasn't: "Will it feel like menstrual cramps?" (I explain that dilating the cervix will cause some minor pain, and the local anesthetic she'll receive usually causes cramping.) "Will the nitrous oxide gas put me to sleep?" (All it should do, I reassure, is create a relaxed feeling of well-being.)

"Will the abortion interfere with future childbearing, when I'm ready to have a baby?" (I emphasize that one or even two abortions will not have that effect, but that the woman who makes abortion her regular fallback method of birth control is headed for trouble.) "Are complications possible?" (Mild fever and a low-grade endometritis are the most common risks, but in the years my partner and I have been doing this, complications have been extremely rare.) "Can my boyfriend be present?" (If you feel you really need him, but we don't encourage it—especially if he's under eighteen. An experienced nurse will be at your side to support you, hold your hand, and talk you through the procedure.) "Can my mother come in?" (If it will make you feel better, certainly.)

Sometimes I sense feelings of hesitation or reluctance. A young woman may say, "My boyfriend [or my mother] wants me to do this." Or, "I guess I have to do this." Or even, "I don't really want to do this."

"Well," I ask, "have you considered that you don't *have* to do something you don't want to do? We all have choices in life, and it's not too late to change yours. If you're not certain, take some more time to think it over. I really don't want to do this unless you are absolutely sure."

Given that opportunity to say No, almost always they say—firmly this time: "Yes, I'm sure now. I want to do it."

But there are occasional exceptions. I remember a dark-haired sweet-faced girl of twenty—she reminded me of old

Kodachrome family keepsake snapshots of my mother—who told me sorrowfully that she wanted to get married, but her boyfriend insisted on an abortion. She had presented herself dutifully to have it done. But on the table, as my nurse placed the anesthetic mask over her face, she suddenly shook it off. "No," she said, "stop, please! I can't go through with this. Not for Carl, not for anything!"

I smiled. "That's fine," I said. She slid awkwardly off the table, returned to the examining room, dressed, and quietly left. I saw her to the door, feeling glad that I hadn't done an abortion on someone who didn't want it done.

For most patients, we use nitrous oxide and analgesia. I wait a few minutes for the local to take effect. This is no time for small talk. I want my patient to relax while she inhales the gas. It's a time for me, too, to relax, so that a few minutes from now I can perform a swift, safe abortion. I close my eyes and meditate. I am, I know, presiding over a tragic moment in my patient's life. But I don't think about whether what I'm about to do is morally right or wrong, or whether she is correct in doing what she's doing. That's all been handled beforehand.

Most patients lie quietly. When someone is really tense —younger patients understandably are—she'll cringe, press her thighs tightly together, wriggle and writhe on the table. Then, performing the procedure is almost impossible, akin to shoeing a bucking horse. But a fast-working injection of intravenous Valium abates my patient's tension. I grasp the suction curette and carefully vacuum out what we blandly and clinically refer to as "the products of conception." I follow with the curved stainless steel curette, gently probing inside the uterus with a circular scraping motion to be absolutely sure all's clear and there'll be no complications.

Unless my patient has insisted, "Please, just do it. Don't describe it," I tell her what I'm about to do before each move I make. Knowing that this or that "will hurt a bit," she also knows what won't hurt at all. Still, try as I do to make abortion painless and compassionate, for some women anesthesia blunts the pain but not the misery.

Occasionally, as I begin to scrape, a scream rips through the room. My nurse turns up the music volume to muffle, and I turn on the whirring, whirling hematocrit machine to drown out, the bleak, despairing cries of uncontrolled hysteria. I remind myself that this is anguish, not pain. But whether the hurt is psychic or physical, it hurts to be causing it.

I am seated, wearing a surgical mask and the hiss of nitrous oxide makes conversation difficult. I'm painfully aware that to the woman lying in stirrups on my table desperately wishing herself somewhere else, the abortion I am performing is Greek tragedy on a tiny but terrible scale. But I know my nurse is holding her hand, speaking softly to try to calm her. I detach myself as much as I can and complete the job as quickly as possible.

When it's over, I apologize for any pain I may have caused. My patient, embarrassed by her loss of control, often apologizes in turn. I assure her that her reaction was completely understandable and perfectly okay.

When my patient drops her paper gown in the wastebasket, dons her clothing, and departs, often she looks reborn. The weight in her womb with which she came in, the one she couldn't bear, is gone. But another weight may have replaced it, an invisible one that she'll carry around for the rest of her life.

Many would say this is a hell of a way to make a living—that I'm a profiteer reaping benefits from women's suffering. I've thought about that a lot. Probably a lot of people—patients, other doctors, even friends—have, too. Is the answer I give myself just defensive rationalization? I don't know. I do know that pretty much the same charge could be made against a doctor treating any patient who urgently needs care: the middle-aged man hemorrhaging in the hospital ER or the child dying of leukemia. I know that when I sit at the foot of the procedure table waiting for that paracervical block to take hold, I give no more thought to the payment my patient gives the receptionist than I do when I deliver a baby. Yes, I'm paid for what I do. But I don't do it just because I'm paid.

Would I be happy if abortion suddenly became as medically obsolete as the leech? If the fail-safe contraceptive methods researchers are working on suddenly proved successful? Darned right I would. Sure, a sizeable source of office revenue would instantly dry up and blow away. But I'd breathe as deep a sigh of relief as my patients would.

Would I be happy if women all opted for adoption instead of abortion? Again, yes. We do get such women occasionally, and we're happy to help them find good families to place their babies with from a long list of patients and friends unable to have children of their own. (Unfortunately, we can't do much for the hundreds of strangers who contact us from all over the country.) Jack has been placing such babies for some time, usually because their natural mothers don't believe in abortion or come in too late to have one. I started doing so only recently.

It's a wonderful solution for both baby and adoptive parents. But not many women are willing to carry a child for nine months and then give it up. It takes an unshakeable belief in the personhood of the life growing within you to be willing to go through months of stigma and discomfort to save your baby for someone else. When a woman has that strength, I'm proud to support her. I don't like doing abortions any more than women like having them done. We're both trapped by biology and circumstances.

But as long as abortions are needed—and with all the religious and political divisiveness and emotional turmoil they generate, I hope it will not be much longer—I'll be around for women who choose to terminate unwanted pregnancies. Feeling very lucky that the law is with instead of against me, and very fortunate that I was born twenty years later than Dr. Henrie.

PART THREE

BECOMING HUMAN

Leaves from an Ob/Gyn's Journal

The snow is falling outside the ski lodge in Vermont. I am euphoric at this opportunity for a break in my routine, eager to hit the slopes tomorrow. But Madalyn is strangely subdued, and the blazing fire does little to brighten her spirits. We lie quietly on the rug in front of the hearth, enjoying the warmth of the flames. Separately. Not touching. Feeling romantic, I slide an arm around her. When I try to draw her toward me, her hand unhooks my arm.

"No, Henry," she says firmly, her eyes avoiding mine. "I want to talk."

"So, talk," I say, a little ungraciously.

"I'm not happy, Henry. I haven't been for a long time." She pauses. "I've been thinking about it a lot," she continues, choosing her words carefully, "and I'm not sure I love you anymore. Right now, I'm not sure what to do. But I know our marriage is in big trouble. We can't keep going the way it's been."

"What's wrong?" I mutter, not really believing anything is wrong and nettled because her words have shattered my romantic mood as brick shatters window pane. What could be wrong? My practice is flourishing. We have three wonderful children. Money's no longer tight, we're planning to build our dream house, and we even have time for a vacation. "Why this sudden bombshell? I don't understand."

"You're right. You don't understand." Her voice is picking up strength, and the high-tensile hardness of its underlying resolution is frightening. "Maybe my speaking up is sudden, but the unhappiness isn't. I think I've been miserable for most of our marriage."

8

Madalyn's Mutiny

ON OUR WEDDING day, Madalyn's father took me aside after the ceremony. Glancing fondly at his daughter, the train of her white lace gown gathered in one hand, dancing an exuberant lindy hop with the best man, he said, "Hank, take care of my little girl." And that's what I did.

Fifteen years later in that ski lodge I found that I hadn't been doing as good a job as I thought; and, in fact, that it was no longer okay to "take care" of her. Madalyn's revelation changed forever not only my marriage but my practice of ob/gyn as well.

Her words, when they finally sunk in, stunned me. I thought I was a good husband, a husband who loved his wife, and I suppose I thought that making love to her two or three times a week—faithfully and exclusively to her—conclusively authenticated that. I also suppose that I was a totally unconscious jerk.

Consciousness didn't come easily. At first I kept thinking that the whole thing didn't make any sense. Why now, after fifteen years? If she wasn't happy all that time, why hadn't she walked out—or at least told me?

By morning (we talked all night, probably more meaningful words passed between us that weekend than in all our married years before), I think I understood why she hadn't spoken up earlier. She was young and had convinced herself that that was the way it had to be when you were married to a young doctor. He's hardly ever home, and when he is home, he's so exhausted he falls asleep right after dinner. And then the phone rings and he's gone again. "I loved you," she told me. "And I didn't really know what was wrong. I didn't want anything to be wrong."

She made up excuses rather than face the fact that something was awry in our marriage. When she was unhappy in the air force, she told herself it was the problem of two little children and the close quarters of a tiny frame house. She even felt guilty being angry. "You were out there at the hospital saving lives and bringing babies into the world," she explained. "And at least you came home. Most of the other women at the base were married to pilots who flew all over the world and were away for weeks at a time. I didn't feel I had the right to complain."

It was hard to believe it had been so bad for her and I hadn't even noticed. Every day, I went out to the work I loved, experiencing excitement, stimulation, and reward. She experienced diapers, dishes, dirty faces, and more diapers. And no one but toddlers to talk to. I had no idea how she was aching for adult conversation and companionship when I came home. All I wanted to do was unwind, sleep a few hours, and then go out again.

Of all those years in the air force, Madalyn could only remember one day that was really special. I'd always known it was a special day to her; I'd just never realized it stood alone.

I might have forgotten it entirely if Madalyn hadn't made it a permanent holiday on the Eisenberg calendar. It began on a Veterans Day at Dover Air Force Base. Her mother had offered to babysit so we could drive to Wilmington to buy something or other for the house. "We were looking for material so I could make drapes and the neighbors couldn't look in," she reminded me. "We stopped at that dinky little luncheonette and had a tuna fish sandwich and hot chocolate. I don't know why, but to me, that was so romantic and wonderful. Maybe because it was just the two of us, with no phone to call you to the hospital or kids to pull at my skirt and ask for cookies."

Every year since then Madalyn had insisted on celebrating Veterans Day in a luncheonette with tuna fish and hot chocolate. But I'd only discovered how special it was to her the previous Veterans Day, when she said she wanted that sandwich and hot chocolate, and then started to cry when I told her I wasn't hungry. I thought it was dumb, but I drove for miles to find a luncheonette sleazy enough so she could revisit that memory. I reminded her now of how magnanimous I'd been: "If you remember, I forced myself to put away a big tuna sandwich and hot chocolate. Now doesn't that qualify me as a first-class, romantic, self-sacrificing Starkist husband?"

"You may be a first-class doctor," she told me, unwilling to let me joke my way off the hook, "but you're a lousy husband. And you're not much better as a father. You're going to have to do something about both things because . . ." (I can still remember that pause; it was the moment I realized how really serious Madalyn was) "I am so close to the end of the line that I'm almost ready to get out."

My first reaction was disbelief: I couldn't be that bad. I loved her and the boys. I'd been doing all this for them.

Then defensive mechanisms came into play: If I wasn't perfect (and who is?), there was a good reason. I hadn't spent as much time with my sons as some other fathers, but that was because during the training years it had been impossible, and in the practice start-up years it had been difficult. I'd always tried to make the special Little League games and family get-togethers. Could I help it if, when we had a day at the circus planned, a patient decided to go into labor? Or if the phone summoned me to the emergency room in the middle of a birthday party?

I certainly didn't skimp on time with Madalyn out of choice. Sure, movies or dinners out were rare, but that was because up until recently we couldn't afford the babysitters. And sure, when we did go out my beeper squawked half the time and I'd have to rush off, leaving her to be driven home by friends. But wouldn't I have preferred the uninterrupted night out? True, Madalyn ate a lot of dinners alone with the boys and reheated a lot of cold ones for me—but not because I enjoyed keeping her waiting or reheated dinners. The lesson drilled into my head in internship and residency had been: When you're a doctor, your patients come first. What I hadn't realized was that the way Madalyn perceived it, the family came last.

In the months that followed, as Madalyn and I struggled to

save our relationship, I tried harder to see things through her eyes. I'd been so involved in becoming and being Dr. Eisenberg, that that perspective had never occurred to me. What I saw was that, even in the early years, our relationship wasn't anything but two lonely people living together, coming together for meals, and for sex, and for shopping, and in times of crisis. We had walked together down our predetermined path without any real questioning or looking at where we were headed and why. For me, the map had read: You're going to get married, you're going to be a doctor, you're going to have a family and a practice, and you're going to be successful. For Madalyn, the directions were only: Get married, be a supportive wife, and have a family. Now that path had taken us to a dead end.

As a "women's doctor," I thought I knew a lot about women. I did about their bodies, but not much about what went on in their heads. Madalyn, in asserting herself for the first time, taught me some things about what women want and don't want. What she didn't want was to be Mrs. Dr. Eisenberg. At least, not anymore. That was news to me. I'd always thought that was who I'd married, and for a long time, that was the way I'd wanted it. But it began to come clear to me that she was not going to be satisfied with being my satellite anymore. And the more I thought about that, the more I realized that other women—my patients—might have as many unexpressed reservations about me as Madalyn. Possibly more.

Was there a connection between the way I had taken my wife for granted, the way I had played lord and master with my family, and the way I treated my patients? Motion pictures danced through my mind:

Madalyn undergoing a breast augmentation. Me bringing home literature about it from the office. Like many others who grew up in the postwar forties, I'd been sold by the slogan: "Better things through chemistry." And I was sold on those new silicone implants that could increase a woman's breast dimensions "naturally," particularly when plastic surgeon friends reported success with them. Since Madalyn had complained about her breasts sagging after three pregnancies, I thought she might be interested.

I'd certainly never complained about her bosom, but she'd joked several times that her "squishy" bust couldn't measure up to the firm, youthful breasts of my young university campus patients. And my act of bringing home the literature and showing it to her could have seemed to her an unspoken opinion and complaint. (Possibly it was, and I just wouldn't admit it even to myself.) I thought at the time that my message was that I loved her, wanted her to look her best, and would support her if she chose to use new developments in plastic surgery to restore her former youthful shape. But maybe there was another motive. If I wasn't playing God by trying to control her life, it could be argued that I was doing so by tinkering with the life processes of creation and change.

We made an appointment for a consultation, and a few weeks later she had the surgery—in Philadelphia, so it would be her secret in Syracuse. I chose the busiest plastic surgeon in town, but busy turned out to be not necessarily best. We'd specified medium implants, but somewhere on his assembly line someone made a mistake. He implanted the largest size, and in a woman as petite as Madalyn, they looked monstrously out of proportion.

At first, she was pleased with the attention she got in shopping expeditions and on campus. Sibilant whistles accompanied her everywhere. Gentlemen eagerly sprang forward to open doors. And when she explained to puzzled women friends that her sudden prominence was the result of a new birth control pill I'd put her on, I was deluged at the office with requests for a prescription.

But within six months, Madalyn's reborn breasts hardened to the consistency of Carrara marble, and the only way she could sleep was flat on her back. When she jogged in a T-shirt on the winding road near our home, bug-eyed drivers narrowly missed crashing into trees. Miserable, she had the implants removed on the anniversary of their insertion.

Had I, I wondered now, really considered the personal aspects as well as the scientific ones before I urged the procedure on her? Had I been salesman, not medical adviser? Had I taken the time to be sure it was something she truly wanted to do? Very possibly not. And possibly I wasn't any more considerate of the feelings and unspoken needs of my patients when I urged a procedure on them.

Madalyn picking out a long dress with flowing scarf to wear. Me suggesting she'd look better in the knee-length flannel skirt and tailored white blouse. I wasn't honest with Madalyn. I didn't tell her that I wanted her to "blend in" the way I did, that the only statement I wanted her clothing to make was that she was Mrs. Eisenberg, the doctor's charming wife. I just frowned and told her how great she'd look in the skirt and blouse outfit. Most of the time, she meekly acquiesced, cheated of the right to express her individuality and flair for color and the joy she felt when she did. I'd breathe a sigh of relief. I was uncomfortable with flamboyance; it wasn't me.

Thinking about it later, I realized that was pretty dumb. It wasn't supposed to be me; it was supposed to be her. She'd felt that, but couldn't say it. Her resentment just kept building up until we got to the ski lodge. There, finally, it exploded.

When we talked it out, I was able to understand her need to dress herself for herself. To let color splash out in her clothing as it later came out in her painting. Though, I freely confess, I'm pleased when she dresses for me sometimes.

Again, there was a parallel in my practice: imposing my will, not inviting patients to express theirs. They had their babies the way I decided they should. I never even considered that they might prefer something else, or if they did, that what they preferred mattered. Could I change that as I had begun to change my attitude toward Madalyn's wardrobe preferences? Could I grant that a woman had the right to do it her way, whether it was in something as seemingly minor as the clothes she donned or as significant as the way she delivered her baby?

Madalyn in bed with a bad cold. Madalyn on the sofa with a painful headache. Me acting hostile, angry, unsympathetic.

"I don't understand it," she said one day. "How can a physician who's supposed to deal with healing people and be a caring person in the presence of illness turn into such an ogre whenever I get sick? If you do that with someone you're supposed to love, how do you act with your average patient?"

It was a good question. I couldn't answer it until I started looking at images from the past that might have had something to do with it. When I did, that boyhood fight with Rocky played back on my mental monitor. I realized that from that humiliating afternoon on I had hated weakness—hated it in myself and disliked it in others. So, clearly part of the problem was a personality defect I had to work on. But my attitude had been strongly reinforced in medical school and in training, where weakness was something you weren't supposed to have—and if you did have it, you hid it. When I saw weakness

in my wife, even wearing the face of illness, I found it
intolerable.

I didn't mind it in patients with clearly defined physical
problems. I could call that an illness and treat it. It was
generalized ills that I was uncomfortable with: undefined
pelvic pain, headaches or menstrual cramps that appeared to
have large emotional components. Of course. The surface of
psychosomatics had barely been scratched in my training. No
one had ever given us the news that most patient complaints
don't require a top-notch diagnostician and a battery of lab
tests, just a compassionate human being and some reassuring
words.

Yet from me (and, I'd wager, from a good many of my
colleagues), those patients, though the most numerous of all,
got compassion least of all. Patients flood doctors offices with
somatic complaints of emotional origin—reactions to personal
or professional circumstances they find too difficult to face up
to. We react by giving them every lab test we can think of, by
wishing they would take their pains to another doctor, by
referring to them as "crocks," and (with our so-nice-to-see-
you-again smiles on automatic pilot) by secretly resenting the
stubborn failure of their maladies to succumb to our remedies.
They certainly don't do a lot for our omniscient self-images.

"Can you imagine," Madalyn had asked me scornfully,
"going to a doctor who doesn't like someone who is sick?" I
had to wonder if any of my patients had ever asked themselves
that question. If they had, it could easily have happened
without my knowing it. It's like bad breath. Patients never tell
you. They just drop out of your practice and go to someone
else. As it happened, the only one willing to tell me was my
wife, and it took her years to muster up the courage.

All those years, I'd continued blithely along thinking everything was fine—in our relationship and in my practice. It was
not until I looked at myself in the glaring spotlight of
Madalyn's dissatisfaction that I began to see that I needed to
take a closer look at relationships with my patients as well. If I
had been blind to my own wife's needs, how much more must I
have failed to detect the needs of other men's wives?

Leaves from an Ob/Gyn's Journal

My eyes are closed and the darkened room is quiet as I listen to a gentle passage from Leboyer's *Birth Without Violence*. In soothing tones, a rebirther beside my bed urges me to re-create my own birth experience. "Relax . . . relax deeply . . . breathe deeply . . . focus on your breathing . . . feel the warmth of the fluid surrounding your bare body . . . hear the gentle beat of your mother's heart . . ."

I enter a serene alpha-state guided fantasy and am transported back to the womb by the whispered urgings: "You are in the warm safety of your mother's body . . . you are happy, comfortable . . ." I feel peaceful, calm, a sense of floating tranquilly in a private sea of amniotic fluid.

"Birth is approaching," the voice warns. Suddenly, my voyage is violently interrupted. A large hand grips my ankle. I am yanked roughly out of the wonderful warmth and darkness of my mother and into a world of chilling cold and blinding light.

Naked, dangled in midair, I feel pain slap my buttocks, and I howl my anguish with my first breath of air. Someone carries me down a long corridor, and I sense that I am being separated from my mother. My crying intensifies. Terror envelops me.

9

The Great Patient Revolt

IF MADALYN'S REVELATION in that ski lodge hadn't shocked me into opening my mind, I don't think I would have been receptive when, browsing in a bookstore one day, I spotted the title *Rebirthing,* by Leonard Orr. Intrigued, I picked it up. It suggested that the experience of birth, as practiced by modern obstetricians, is a rude awakening, a nasty time for the fetus becoming a person. It warned that the imprint of that trauma could remain with the individual for a lifetime, affecting behavior and health.

The rationale was simple. In the womb, oxygen is delivered through the placenta and umbilical blood vessels. After the baby is born, its lungs take over and breathing begins. But there is a transition period of from three to ten minutes after birth during which both systems work in tandem. Even though the lungs are operational, the placenta continues to function, supplying oxygenated blood to the fetus. Only when the cord stops pulsing does the placenta cease supplying oxygen to the newborn.

Routinely cutting the umbilical cord immediately, the book hypothesized, is as frightening to the infant as a policeman's chokehold is to a prisoner. There is an alarm reaction: Breathe through these untried lungs or die. Upending the infant and spanking it may be an effective way to shock the newborn into switching from one respiratory system to another, but it's also barbaric. That trauma, the rebirthers suggested, was why throughout our lives we associate breathing difficulties with imminent death, and why so many of us, particularly when tense, find it "hard to breathe."

It all seemed so obvious, so reasonable, that I was amazed that I had never considered that connection. Why shouldn't there be an imprint in the adult mind of life's first, possibly most traumatic experience? A sort of video tape that can be played back later on the VCR of the subconscious. There's lots of evidence in psychiatric literature that images from the past, even of early infancy, may be vividly recalled under analysis or hypnosis. Influences from the past, good and bad, subconsciously direct present actions. You meet a girl, and her cologne reminds your subconscious so much of your mother (who wore it, too) that you marry her. You hear a snatch of a vaguely familiar tune, and you inexplicably become panicky. What you don't know, but your subconscious does, is that that tune was playing on the radio in the dentist's office the first time you ever had a tooth drilled.

Shortly after reading the book, I saw an ad in the local paper that there was to be a rebirthing seminar in Syracuse. I arranged to attend it. Impressed by what I heard about the impact of the moment of birth on the rest of our lives, I decided that as an obstetrician it wouldn't hurt to have done to me what I did to others. I'd always regretted I couldn't experience childbirth from the point of view of the mother. Maybe I could at least experience it from the viewpoint of the child. I signed up for a rebirthing. (Would I be thought a flake? I didn't care. It sounded interesting.)

Was the recreation of my birth experience real or imaginary? It's hard to believe that I could dredge up from somewhere deep in my unconscious with such vivid clarity a forty-year-old experience—if it was my experience. If, indeed, I was a breech baby—a footling—that's only a one in twenty-five occurrence and would make my rebirthing experience all the more surprising. Whether it was memory or imagination doesn't matter. Rebirthing awoke in me an awareness of fetal consciousness that hadn't been there before. It reminded me that birth isn't just a mechanical exodus, it's a pivotal emotional experience, an aspect every bit as important as the

Apgar score. It might be a good idea for babies to grade us as we grade them. I remember the general practitioner who took care of me in my early years as a caring and wonderful man. But if my rebirthing memories are correct, I'd have to flunk him in obstetrics.

The rebirthing experience kindled a tiny flame in me, one that said, "There is something more to delivering babies than I have yet experienced." Actually, the flame was probably *re*kindled. Nearly ten years earlier, I had had another experience that told me the same thing. But it seemed that at that point neither I nor the rest of the world was quite ready to believe it.

It was 1967 when my receptionist buzzed me to say that Dr. Aubry was on the line.

"Dick," I said, "I hear you're off to the wars."

"That's right. From now on, you'll have to call me Captain Aubry. But it'll be a long distance call. Saigon or someplace like that. That's why I wanted to talk to you. I have a patient in her first trimester I'd like to refer to you—the wife of an English prof at the university. Think you can fit her in?"

Dick Aubry was a professor at Upstate Medical Center, one of the best and the brightest, and later to become its Director of Obstetrics. "I'll be happy to take her on," I said.

"Good, but there is one thing you should know. I've gotten interested in Lamaze techniques lately, and Mrs. Green is a Lamaze patient. There's nobody else in town doing it, but I told her I thought you were open to new ideas and might be willing to try it."

I *was* open to new ideas. But mostly they were ideas that came from medical journals, not from patients. And though I didn't know much about the Lamaze technique than that it was named for the French obstetrician who developed it, the concept seemed a little far out. But I respected Dick and so decided to give it a try.

Karen Green was intelligent, enthusiastic, and I liked her on sight. It's well that I did and that she was an exuberant feminist, not an abrasive one. Otherwise, at that stage in my life, I could never have accepted her defining the rules of our patient-doctor relationship.

She wisely began by giving me a copy of *Thank You, Dr. Lamaze* by Marjorie Karmel and suggesting that I read it before making up my mind whether or not to take her as a patient. After nearly ten years of delivering babies, birth was as old hat to me as navy blue ribbons to a milliner, but I was deeply moved by the author's description of her childbirth experience and the joy that seemed to flow from it. Her description of the Pavlovian conditioning that helped her through the experience feeling little pain was startling. To an ob who routinely used medication to ease the agonies of labor and delivery, the thought that a nonmedicated approach to dealing with the pain was possible was tantalizing. So tantalizing that it wasn't until I'd turned the last page that I realized I'd missed the first period of a Syracuse home basketball game I'd been looking forward to all week. Before leaving for the game, I picked up the phone to call Karen and say one word: Yes.

My reason wasn't just enthusiasm for the Lamaze method. I had recognized pieces of myself in the patronizing obstructionist doctors the author had met in the U.S. when she tried to replicate in New York her Paris experience with Dr. Lamaze. The portrait she painted of these obs was unflattering, and I was determined not to resemble them.

We learned together, and more often than not, my patient was my teacher. When the big night arrived, I'm not sure who was more excited, the eager couple or the anxious doctor.

I was already waiting when Karen Green was brought into the labor suite at Community General. It was difficult to tell that she was in active labor. Unlike so many of my patients, she didn't double over in pain, grimacing tightly, with each painful contraction. Instead, she closed her eyes and concentrated on her breathing exercises.

"No butting in when I'm doing my breathing and panting," Karen warned between contractions, when she was settled in a labor room. "And no examining me or talking to me when I'm having a contraction. I don't want to be distracted when I most need to concentrate." It was difficult for me, after all the years of taking charge, to stand back and not interfere with Karen's labor. But for the first time I could remember, I followed the patient's orders.

One of my greatest advance misgivings about this whole experiment was having a father in the labor room. We'd never done it, and I had to get special permission from the chief of the department. But Rick's presence worked out exceedingly well. I was impressed with how helpful he was, wiping Karen's brow, feeding her ice chips, reminding her of her breathing exercises during contractions, her relaxation techniques between them. I found I didn't resent his presence as I'd feared I might. With his help, and her Lamaze training, Karen handled her contractions calmly. Early on, when I might routinely have administered a shot of Demerol, I kept my hands in my pocket.

As the contractions increased to every two minutes, Karen's legs started to tremble—an indication she was entering the transitional phase of labor, the one that leads into the pushing and delivering stage. A pelvic confirmed the fact that her cervix was nearly eight centimeters dilated. "It won't be long now," I told her. When she grunted, "But how many centimeters?" I could see that she felt my be-a-nice-little-patient reply was patronizing. It was difficult to keep in mind that in this birth, the patient was my partner.

In the delivery room, our experiment continued—though hospital rules did not allow the father to join us. After twenty minutes of well-organized pushing by Karen, the baby's head had not yet crowned. That was the moment I frequently gave an epidural to numb the lower body, then gently used forceps to ease the baby out with no help from mother. But not this time, I reminded myself.

An hour and fifteen minutes later, little Amy Green emerged into the world, pink and spunky. I don't know who was more exhilarated—Karen or me. I hadn't been as excited about a delivery in years, maybe since my very first.

Karen Green was the first woman I'd ever attended whom I looked upon as more than just the package the baby came wrapped in. I marveled that she was so absolutely radiant even after all those hours of labor, with no medication at all. Her head framed by a damp halo of dark hair, she had tears in her eyes as she thanked me for delivering her wonderful baby.

"I didn't deliver her," I told her. "You did. I just assisted." At that moment, I was confident that my practice of obstetrics would never be the same.

It was a nice sentiment. And I meant it. But reality was a brick wall—a hospital wall. The hospital was not receptive to Lamaze births. And I suppose that I wasn't fully ready for it either; I was too rigid, too up-tight. Gradually my enthusiasm waned, and I found my practice little different from before Karen Green—with the exception that now I had no qualms about allowing a woman to deliver with no medication at all if that was her wish.

Alice Wallace's wish ten years later was a lot more complicated. Alice and her husband, Peter, were good friends of mine and parents-to-be who'd been rebirthed about the time I was. They were so impressed with Leboyer's *Birth Without Violence* that on their next visit they asked me to deliver the baby by the Leboyer method. Even more thoroughly than Karen had, Alice laid out the rules by which she expected to deliver.

I respected and admired Alice, but I saw that to satisfy her requirements, I would have to back off from a bunch of positions that I'd always thought important. I wasn't at all sure I could—or should.

"I don't want an enema when my contractions start," she told me—sweetly but firmly. "And I don't want my pubic area shaved. It's degrading, and I've heard that the postpartum burning and itching as the hair grows back is uncomfortable."

"You have to understand," I said, "that doctors have been ordering these things for a long time, and not just on whim." As the doctor, the one with all the answers, I figured a little education would change her mind.

"The reason for the enema is twofold," I explained. "First of all, a bowel filled with hard fecal matter can compress the birth canal, making delivery more difficult. And secondly, any fecal material in the intestine tends to be forced out during the pushing phase. It's embarrassing for the mother. And it contaminates the sterile area where the baby will be landing. A timely enema reduces the problem. As for shaving the pubic area, that's just another precaution to ensure a sterile field. If you had a wrist operation, the surgeon would order you shaved clear up to the shoulder. The enema and pubic shaving are routine insurance based on the germ theory of disease."

For a long time, I had carried the baggage of certainty about all the beliefs accumulated in my years of training. I was a doctor who knew what was best for the patient, and that was the way I practiced. I'd become moderately successful after five or six years, and increasingly successful after that. Why change my philosophy when there were so many women out there who accepted it? But Alice was different. She was of a new breed, and she shook my certainty.

"If anyone believes in the germ theory," she argued, "the French do. After all, Pasteur was a Frenchman. Do you think

Leboyer would be doing these things if they resulted in higher infection rates?''

When I double-checked, I found that she was right. Recent studies had shown the infection rate no higher when the pubic area wasn't shaved. In fact, some studies found it lower because the tiny nicks caused by shaving can be breeding sites for bacteria. As for enemas, research indicated that the compression of the birth canal is highly unlikely if a woman has had a bowel movement within the past twenty-four hours and no fecal mass is felt in her rectum on examination. Since many women experience diarrhea with the onset of labor (one of nature's little strokes of genius), the presence of a significant amount of fecal matter is highly unusual. In addition, I found, many doctors were already doing deliveries without enemas. They avoided exposing the infant to infection (a remote possibility to begin with) by whisking away any excreted fecal matter with the disposable gauze pads under the woman's buttocks and replacing the pads with fresh ones. With one blow, Alice had killed two of my sacred cows.

There was more. Arm and leg restraints, too, would have to go. No one had ever clamped my feet into stirrups and pinioned my hands in restraints at my sides, and now thinking about it for the first time, I could imagine the sense of helpless terror that I'd feel. But what about the possibility of her kicking out at the height of a contraction and interfering with my work? Or of her lashing out with unbound hands into the sterile field in which the baby was to arrive? Alice assured me that she would be in control. She wouldn't kick her legs or swing her arms.

To do it Alice's way was to surrender a great deal. In the medical model, the all-knowing doctor makes the laws and the patient trustingly obeys them. Alice was proposing we turn this model inside out. But on contemplation, I had to agree she had a point. Here in this moment of great and awesome power, when woman and God are working together to bring a child into the world, should she not be free and unfettered to experience that power? Surely, doing it the way the patient wanted it done—supporting, exhorting, showing that I cared, letting her know that this was her experience, interfering only when necessary—was worth a try.

When I agreed, I found Alice was not through with me yet. She made an additional and far more unsettling request: ''I want a home delivery.'' The Wallaces weren't the first couple to make that request, but I'd always said flatly, ''No, it's unsafe. It's a long backward step into the Dark Ages. Too many things can go wrong.'' But Madalyn and I and the Wallaces had such a warm relationship that I felt somehow that it would be a wonderful experience and everything would go right.

Alice was in her fourth month, radiant and active. I knew that clinically she was a very healthy woman, with a normal pelvis and no risk factors in her history. Equally important, her intention was to do it, and when someone has that strength of intention, it creates an irresistible force. I agreed.

Peter's voice was calm and confident when he called early on the morning of a Fourth of July holiday to say that Alice was ready. I was, too. I'd packed a bag at the office with everything in it I could imagine needing, and it was sitting in my car trunk all set to go.

Madalyn was anxious but excited, unsure of what she could contribute in an emergency, but happy to be there if only as a friend for this special moment. There was no emergency. Alice delivered in her bedroom, and it was different from anything I'd ever done before. Leboyer's book was our text. It was beautiful—no hospital rules and regulations, no distractions, no nurses, no changes of shifts, no bright lights, no spanking. Not even the need for an episiotomy. Alice didn't tear—almost unheard of in someone having a first baby—and the baby had an immediately perfect Apgar.

The cord still attached, the tiny newborn was bathed in a basin of warm water by Peter and Madalyn at Alice's bedside. She seemed to appreciate the return to the womblike environment and looked around contentedly. Her lifeline to her mother wasn't cut until it stopped pulsing, giving her plenty of time to switch respiratory systems. Finally placed in her joyful mother's arms, the child was peaceful, contented (Hillary has continued to be a delightful and unusual child), and the very next day her happy parents, with Alice in remarkably fine condition, took her to the office of a pediatrician I'd previously arranged for them to see.

This time there was no doubt that my practice of ob would never be the same. The Wallaces had helped Madalyn tug me—not exactly kicking and screaming like a newborn, but with a good many mental reservations—off my demigodlike professional pedestal. And I, who'd always acted as though I was the one having the baby, learned to take a backseat to the real stars of the delivery room: mother and child.

Not a moment too soon. I'd performed that "miracle of birth" 1,000 times or more. I didn't think of it as a bore, but it had become something of a chore. Science and technology ruled my practice. I meticulously followed my medical journals' latest and most modern dictates, from amniocentesis to zygote studies in twins. But the fizz was gone. Delivery had become a mechanical, joyless service to be rendered. The idea was to do a good job, avoid complications, and get it over with as soon as possible. There was no challenge, no excitement. Most deliveries were easy, routine, and repetitious—like changing the oil every 2,000 miles. I'd become, it seemed to me, a kind of baby mechanic.

That day told me something. In order for me to really open up my life, to be the kind of person Madalyn wanted me to be, that I now wanted to be, I had to be willing to experience new things, to be open to new ideas, even if that meant reexamining and occasionally rejecting solemnly proclaimed old truths. After all, old truths were continually becoming new fallacies. It was less than a hundred years since an esteemed physician had warned at a convention of the American Gynecological Society that infertility was caused by the wearing of high heels—that the unnatural elevation tipped the wearer's uterus. And only a few years later, jolts of electricity to the embryo were hailed as a new scientific treatment for ectopic pregnancy —though they killed the mother as often as the baby. At about the same time, the ultimate solution to the problem of "hysterical disorders" in women was declared to be the removal of the ovaries. The trick, I realized, was to save the baby while periodically changing its bathwater. Therein lay not only greater professional satisfaction but perhaps even a return to my young resident's enthusiasm, when everything was new, different, and for the first time.

With such results, and after so rewarding an experience, you might think that I'd make home deliveries a specialty. Not so. Jack and I considered it seriously, but concluded that there were just too many good reasons to avoid them. If I've learned anything in obstetrics, I've learned that life-threatening situations (for mother or baby) can arise in seconds. Without warning (except via a fetal monitor, not available at home), a fetus trying to make its way into the world can go from being okay to being not okay to being critical and needing the immediate salvation of a cesarean section—which requires the sterile enviornment and high-tech equipment of a delivery room. The mother can unexpectedly hemorrhage postpartum and go into shock, or suffer large tears of the vagina or cervix that require blood or plasma tranfusions or anesthesia for suturing. The placenta could separate prematurely or the cord wind around the baby's neck—both of which could threaten the oxygen supply to the fetus, and either of which might require immediate surgical delivery. In many instances there is absolutely no way to get to a hospital in time, unless the patient happens to live across the street or around the corner.

If the attendant at a home birth is not experienced, the risk is greater: If, for example, the membranes rupture and there's greenish meconium in the fluid, it could signal that the baby is in trouble. Or it could be old meconium from the cord around the fetus's neck three weeks before labor began and have absolutely no significance. A fetal monitor helps make the distinction.

I suppose anyone has the right to make personal choices in life—even to jump off the Golden Gate bridge. I wouldn't say, ''Go ahead and jump!'' but I might think twice about plunging in to the rescue. If a couple chooses home birth, based on their instinct that it's going to be all right, that's their prerogative. But it's not health care that I feel safe in providing.

Just one hemorrhage or compromised infant, and I'd live to regret it. But without backup hospital resources and technology, my patient or her baby might not. What you'd do in a perfect world—one free, at any rate, of peer pressure and plaintiff's lawyers—and what you actually do in the imperfect one we live in are two entirely different things. Recently, I read of a doctor in rural upstate New York who found that out. He was driven out of practice by the state because he did home births. What his results were I don't know. I do know that the suspension of his license must have left his world a shambles.

I had proven to my own satisfaction that home births can be beautiful. I chose to lobby at my hospital for the closest thing to them: deliveries in a room that looks and feels like home. It wasn't too hard a sell. Administrators and more conservative obs understand that if a hospital doesn't have birthing rooms in today's world with the consumer in the driver's seat, it's going to lose patients to hospitals that do. Now we have them—with easy-chairs, pictures on the walls, chintz curtains. All the comforts of home, but with the security of the hospital outside the door.

The comforts of home are psychologically important for the mother and father in the birth triad, but don't mean much to the newborn. What does, however, I feel is coming into the world in a peaceful way, as Leboyer had blueprinted it. So I dimmed the lights for normal deliveries. And I reconsidered a hasty cutting of the umbilical cord. No one clamps a cow's cord, or a collie's. When it stops pulsing, the mother bites it off. So I saw that I had an opportunity to affect in a positive way the well-being of many hundreds, even thousands of newborns. And, like many, if not most, of my colleagues—some of whom came to it earlier, some later—that's what I've done. When a newborn enters the scene these days there's no rush to cut the cord, except in cases where not clamping immediately would be harmful—such as with Rh-sensitized infants, or a baby already in respiratory distress who needs to be resuscitated. The transition from nonassisted breathing to lung power is smooth and natural.

Though I'd realized as long ago as Karen Green's delivery that pain medication wasn't an automatic given in childbirth, I'd still been giving it almost automatically. Most often that had been in the form of an epidural block, in which the anesthesia is injected into the space outside the spinal cord, bathing nerve roots in the area and numbing the patient from the injection site down. Two drawbacks to routine use became apparent in the education I got from Karen Green, the Wallaces, and others. First of all, many mothers don't like it because it turns the last stages of labor into a nonexperience. They can't feel the contractions, so they feel they're not experiencing labor. Second, administered as it is well into the active phase of labor, anesthesia can interfere with the normal rotation of the baby as it moves into the best position for delivery, necessitating the use of forceps or otherwise complicating delivery.

I was proud of my skill with forceps. When I started practice, these long curved steel fingers were almost routinely used to shorten the second stage of labor and "gently" pry the baby from the birth canal. But now I realized that if I walked into the nursery and clamped a pair of cold metal pincers around the head of a newborn to tug him out of his crib, the result would most certainly be a terror response. Why should extracting him from the birth canal that way be any less terrifying?

Also in the armamentarium of modern obstetrical torture implements—not devised to torment the fetus but having that effect—is the internal fetal monitor. Again, if I attached a clip to the newborn's scalp after birth, he'd certainly cry out in pain. Similarly, I suspect that when the clip is attached before birth to monitor the fetal condition during labor, the discomfort is there. We just don't hear the cry. So, though this type of monitoring is a somewhat more accurate way to gather information, I resolved to use noninvasive external monitoring whenever possible.

Because some women are uncomfortable even with the external monitor—which requires a belt attached around the abdomen with one monitor to read the fetal heartbeat and another belt with a gauge to pick up contractions—I monitor continuously only in high-risk situations. This gives the woman in labor the chance to walk around between monitoring moments. If she strenuously objects even to that, I try to create a situation in which we share our feelings and concerns. She tells me what's worrying her. I tell her what's worrying me. That way, we each make clear what we can afford to give up and where our "uncrossable line" is, so that we can compromise.

I make it clear that I want to assist her to have her delivery her way. If signs are good (amniotic fluid is clear, the baby is in the head-down vertex position, and what I see in fifteen or twenty minutes of monitoring early in labor looks pretty good), I probably won't require any further monitoring until the delivery stage. If the signs aren't good, or if they change for the worse, I let her know that she will go back on the monitor.

I find that to most women, however, the monitor is a very welcome birth tool. That sweet sound of a regular fetal heartbeat is the most beautiful music they can hear during labor. In lengthy or high-risk labors, with considerable stress on the fetus in the birth canal, each reassuring beat tells them that their baby is A-okay.

I didn't chuck my old way of practicing obstetrics and adopt a new one in the twenty-four hours after Alice Wallace's delivery. Some changes took months, even years, to effect. Some things I'm still learning.

Recently we had a patient who was so demanding I almost told her to go elsewhere. Liza Brody wanted her sister, a midwife from Vermont, to deliver her. She wanted her husband and mother with her, as well as her sister (something we couldn't swing because of hospital rules limiting coaches to two). We ask all our ob patients to fill out a preference list, which accompanies their records to the hospital, and there were more than forty special requests on Liza's birth plan. She did not want a shave or an episiotomy, an enema or IV, a fetal monitor or artificial rupture of membranes, labor stimulants or pain medication. She wanted to wear her own clothes, have unrestricted mobility, and free access to the bathroom. And she wanted to record the event with camera and tape recorder. My first reaction was negative.

When she arrived at the hospital there was an initial period when we tested each other, each wondering how far the other would go. But her birthing was a marvelous experience for me, as well as for her. During part of her labor she stood upright, supported by her husband and sister, bending at the knees and waist with each contraction. She also did some pushing on the toilet with pillows behind her. Her sister, with special permission I'd been able to arrange with the chief of ob/gyn, eased the nine-pound baby out—amazingly without a tearing. They thanked me enthusiastically. I returned the thanks. I'd picked up a couple of new birthing positions and expanded the frontiers of my flexibility. I owed them at least as much as they owed me.

If I hadn't already been working with a midwife, I certainly would have balked at my patient's delivery being assisted by one. But Jack and I had had a midwife on our staff since the early 1980s. Ellie McLees had been an ob nurse at Community General and decided to train as a certified nurse-midwife. Jack and I told her to give us a call when she got her certification. She did and we hired her, but it took a lawyer to win her hospital privileges. The only other midwife delivering in a Syracuse hospital was at another institution.

As part of the bargain struck with the hospital, careful protocols were drawn up outlining in great detail those things she had to call us for consultation on and those she could do herself—when we had to be there and when we didn't. At first, everyone watched her every move to make sure she didn't overstep her privileges. There was some early territorial conflict between her and the nursing staff. Although, in a sense, one of them, by virtue of a couple of added years of training, was bearing more responsibility, earning more money, and having more fun. But those tensions soon dissolved, and so well have the age-old and new skills that Ellie practices been accepted that two other nurse-midwives, employed by another local ob, have since been awarded hospital privileges. And we're thinking of hiring another ourselves.

When a patient comes into our office, she's told that we are a team that will take her to term: Jack, Ellie, and I. We have a rotational call system, and one of us will deliver her. Ellie's been a heavy hitter on the team from the first, developing a postpartum program and patient education materials, and spending a lot of time discussing things we know are important, like nutrition, that we don't always have time to go into in detail.

The first real test of our practice relationship came with the first patient who declared a preference for a midwife at her delivery. I said nothing, but I suspected moodily that it said something about this new patient's negative feelings toward doctors.

Now, instead of feeling bruised and wounded, I make a special effort to earn such patients' trust, so that if their deliveries happen when I'm on call, we can both be happy. I want them to know something that I only recently discovered: that midwives don't have an exlusive patent on knowing how to communicate caringly with patients.

But not every patient wants a midwife, a drugless labor, or a homelike birthing room. In fact, not every patient wants Lamaze, Leboyer, or any part of Le Modern Approach. I have to admit that, much as I enjoy shared responsibility, it's refreshing and less stressful—no negotiations, just simple prescription—when I get a good old-fashioned patient every once in a while. The preference lists of these women let me know right up front that they want an epidural during delivery —they don't want to feel the contractions. One came in the other day who didn't want to feel anything. She's only twenty-five, but she sounded like her own grandma.

"Spare me that childbirth education and deep breathing stuff," she said on her first visit. "This is my fourth baby, and for me there's only one way to have them. Give me a general anesthetic, put me to sleep, and wake me up when it's all over." I could see there was no use arguing. Besides, it's kind of fun playing God now and then.

Leaves from an Ob/Gyn's Journal

Like a gaggle of gosling following mother goose to the brook, a covey of Philadelphia General Hospital interns and residents trails respectfully after the chief of the ob/gyn service as he rounds from bed to bed and ward to ward. I am among them.

Dr. Williamson's black leather wingtip shoes gleam as though fresh from a rendezvous with a street corner bootblack. His softly lustrous gray tweed suit fits as though a small but dedicated army of custom tailors sewed it upon his lithe frame. Everyone reveres him. He possesses all the things I hope some day to have, and he is all I want to be. But my relationship with him consists principally of worship from afar and noting any treatment he orders on my patients' charts.

He pauses briefly beside a middle-aged woman with a post-operative vesico-vaginal fistula, propped up in bed reading a copy of *Reader's Digest* at arm's length. "Order an ophthalmological consult for Mrs. Sweeney," Dr. Williamson commands. "She's going to be spending a lot of time in bed, and we ought to fix up that hyperopia of hers so she can read with a little less trouble."

"Excuse me, Dr. Williamson," one of the brasher residents challenges. "As an ob/gyn, isn't the patient's vision a little out of your line?"

Williamson turns and eyes him thoughtfully. "Strictly speaking," he says mildly, "you're right. But there's one thing I try to remember: I'm concerned with the whole patient, not just her breasts and pelvic organs. I'm a doctor first and an ob/gyn second."

10

Off the Pedestal

IT TOOK ME years to realize how important that little comment of Dr. Williamson's was that morning in Philadelphia. It was drowned out by words in my training that I thought far more significant: "A unilateral pain in the lower abdomen accompanied by vaginal bleeding may signal . . ." Or, "The treatment of choice for fibroids is . . ." Or, "You grasp the scalpel this way . . ."

Fortunately, the recognition that there's more to being a doctor than just being a good technician and getting good results came before it was too late for me to do anything but turn the thought over endlessly in my mind while rocking on a retirement porch somewhere. Thanks, again, to Madalyn.

I couldn't expect my patients to tell me. Why should they? We all have Passing Ships relationships in our lives—with unfriendly neighbors, brusque colleagues, disinterested store checkout clerks. We learn to expect and accept them. Exceptions come as pleasant surprises. In any case, the doctor who treats you like a common cold instead of a person is okay as long as he knows his stuff. So much the better if he manages to force his facial muscles into a smile of greeting. It may not look as if he means it, but at least, he's trying.

If even my best patients wouldn't tell me, Madalyn did. She made me see that I had wrapped myself up in *materia medica* like a mummy and that, like a mummy, I found it difficult to bend. As a husband, it made it difficult to have a complete relationship. As a doctor, it made my relationships with patients perfunctory and unrewarding.

If Madalyn made me start thinking about humanizing my practice of medicine, a remark by my partner, Jack, made me take action. Jack presented me with evidence that I needed to rearrange the furniture in my head when he said in his quiet, low key way, "Henry, I've had a couple of patients tell me lately that they'd rather see me than you. I don't know their reasons, but I figured you'd want me to tell you."

My first reaction was embarrassment, my second rationalization. Of course, some patients would naturally prefer Jack to me. Some would prefer me to Jack.

But I knew there could be more to it than that, and I didn't want anyone leaving the office believing I didn't care about them. Nor did I want to appear godlike and intimidating to my patients—which, God knows, I probably had been for years. I wanted to be loved, but I would settle for being approachable.

Still, it's one thing to have that as your purpose and another to communicate it to patient after patient, day after day after day. So I started doing mental deep-knee bends to figure out how to change.

If I needed a role model, the caring silver-haired GP who'd delivered my sister-in-law's first child would be as good as any. "I was nineteen years old and terrified," she told me, "lying in the delivery room. Then I heard Dr. Zoll's voice as he came off the elevator. It was as if I'd been given an intravenous tranquilizer. Instantly, I felt calm and relaxed. I realized later that I never felt another pain after he arrived. The delivery was so easy I told him I'd have a dozen." It was a good bet Dr. Zoll wasn't wrapped up in *materia medica*.

But when I thought about it, I realized I already had a role model of my own. One of the most beloved obs I could remember was an attending at Yale, whom we residents looked upon as something of an eccentric. Why, we wondered, was Dr. Wilkes living in the fuddy-duddy obstetrical past? Why didn't he take advantage of new techniques that even we, his juniors in years and experience, were familiar with?

The "more modern" obs at Yale let fully dilated patients push for twenty minutes, then administered saddle blocks or epidurals and carefully delivered the baby with forceps. Wilkes waited patiently for nature to take its course. Now I know his reasons, but then I didn't understand, though it should have been obvious from his results. Along with the hospital's lowest incidence of inductions, he had the lowest incidence of vaginal lacerations and postpartum bleeding. And his patients loved him. That, I thought at the time, was nice—but less important than learning how to use forceps with flair.

Later, my early Lamaze patients convinced me that that old-fashioned eccentric from Yale had had the right idea. My eyes were opened to a kind of medical practice I suppose I knew existed, but hadn't really believed was compatible with modern obstetrics. One in which the doctor moves beyond the technical sphere of medicine to the human part, develops caring relationships with his patients, and provides not only the services he wants to give, but those his patients want.

I made some false starts trying to get closer to people. One was experimenting with pot. People talked about the way marijuana could open up a closed personality. I thought it would make me bloom. It only made me forgetful. But my explorations into the human potential movement, at about the same time, taught me something valuable about human relations. And the first lesson I learned was how to make contact with my closest human relation: my wife. Not in the self-centered way I always had, relating to her as an appendage, but as a person in her own right.

No more returning home and flipping on the TV, flopping down in an armchair and groaning, "Boy, am I tired!" Madalyn was exhausted at the end of the day, too. Instead of just asking, "What's for dinner?" I asked, "Anything I can do to help?" And I began doing things. Ordinary things that in other homes might have been taken for granted. Drying dishes. Picking up toys. A quick vacuuming of a coffee grounds spill. Instead of focusing conversation on my day at the office, I asked about hers. Instead of complaining when she wanted to see friends I wasn't crazy about, I made the effort to enjoy their company. (To my surprise, I found I did.) Instead of replying, when she asked me to go to a parent-teacher conference at Jordan's or Bruce's school, "That's your department!" I began to participate and to be available at home to discuss our children's problems.

When Madalyn, more or less in desperation, had taken her first art lesson—at the Officers' Club at Dover Air Force Base—I had been patronizingly pleased. Here was something to broaden my homebound wife's horizons. But now I became as serious about her work as she was. I suggested titles for her paintings, accompanied her to shows. When, fearing rejection, she hesitated on the sidewalk outside a Manhattan or a Woodstock gallery with her samples, her flagging courage revived after a you-can-do-it-honey pep talk. Come on, aren't those all things any spouse should do? Sure. But I'd always considered myself a doctor first, a husband second. I'd never done ''spouse things'' before. When I regressed—I still regress—Madalyn, spunkier with each new achievement and success, was never slow to remind me. ''Come off it, Henry!'' was the way she aptly put it. The ''it'' was my pedestal.

I'd made contact with my wife; now I wanted to make contact with the other women in my life, my patients. For years, my opening gambit, one I'd picked up in training from my seniors, was, ''Do you have any problems today?'' It was the right question for me then, because it suggested a narrow answer: about troubling body dysfunctions, which is what I was comfortable talking about. Because it let me set the parameters, it kept me in command. Opening the floor to more complex issues, even to friendly banter, wasn't easy for me. I worried about the kinds of responses I'd get if I asked, ''Is there anything on your mind that you'd especially like to talk about?'' or ''What's new in your life?'' But I was determined to try. And I've been pleasantly surprised at the things that pop up when I press the button.

Mostly, of course, I still hear about bodily problems: staining, vaginitis, premenstrual syndrome. No matter how open-ended my question many patients are still programmed to give a medical, rather than personal, response. If they're troubled by an acute medical condition, that's only common sense. But others take my cue and raise sexual and marital problems. Some go further, blurting out their frustrations, concerns, fears about their emotional health, their children, their husbands, careers, even employers. It's almost as though all these years they've been waiting for someone to ask.

''I've been thinking for some time,'' said Mary Rogers, an attractive thirty-two-year-old responding to my open-ender, ''about becoming a single parent. I want very much to have a baby. Friends who aren't parents are very supportive, but friends who are, especially single parents, think I'm crazy. What do you think?''

That was a question she'd have been unlikely to ask the old Dr. Eisenberg. But it was one ''the new improved'' Dr.

Eisenberg felt comfortable discussing. "Medically," I told her, "there would be no problems. But it sounds as if you need to do more research to try to figure out what life would really be like. When you've made up your mind, whatever decision you make, you can expect total support from everyone in this office."

My preliminary conversations with patients often sound like small talk. But by listening with both ears and what's in between, I learn a lot. When I ask an expectant mother how she feels abut her pregnancy, about her interests, her job, what she eats, what kind of exercise she does, and how her relationship with her husband works, I'm not just being noisy. Besides giving me a chance to get to know another human being better, her answers will help me be a better doctor.

If she says that she's exhausted all the time and has constant back pain, that may tie into information acquired earlier: that she's a saleperson on her feet all day. That suggests that she ease her pain by putting a low box behind the counter (akin to a back-saving saloon brass rail), and periodically resting a foot on it. If she says she's depressed, we can discuss her ambivalent feelings about the new life developing inside of her—feelings that are perfectly normal. When she tells me, as Alice Wallace did, about something new in childbirth that she's read about and would like me to try, her visit can be as educational for doctor as for patient.

When a wife confides the fear that her husband may be having an affair, I'm clued into the possibility that the pelvic pain that brought her to my office may stem from an STD, a sexually transmitted disease. If she bemoans a troubled teenage son, I consider stress as a possible cause of her lower back pain. If she brings up nothing more than a happy report of a new job, or the news that her softball team just won the division championship and she was the Runs-Batted-In champ, then I know more about her world than I did before. The personal notes I dictate after one visit enable me to jog my memory before the next visit—when I will go into the examining room ready to meet someone I know and can more quickly put at ease: someone I can talk to about her softball team's chances for a pennant next year instead of just her urine specimen.

Getting personal with patients has required no small effort to overcome my own inhibitions. For years I repressed remarks that I thought were unprofessional or I feared might be misconstrued. Even little comments like, "That's a pretty dress you're wearing today. The color is very becoming." Or, "You cut your hair, didn't you? It looks great!" Now I see that for me to squelch such thoughts deprives me of an opportunity to tell patients something that's not only true for me, but that they would enjoy hearing and that could make them more comfortable raising personal issues later.

For years I never touched a patient, except in clearly professional ways. I feared that, like a compliment, a pat on the shoulder might be misinterpreted. Today I realize that contact—the laying on of hands—is important. When a woman has delivered a baby, a good hug is in order. When she's anxious about impending surgery or upset about her results, taking her hands in mine may offer reassurance and tell her that I care about what happens to her.

Getting personal, of course, involves taking risks. It's a lot safer to stick to advice on painful menstrual periods. Like the morning when, making friendly conversation, I told a patient at great length how much I liked and admired her husband, and how deserving he was of success. I attributed the marked tightening of her facial muscles as I talked to tension about a Band-Air sterilization procedure she was there to discuss. When I finished my eulogy, to my great embarrassment she explained why she wanted the procedure. Her husband had left her, and she felt she needed protection in case she developed another relationship. I apologized profusely. She forgave generously.

But you risk more than egg on your face when you strive for intimacy with others. You're forced to admit your own vulnerability, your own humanness and fallibillity. To say, "I have trouble with that, too," swings a wrecking ball at your pedestal. But coming down to earth seems to have improved rather than disturbed my doctor-patient relationships. It's not easy to talk to a statue.

My open-ended essay questions take up more time than my old short-answer quizzes, and I make a conscious effort not to rush people in and out of appointments. But it's possible my more human policy may be considered inhumane by patients impatiently turning magazine pages outside in my waiting room. Especially those who just want their Pap smears, are handling their personal problems quite well, thank you, and may be less interested in establishing a warm doctor-patient relationship than in getting back to the babysitter or the office. Since patients tend to keep such feelings to themselves, I can only guess that they exist. For the most part though, people seem to leave the office in a happier frame of mind. I know I do.

My more open approach to patients came just in time to keep me in step with the consumer revolution in medicine. Patients are insisting that doctors listen more, respond more, explain more. (When the Alabama Medical Society did a statewide patient survey, they found that "an explanation of my condition" headed the list of what patients wanted from their physicians.) Most people no longer wanted a surgeon who acts as though he not only takes our gallstones at Mt. Sinai, but also chiseled the Ten Commandments there. For many, though not all, familiar maxims like "leave it to the doctor" or "doctor knows best" are going the way of the ten-dollar office visit. Most patients today are looking for partnership with their M.D.s, and judging from my own experiences, they don't want to be silent partners.

Not too many years ago, such patients would not have been among my favorites. Now I know that the woman who is well informed and participates in the decision-making process and choices that affect her life and health is not only a better patient but makes me a more effective doctor. When her period is late, she's more likely than a passive patient to pick up a home pregnancy test at the drugstore, and if it's positive, call my office for an appointment. That's good. The earlier an expectant mother gets medical care, the better.

If she thinks I'm not paying enough attention to persistent lower abdominal pain, she doesn't bite her tongue, she speaks her mind. When a patient takes that kind of active interest, I'm more likely to make the all-important early diagnosis that will prevent serious consequences. So, though I, and I'm sure many of my colleagues, at first found the new generation of educated, activated patients hard to take, we're learning to respect and appreciate them.

Not all of us have reached that point. Some, like me, are changed by a gently prodding and pushing Alice Wallace, sharing her beliefs and concerns. Others only draw up the

wagons in a tighter circle, threatened by the patient who claims
to know something they don't. But the woman in search of a
doctor-patient partnership needs the courage to face the wagons down, and in a tone inquiring rather than confrontational,
say something like: "Doctor, I don't think you've really heard
a word I've said. Isn't my input important to you?" She may
not only improve her own relationship with the doctor but
also—by making him aware of his communications problem
—that of other patients as well. Then again, she may not; in
which case her best bet is to seek another physician.

Having open relationships with patients may initially be
threatening to the physician who hasn't tried it. It was to me.
But I enjoy my practice more now that I can say the things I'm
really thinking, now that I can admit I don't know all the
answers, now that my patients can feel freer to express their
needs and feelings. And their doubts.

I don't have to wonder, as a passive noncommunicative
patient walks out my door, if, unconvinced of my diagnosis,
she is headed home to ignore my instructions. Before the door
closes behind her, I've made every effort to be sure she has no
qualms. I no longer assume a patient is comfortable with my
plans for a particular procedure. I give her the chance to say
No, which gives me the chance to discuss alternatives.

Bilateral honesty also creates the opportunity to discover
early on whether we are (a) compatible or (b) on a philosophi-
cal collision course. She may refuse to consider the possibility
of a cesarean section no matter what the circumstances or,
because of a book she read, be dogmatically opposed to fetal
monitoring even in a high-risk delivery. If so, our relationship
is just not going to work.

Some failures are possible to predict even before the patient
and I meet. One woman sent us a questionnaire the size of a
credit bureau report to fill out as a kind of test Jack and I had to
pass before she would consider us for managing her delivery.
Among other things, she wanted to know not only our age,
training, experience, and the medical societies we belonged to
(certainly relevant), but (arguably confidential) our marital
status and number of children. Her final question asked
whether we had read and agreed with Dr. Bradley's book
Husband-Coached Childbirth.

That did it. I hate to generalize and I'd rather make friends
than enemies. But Jack and I have found that the unyielding

confrontational attitudes that dogmatically devoted Bradley followers bring with them to the office create frictions even with physicians who make every effort to give ob patients major control of their childbirth experience. A patient can't have two doctors—her own ob and Dr. Bradley—particularly when one of them, Dr. Bradley, appears absolutely certain that the only right way to do things is his way. We decided it would be best for her peace of mind and ours if she shared her childbirth experience with some other doctor.

Doctors have to take stands, too, and to my mind such patients carry medical consumerism a couple of steps too far. I'm all for the self-care movement, encouraging the patient to take more responsibility for his or her own health care. It makes a lot of sense. It's become a cliche, but I happen to believe it's true, that very little a doctor does for patients is as important as what patients do for themselves. You make daily choices between the Whopper and the salad bar, the hammock and the jogging trail, cigarettes and peanuts. You decide whether to go easy or go overboard on alcohol, to repress or report a worrisome symptom to your doctor, to routinely get preventive Pap smears and breast mammograms or regularly postpone them. We can contribute years of training and experience to a relationship, but no physician has more power over your life and health than you do.

Once I might have said brusquely to a patient waving a clipping touting the media's latest medical miracle, "I'm your doctor, not *Prevention* magazine. I know ob/gyn and your body better than the writer who wrote this and the editor who published it. Here's what I think is best for you, and I certainly hope you'll continue to follow my advice." It would be clear from my tone that the discussion was over and that the next patient was waiting. I've come down off that high horse. Now I take the time to read the article and discuss it with my patient. We may both learn from the experience and, instead of weakening, our relationship is likely to be strengthened.

Not long ago, a highly intelligent and civically active patient of mine in her forties came in with a brief article from a feminist health publication. "Please look at this," she said. "It says taking estrogen for menopause complaints increases the risk of cancer."

I had suggested she begin hormone replacement therapy

(estrogen for the first twenty-five days of every cycle, progesterone from day sixteen to twenty-five every third month) for
the disconcerting hot flashes she'd been experiencing and to
ward off possible osteoporosis. Now she was challenging this
treatment.

"What this article you've shown me says is correct," I said,
"but only as far as it goes. The risk of cancer of the
endometrium (the lining of the uterus) is increased in women
taking estrogen therapy. But—and it's a very important
but—research shows that when the estrogen is supplemented
periodically by progesterone, as it is in your case, not only
does the combination therapy *not* trigger cancer, it seems to
inhibit it. The progesterone may also protect against an effect
sometimes attributed to unopposed estrogen: cancer of the
breast."

"Well, why on earth doesn't this article say that?" she
demanded.

"That's a question you'll have to put to the editor," I
replied. "But I have a question for you. What do you know
about osteoporosis?"

"I know it has something to do with weakening of the bones
and it's more common after menopause."

"Right. But do you know that it is reponsible for far more
deaths—about 200,000 a year, mostly from hip fractures
—than endometrial cancer? That it's the reason so many
women develop dowager's hump and lose inches in height
when they age? And that taking the estrogen plus 1,000
milligrams of elemental calcium in a daily supplement can help
prevent the disease?"

"Not really," she said. "I guess I've only heard the
negatives about estrogen."

I went on to explain that she was a prime target for
osteoporosis because she was small and thin and had been a
smoker for many years. The fat cells in heavy women produce
some estrogen of their own, protecting them somewhat against
bone loss. Smokers are also more prone to osteoporosis,
though her quitting recently was a point in her favor. I also
recommended her starting an exercise program. Weight-
bearing activity (jogging, walking, bicycling) helps strengthen
bones. As long as she was on the hormone therapy, we would
monitor the condition of her endometrium regularly, as an
added precaution.

If, in spite of all I'd said, she still preferred to let a magazine piece be her doctor, I could at least feel I'd done my best. In the end, though I could inform and educate, she had to choose. She did. She chose to begin the hormone replacement therapy.

That was one battle won, but like the pediatrician's war against otitis media, the ob/gyn's war against media poisoning is never done. Not all press and TV reporting, of course, is inaccurate. Much of it is quite good, and its early warnings and instant education can be very valuable. The problem is that, for reasons having to do with ratings, revenue, and the need to catch busy people's attention, too much of it is alarmist.

Pregnant woman have heard so many dire warnings about medications that "Take no drugs!" has become the expectant mother's eleventh commandment. Even our own staff, among whom pregnancy has recently been epidemic, is not immune. So our nurse, Dagmar, was not amused when, in her sixth month, she absently swallowed with her early morning orange juice what she believed to be her queen-size prenatal multivitamin. Puzzled, she observed it still sitting where it had been on the kitchen counter a moment before. Two oversize pills—her pink, Fido's green—had been side by side. "Oh my God!" she shrieked. "I've taken the dog's heartworm pill!"

The bloodshot eyes Dagmar came to work with several hours later were caused not by the pill she'd swallowed, but by her understandable hysteria over having taken a medication designed not to nourish but to kill. She'd spent half the morning trying to make herself throw up, the other half crying. Needlessly. The low-dose heartworm pill was harmless, particularly to a fetus at so late a stage of gestation. The only painful side effect was the greeting Jack inflicted on her at the office for the next few weeks: "Good morning, Dagmar. Are you barking yet?"

Pregnant women *should* be mistrustful of medications. Ever since the thalidomide and DES disasters, we all are. They should certainly avoid taking any drugs that aren't recommended or prescribed by their obstetrician, or by a doctor who knows they are expecting and is familiar with the safety of the drug in question for pregnant women. But they shouldn't be mistrustful or every medication an obstetrician prescribes. Unfortunately, many women are and either refuse directly to take the drug or, perhaps more commonly, politely accept the prescription, then let it go unfilled.

That's where a good doctor-patient relationship helps. A doctor who has rapport with patients can carefully explain that the risk, if any, of the particular drug being suggested is far outweighed by its benefits. If it weren't, he wouldn't be prescribing it. Most of us have had to debate more than one underinformed and overanxious mother-to-be to persuade her to take an antibiotic for a urinary tract infection. The antibiotic has been shown to cause harm to neither mother nor child. But, left untreated, a UTI can cause premature delivery of the baby, kidney infection, and in extreme cases, even kidney loss to the mother. That's a risk-benefit ratio any expectant mother can understand.

Also thanks to the media, we see more and more patients who are up in arms against episiotomies. Sometimes the too-eager-to-please physician gets carried away by the patient's enthusiasm. I did one day when a woman in labor stubbornly resisted an episiotomy. "Okay," I agreed, "we'll do it your way." After all, I reflected, didn't my nurse-midwife say that she doesn't do them? (I learned later that she often does). So I rubbed oil all over the perineum in Ellie's midwife style, making it extra slippery. Then I massaged it, making it more pliable. Finally, slowly, very slowly, I eased out the baby's head.

"What a marvelous technique!" I thought jubilantly. "Why haven't I done this before?" Then came the rush of blood from the jagged tears in the birth canal. I had acceded to my patient's request, but it hadn't turned out to her benefit. She emerged from the delivery room forty-five minutes later traumatized internally by the scores of sutures I'd had to use to mend her unnecessary lacerations. And I emerged with a lesson I'm not likely to soon forget: Listening to what a patient has to say is desirable. Letting it overrule your own judgment isn't.

Now I carefully explain to people that, if I'm doing their delivery, it's very unlikely that they won't have an episiotomy. Not because I want to get the second stage of labor over with quickly, but because I want to avoid an unpredictable and nasty laceration. I won't do big, wide incisions or the lateral ones that are required when you use forceps. I do the smallest one practicable. I know it may be uncomfortable for a few days, but a lot less than the repair of severe lacerations would be.

It's not easy to No a patient who, in these times of doctor

surpluses, may simply drop out of your practice and find
someone willing to say Yes. But the doctor who doesn't stick
to doing what he believes is sound medicine may expose
himself to that hydraheaded monster of 1980s medical practice:
malpractice litigation. The person who insists that it be done
his or her way is often the first to sue when something goes
wrong. So we find ourselves in the vise of sued-if-you-do,
damned-if-you-don't, and the only way to extricate ourselves is
to work hard at building mutually trusting and respectful
doctor-patient relationships. And pray a lot.

Many of the charges Madalyn hurled at me in front of the
fire in the ski lodge at first baffled me. "Just because you're a
doctor, do you have to act like God?" she asked scathingly.
My only reply then was, "Madalyn, that's ridiculous!" But
what my wife said is repeated so often about doctors that there
has to be some fire under all that smoke. If we do act godlike,
one reason is because some patients who come to the altar that
is our office want us to be. When you've got cancer, you go to
your doctor hungry for a miracle—at least, a miracle drug.
You want a wise, comforting healer to lay on hands and
vanquish the evil enemy within.

The ancients believed that their shamans, their medicine
men and women, drew special powers from God. Believers
went to Lourdes, the superstitious went to witch doctors. And
doctors of medicine did nothing to discourage all that unde-
served faith. They gloried in it, pontificating—like
Hippocrates—that "a physician who is a lover of wisdom is
the equal of a god." There were, of course, always doubters,
saying—like Diderot—"The best doctor is the one you run for
and can't find." But today, skeptics and iconoclastic
consumerists notwithstanding, the god-doctor parallels continue: "I just put myself in the doctor's hands." "You should go
to my doctor. I really believe in him." "I pray the doctor can
save her." When health or life are disturbed or threatened, we
want the doctor to be, like God, all-powerful. But there is a
related wish: that he also be loving and compassionate. The
doctor-god isn't always.

The doctor as God isn't just a patient creation. We doctors
—from the earliest medicine men right up to today—have
done a lot to encourage it. Partly, it's a way (conscious or not)
of protecting our positions: If we are gods, we don't have to

admit what we don't know, which can be plenty. The divine right of doctors includes the right not to be challenged or questioned. I saw that in my superiors during my training, and took the mantle for myself. I enjoyed the status, though I didn't consciously acknowledge that it existed. I encouraged patients to surrender their power ("Don't worry, Mrs. Smith. Just leave everything to me.") and have unbridled faith in me. I've come to believe that the relationship between doctor and patient works best when the patient doesn't relinquish all power and control to the physician, when it's understood that the physician isn't omniscient, only human.

Interestingly, I find I have more power since I gave it up. Not the authoritarian kind of power a hurler of lightning bolts might have, but the power to really move people, to change their lives, to help them live up to their potential, to recognize that they are the source of what happens to them.

In the past, I saw the patient who didn't change when ordered to as being guilty of weakness of character. When patients continued to be obese, or smoked, or didn't exercise, in spite of my repeated zealous attempts to convert them, I cared for them, but less and less about them.

Now, my God complex outgrown, I take a second look. I looked one afternoon at Gloria Gleason, whose weight in the fifteen years she'd been my patient had ballooned nearly a hundred pounds, in part, I sensed, from problems at home. In the past, I'd tried in vain to persuade her to lose weight, and I'd finally stopped raising the issue. Now I tried again.

"When I first met you," I said, "you were a beautiful young woman. You're still young. If you lost some of that weight you put on during your pregnancies, you'd still be beautiful. Should we talk about it?"

We talked. I talked as much as she did. I admitted that I hated myself when I put on a few extra pounds. That gave her the opening to admit that she hated being fat, too. I told her about my problems trying to keep my weight down. She poured out hers, which included a husband with an agenda of his own who wasn't supportive of her weight-losing efforts, and children whose leftovers it seemed were better eaten, than thrown away. I told her how I'd coaxed my whole family into the Pritikin Program, and how we had all benefited. I suggested she might like to try it herself.

I think she left the office in a daze. She certainly must have been thinking, can this really be Dr. Eisenberg? Does he really have trouble with weight and pigging out just like me? Whatever she thought, she came back to her next visit several pounds lighter. And she was confident of losing more.

But you can't win them all. Some patients are just not going to succeed in making even ardently desired changes. I've had to learn to accept that—and to let patients know that I do. Otherwise the patient who fails to make a prescribed change or to meet an urgently recommended goal may be too embarrassed to come back.

Patients who ought to be thinking about life-style changes come into the office every day. Jane Kramer, twenty-six and considering having her first child, came in for prenatal counseling. She needs a lot of it. She eats only one meal a day and smokes heavily. I outlined for her the need to begin taking care of herself before she is pregnant. If she wants a healthy full-term baby, she has to stop smoking and improve her diet. We discussed just how she could do both. The sooner she starts acting as though she is already pregnant, the better.

Myrna Morrissey, a short blonde woman in her late thirties, had an appointment the same morning. She has no children and has been on the pill for eighteen years. It was her first visit. She wanted a checkup and more pills, but I hesitated when her stained fingernails and tobacco breath told me that she was a heavy smoker. The gurgle when she laughed told me more: that she has chronic congestion in her bronchi.

This was a patient who might not want to hear my message, but I delivered it anyway: that a smoker over thirty-five on the pill has a risk of stroke four times greater than normal. I suggested that she cut her risk and improve the quality and length of her life by joining a smoking cessation program. She could go on taking the pill for another six months while she made that effort, but I would not support a potentially serious threat to her life and health by continuing her presecription beyond that point. I want to be her doctor, but not her accomplice in repeating the behavior that's taking her down the inevitable path to her stroke, her coronary, her grave.

To be a good influence, a physician has to set a good example. I know I wouldn't want an obese doctor with an ashtray full of cigarette butts to tell me I need to lose weight and stop smoking. Until we start practicing what we teach, doctors with pots are in no position to call their patients' kettles black.

That's a shame, because there's such an opportunity for us to put office time to use counseling, educating, and helping patients find the power within themselves to change. I see patients who are overweight, or smoke, or don't eat sensibly, or don't exercise, or don't communicate with their mates, or don't use birth control—a good many of them with all of the above problems. The barriers to change seem insuperable to them and daunting to me.

But, since I'm a partner in their health care, it's my responsibility to say, "Hey, take a look and see if this is what you really want to keep on doing. Or can I help you choose something better?"

Leaves from an Ob/Gyn's Journal

It's been one of those days . . . and nights. A delivery at three in the morning. A few hours' sleep and then hospital rounds at eight. A nonstop parade of office patients ever since. I look at my appointment schedule with a sigh of relief. Only two more patients to go.

I step into an examining room to see the first of them, a quiet young woman starting the third trimester of an uneventful pregnancy. She's been my patient for five or six months. She has always come alone, but today a tall, bearded young man in plaid shirt and dungarees is with her. She introduces him with a mixture of pride and embarrassment. (Why the embarrassment, I wonder.) His handshake is firm, matching his down-home farmboy look.

"I'm happy to see you here," I tell him. "The more the father is involved in the pregnancy, the better I like it."

"I'm sure glad to hear that," he says quietly. I have the feeling that he wants to say more, as he nervously twists his gold wedding band during the brief routine of my examination. (Why so nervous, I wonder.) Only when he hears the laboring locomotive chug of his baby's Doppler-magnified heartbeat for the first time does his face turn joyful.

The exam finished, I tell the young woman that all is going well and that she can dress and meet me in the consulting room.

"Umm, doctor," says her husband, at last unburdening himself. "Before my wife gets dressed, there's something we want to ask you." I stop with my hand on the doorknob. "Rachel and I have been talking it over, and we were wondering if you could teach me how to examine her when her contractions start. So I can see how much she's dilated."

I am taken aback. I had a feeling that this visit was more than casual, but I've never had a request like this one before. My first thought is: No way. It's crazy. I'm not going to teach you that. You didn't go to medical school. That's carrying the self-care movement too far.

But I pause for a moment before translating thought into words. I look at this earnest young man and ask evenly, "Why would you want to do that?"

He uncrosses his legs and plants his scuffed and weather-worn leather boots stubbornly in front of him. "Well," he replies, "Rachel wants to do as much of the labor as possible at home. If you tell me what to look for, I'll know when it's time to bring her in."

"I can understand your wanting to do that," I respond. "But frankly, I don't really think it's safe for you to be examining your wife at home. And since I'm responsible for the outcome, I'm reluctant to take the risk." (A quick mental inventory tells me that I am also reluctant to relinquish what, as a doctor, has always been my special province.)

But this man has tugged a lot of stubborn cows to pasture and is not about to take No for an answer. He leans forward. "I understand how you feel, doc," he says gravely. "I know you care about my wife, but you couldn't possibly care about her as much as I do. So you don't have to worry. You just show me what to do. I'll do it right."

I look at my patient. Her lips are pursed expectantly, her brown eyes gaze at me hopefully. I turn again to her husband. "Okay," I say, "it's your wife's body, and if she wants you to do this and you can learn to do it safely—well, it's all right with me. Just bear in mind that there's a lot at stake here—the health and safety of your wife and baby—and it's important not to delay going to the hospital too long."

That said, I am surprised to find that, revolutionary as the request had been three minutes earlier when he broached it, and sternly and adamantly though I would have refused him ten years earlier, it is no longer a big issue for me. I glove him, glove myself, and marveling all the while that this is really happening, show him exactly what to do.

11

Fathers Are Parents, Too

ONE OF AMERICA'S most distinguished obstetricians taught me a lesson that all young obs learned in the fifties: Fathers don't count.

Yale-New Haven Medical Center had a policy that not even ob/gyn residents could witness the birth of their babies. So when my wife went into the delivery room to expel our first child from womb into world, I was shunted to the waiting room with the civilians.

It was, I learned later, a difficult delivery. Waiting, I knew it was a prolonged one. Madalyn hemorrhaged and required blood transfusions, enduring a birth that, these days, is terminated by c-section.

But I questioned nothing. I had taken her to the best in the business: Dr. Buxton, a full professor and department chairman. My part was simple—to wait dutifully outside for the attending obstetrician to emerge and say, "Congratulations! It's a . . ."

Madalyn had lost so much blood that she was anemic after delivery, and painful iron shots were prescribed. Though I was a doctor, I felt powerless—a helpless bystander while people did things to my wife, people far more knowledgeable and experienced than I. That was the way it had always been. That was, I thought, the way it had to be.

Because I wasn't present at Jordan's birth—so near and yet much too far away to squeeze my wife's hand and assure her that the worst was almost over—I didn't really feel like a father to my child. To Madalyn, he was a love object, to me a foreign object who, when we brought him home, was always getting in the way. My intimate relationship with my wife had suddenly ended because a third person, a wrinkled, chronically irritable stranger, constantly cried and demanded attention. In the middle of making love to my wife, the baby "went off." It was worse than the phone ringing. We had the option of ignoring that.

Madalyn was caught in the middle. A young and inexperienced mother, she nevertheless wanted to be the best she could be. We'd been married only four months when she became pregnant. I think we couldn't wait to test her fertility and my virility. We passed both tests, but our relationship suffered.

It wasn't the rules, but rather my eagerness for responsibility, that kept me from witnessing the birth of our second son. I hadn't been at my new post at William Beaumont Army Hospital more than six weeks when Madalyn realized that she'd missed her period. We knew exactly when Bruce happened—in a motel between New Haven and El Paso. This time I resolved to be present at the delivery.

But the morning Madalyn went into labor, I had a hysterectomy scheduled. It was a chance to do surgery, and I wanted it very badly. I hoped the surgery and the delivery wouldn't coincide. I was there for the early labor. Madalyn was in terrible pain, but the anesthesiologist hadn't been trained to do the epidural block that had eased the worst of her anguish during the delivery at Yale-New Haven.

"You do it, Henry," she urged. "You know how."

"I don't really want to stick a needle in your back, Madalyn. I know I could do it, and yet I'm really afraid to." But when she pleaded, I couldn't say No. "Okay," I told her, "I'll do it if it's all right with Colonel Schoenbacher." My commanding officer assented, the shot gave her immediate relief, and she was thrilled that I had done it for her. I felt good, too. I had helped the woman I loved.

But then I was called to the OR for the hysterectomy. "Don't worry, honey," I said, "I'll be back in time for the delivery."

But I wasn't, the block wore off, and she gave birth in great pain. I felt terribly guilty. I could have been there. I could have postponed the surgery or arranged for someone else to do it. But selfishly I did it myself and passed up the opportunity to watch the arrival of my second son. When Ned came along in Syracuse, I stayed with Madalyn through both labor and delivery. Being there to welcome our third son was a far different and more joyful experience than the first two, and I think it helped me draw close to Ned sooner.

Over the years, I think I've been a pretty good father. But if I'd participated in all my children's births, I might have been a better one. Participation would certainly have made me a more sensitive obstetrician—sensitive to the fact that fathers are parents, too. Today, influenced by Lamaze and others, that's a given. The husband is no longer just the harmless butt of expectant-father jokes and the cigar-dispensing clown of yesteryear. These days, he does everything but give birth.

But it would have been, for the first fifteen years of my practice, impossible to convince me that the father's place was in the delivery room. It wasn't only the "Buxton syndrome." I suspect that, like many of my colleagues, I was afraid of husbands.

In all those years, I rarely talked to a husband, seldom even met one until he brought his wife to the hospital in labor. I'd shake his hand, tell him his wife would probably deliver in four or five hours, and suggest he make himself comfortable in the waiting room. If the opportunity presented itself, I'd drop by en route to delivery with a progress bulletin: "She's doing fine. We're taking her to the delivery room. She should be out in about half an hour." More often, I didn't see him until it was all over, when I entered the waiting room to announce the newborn's sex and vital statistics.

Twenty-five years ago, expectant mothers almost never asked to bring their husbands in to meet me. On those rare occasions when they did, I felt awkward, embarrassed, and uneasy. I suspect it was mutual—that husbands then felt inconvenienced by the pregnant state, wanted as little to do with it as possible, and for the most part, accepted childbirth as an exclusively female experience and labor rooms and ob/gyns' offices as an exclusively women's world. Reading a magazine in the waiting room was as close as they cared to get.

I made no effort to involve them. I think I suspected that any normal red-blooded husband would necessarily resent my clinical trespass of his wife's body—must feel that the ob/gyn was, in the crudest sense, a rival invading his turf. So I had a lot of trouble relating to husbands—though probably no more than they did to me. It was nothing personal. He was just one more party involved in questioning and decision-making—or worse, challenging.

Anyway, it was easier for me to establish rapport with an expectant mother than with her husband. As the patient, she developed a greater degree of attachment, so that if the need for a cesarean section arose, it was easier to broach it to her than to a possibly skeptical husband.

Some men, particularly tall men (maybe reminding me of the child-parent relationship in which I always had to look up) or highly successful men, still intimidate me. Those who ask crisp, businesslike questions and expect absolute answers (often there aren't any in medicine) tend to irritate me. Nevertheless, in spite of earlier uneasiness, my rebirthing and Leboyer-Lamaze experiences persuaded me that in the Land of the Pregnant, no husband should be treated as a second-class citizen. He is half the expectant couple, very much affected by her pregnancy, and with an important role in supporting the mother-to-be. If his wife can't sleep at night, he walks the floor with her. If the smell of meat upsets her delicate stomach, he becomes a vegetarian for the duration. If her last trimester falls in skiing season, he wistfully makes do with an exercise bicycle. If she has a cramp or an ache she's embarrassed to call her practitioner about, he's the one to pick up the phone.

The husband who experiences morning sickness and other pregnancy symptoms—from weight gain and food cravings to leg cramps and dizziness—is surprisingly common. Every obstetrician encounters the "couvade syndrome" sufferer. The term comes from the French verb meaning "to hatch," but I doubt that even the president of the Société Nationale de Gynécologie et d'Obstétrique de France understands why prospective fathers who aren't pregnant experience the same kinds of symptoms as their wives who are. Some suggest that it's sympathy, others that it's a subconscious bid for attention because the wife seems to be getting it all. But it could be guilt (for putting their wives in such an uncomfortable condition) or stress (from fear of trying, anxiety over pending family responsibilities, and living with moods that swing like those of the daring young lady on the flying trapeze). In any case, couvade makes a statement. It reminds us that the father cannot be painted out of the pregnancy picture. And today's mothers, firm believers in active fathering, insist that we pencil them in, like it or not. To my surprise, I like it.

So much so that I was the first to stand up at my hospital and speak for the father being in the labor and then in the delivery room. The response I got wasn't heartening: "Listen, I don't want fathers walking in and out of various rooms, perhaps walking in on a patient by mistake," or "We've got women being rolled around here with very little on. All these guys are going to be gaping and staring. What kind of way is that to run an ob service?"

What they found out was that inviting fathers was the only way to run an ob service—and stay in business. When other hospitals in town established family-centered maternity care that included fathers as part of the family, Community Hospital found itself under pressure. Patients opted to go where their husbands could join them and our maternity census fell. If nothing else could do it, that convinced the staff at Community that fathers matter. It also convinced them that to keep patients coming a hospital has to keep up. Now, often inspired by our alert nursing staff, Community frequently spearheads innovation in Syracuse. These days, not only are fathers welcome at delivery, but a second coach as well. Grandparents and even siblings are invited to visit postpartum wards, where once only fathers could tread.

When the young farmer and his wife left my office, I wondered briefly if I'd taught him something that would come back to haunt me in court. ("Yes, Your Honor, Dr. Eisenberg showed me how to do it. And I'm sure that infection to my wife and the baby would never have happened if he'd just told me to keep my hands to myself.") But I concluded it was appropriate for him to learn to do a simple pelvic. After all, he'd been raised on a farm, and this was just an extension of his life experience. I was sure that when it came right down to it, he wouldn't rashly risk his unborn baby's life and would opt against undue delay in getting to the hospital. As it turned out, his wife's condition made the decision for him. With the contractions came a suspicious discharge. They were in their pickup truck and on their way to the hospital within minutes of their call to my office. I can't say I was sorry. I enjoy being on the cutting edge of obstetrical progress. But I don't like getting stuck.

Though almost all husbands want to be involved in labor and delivery, few seek as major a role as my farming friend. I usually offer fathers the opportunity to cut the umbilical cord, and most will do that. But few want to do more. Recently, I went back to the place where my inspiration to be a doctor was born: Grossinger's. It was the site of the first convention for expectant parents, and I, along with several other obstetricians, appeared on a number of panels. One of my co-speakers turned out to be Dr. Robert Block of Turnersville, New Jersey, who earned enduring fame as the first doctor to encourage fathers to "catch" their babies. Intrigued by the idea, I went home to Syracuse ready to let some of my fathers try it. I had only one taker. He was thrilled by the experience, but others feared they might panic and drop the baby. "That's what we're paying you for," was the reply I heard most often.

Where husbands can be most valuable in childbirth is as the wife's most visible means of support. It's a painful, stressful time for her, and there's nothing more reassuring than having the man she loves at her side. He can wipe her brow, feed her ice chips, rub her back, time her contractions, and remind her to breathe during and relax between them. He can be her defender and advocate if a hospital rule upsets her—if, for example, the nurse insists on an enema and the patient is vehemently opposed. He can be her security blanket, her lifeline, her port in this turbulent emotional-physical storm.

Even the most macho of men can turn unexpectedly tender in the labor room. I never fail to find the sensitivity of the father, sharing the experience and wishing he could share the pain (or take it all) very moving. A father in the waiting room misses out on all that. I know I did; I felt left out. So I'm often a little envious of couples privileged to share the childbirth experience. There's no solid evidence of the value of parental bonding with the newborn that everyone talks about, but I have the sense that it definitely cements a marital relationship. The father who is chairman of the delivery room welcoming committee is unlikely to feel, as I did, a certain resentment toward this little wife-stealing stranger, the new center of her universe, who commands so much of her time, interest, and energy. Today, at the six week checkup, I see the father comfortably handling the infant as well as, and sometimes better than, the mother. It's his baby as much as it is hers.

The family birth experience isn't always idyllic. Some father-coaches get carried away. They think they are Vince Lombardi or Barry Switzer, and the good wife is a quarterback obliged to play the game according to a present game plan. "Don't cry out!" Barry shushes his wife. "Concentrate on your breathing exercises. You're doing them all wrong!" During delivery, he may tell her when to push, even "help" by pushing against her head. If she begs for medication, he may express disapproval. (After all, a winning team plays pluckily even if hurt.)

I have to remind Barry that this is not a football game, that he can't take the word "coach" so literally. I explain that it's difficult for a woman to be fully in control during labor, especially when the pain is severe. A plea for medication is not an admission of defeat. It may help his wife cope better with the labor. And only the birth attendant can give the order to "push." Multiple signals only confuse. His wife is having a difficult enough time focusing as it is.

Even when a husband is low key and not putting pressure on his wife, she may respond negatively to his ministrations. The gentlest touch, the most comforting words, can get on her nerves. A few women may demand their husbands leave them alone, even leave the room, particularly during the pushing phase. Sometimes, at this point, a concerned, experienced labor and delivery nurse becomes as important as, or more important than, the father-coach. Even women who've faithfully practiced their breathing and pushing exercises are likely now to need the nurse's special help.

Delivery may present another problem. A few fathers—and the bigger they are the harder they fall—faint at the first sight of blood. This is not a sign of weakness. It can happen to the strongest of men—like triple world boxing title-holder Barney Ross, never kayoed in more than a dozen years in the ring, who swooned dead away while watching his daughter give birth to his first grandchild. It can happen, too, and occasionally does, to medical students observing their first operations. Nurses are alert to this possibility and keep a watchful eye on students and fathers. As a precaution, during cesarean sections, the father is placed at the mother's head, near the anesthetist, where his visibility is limited and so is the damage he can do. If he falls, it won't be into the wound.

Occasionally, in spite of peer and childbirth class pressure, a father will elect to pass up the chance to be present at the blessed event. I usually warn him that he is going to miss out on a very rewarding experience in his relationship with his wife as well as with his new baby. Some will change their minds—all they need is a little encouragement. Some won't. A few think it's not macho to get involved in childbirth. They'd rather watch a Monday night football game in the waiting room. Others have a wake-me-up-when-it's-over attitude. A father's choice may have a lot to do with his wife's attitude. If she doesn't want him there, he picks up the cues.

Whatever his reasons, I press only so far. Sure, it's wonderful to be able to see your baby born. But in this, as in prior generations, plenty of excellent fathers and husbands have paced through it all outside in the hospital waiting room.

Leaves from an Ob/Gyn's Journal

"I don't know how much longer I can go on with things the way they are. Our . . . our personal life . . . there's nothing to it."

In my office, I listen as Mrs. Brown, an attractive woman in her late thirties, tells me how her once loving relationship with her husband has deteriorated. If I've heard it once, I've heard it fifty times—though twenty-five years after the start of the most dramatic sexual revolution in history, it hardly seems possible. The first clue to the cause of her problem is her difficulty in talking about sex. I question her gently, and gradually she relaxes.

"I may be the last woman in the world who's never had an orgasm," she says sadly. "My husband doesn't make love; he has sex. *He* has it. I'm just there while it happens."

Once she's begun, it pours out. A businessman, her husband is all business in bed. No foreplay. No notion that foreplay is not only pleasurable but essential if his wife is to experience orgasm. She goes from resentment to hostility to frequent "no, not tonight" headaches and "just lying there like a mattress." Not like a comforter. And neither of them knows how to talk about it. If they did, they'd never have reached this low point in their marriage.

It takes neither a genius nor a certified sex therapist to see what's needed. It's time for Mrs. Brown to create a context of truth in their relationship, and she can begin it by explaining to her husband why she's having the headaches.

''Tell him,'' I advise, ''that you want there to be more to it for you than just a short period of coitus during which he has his orgasm. Explain that you need to be stroked in a certain way. That you'd like him to caress your back, or pleasure your nipples, or stroke your inner thighs—whatever it is that makes you feel good and stimulates you. If manipulation of your clitoris is what you need to bring you to climax, say so. And tell him that all this won't be just for your benefit.

''Remind him that if you enjoy making love, there'll be less frustration for him, too. There'll be more frequent, more loving intercourse—and more satisfaction all around. When a man is sensitive to his partner's needs, he enjoys not only his own climax but hers as well.''

12

Sexual Medicine

"By the way . . . ," says the patient, about to go out the examining room door. I drop what I'm doing and concentrate on what is about to be said. Often those words or "It's very embarrassing for me to mention this, but . . ." are an introduction to the problem the patient really came to see me about. And the hesitancy frequently means it's a sexual problem.

For a long time, it was just as embarrassing for me. Or more so. When I was growing up, sex was stuff you didn't talk about in my family. And we weren't trained in medical school or residency to talk about sexuality either. Sex was just the process that produced babies for us to deliver or diseases for us to treat. We weren't specialists in the process, only in its products and by-products. And it wasn't something you discussed with colleagues or seniors, asking how they handled it, because that would be an admission of ineptness. It would also have been the blind asking directions from the blind. In those days, our professors and the obs we apprenticed under were as uneasy and ill-informed about sexual matters as we were.

We were taught the textbook categories of sexual dysfunction, of course: premature and delayed ejaculation in men; lack of orgasm and vaginismus, vaginal spasms that prevent penetration, in women. But in practice, I was reluctant to face sex problems. I considered myself an expert in physical conditions of the body. But though I'd bought Masters and Johnson to read up on the subject, I had no confidence in my ability to deal with sex's heady emotional components.

When the subject came up, I blocked or parried it, which is what you do when you don't think you can deal with a subject. I made the problem no problem, saying things like: "It'll get better. Don't worry about it." Or, "Do you love your husband? Do you think he loves you? Then, just give it more time. It'll work itself out."

If that didn't end the discussion, I might say, "If it's really that serious a problem for you, I could refer you to someone who'd be able to discuss it with you." Implying a psychiatrist.

No one had taught me to do that. It was my own insecurity talking. No one was telling doctors to do anything about sex then. But then came the Revolution. Announcements of seminars on sexuality began to appear in American College of Obstetrics and Gynecology (ACOG) programs. And articles began to appear in the journals stressing the need for ob/gyns to develop skills to encourage women to talk about their sexual problems. I wasn't about to encourage women to talk about something unless I knew a lot more about it than they did, so I decided to take a course.

When I took it—a continuing education course in Atlanta —what I learned was that I already knew the nuts and bolts part that they were teaching. The "Common Problems in Sexual Counseling" turned out to be the familiar terrain of premature ejaculation and inorgasmic women. But one point kept coming up that I viewed with alarm: that in order to successfully help your patient, you had to be something of a therapist.

Not totally daunted, I went back to the office and tried. But I felt like a man who'd just learned to play tennis two weeks ago trying to teach his wife. I could show her how to grip the racket and how to keep score, but after that she was on her own. To mix into someone's love life and perhaps mess it up even more seemed too heavy a responsibility.

So when women confided that they couldn't have orgasms, I spent a lot of time talking to them about dildos and learning to masturbate. When that didn't help, I dropped my patients like hot wires, hurriedly referring them to local psychiatrists. No one in town was specifically trained to do sexual therapy, but at least these people had read all of *The Collected Papers of Sigmund Freud*.

It wasn't until I'd taken several human potential courses —for reasons that had nothing to do with sex therapy—that I realized that a sex counselor is not an instructor in how-to-do-it but a facilitator of truth-telling. Difficulties with sex were another form of the same basic human problem we face in other kinds of relationships—our inability to be truly open with one another—compounded by an overlay of inhibitions and hang-ups. Only then did I become comfortable with my role and begin to have some success.

It became clear that talk of dildos and masturbation was all very well and perhaps even necessary, but it had more to do with sex-by-the-numbers than with love. Orgasm without love isn't an oil painting, it's a lithograph. Sexual intimacy at its fullest and most loving is a natural state for human beings. So when Mrs. Green, twenty-four, tells me how wonderful sex was with her husband before they were married, and how it's been downhill ever since the ceremony, my next questions aren't about sex, they're about family finances and careers. A marriage bed can get awfully crowded—with money pressures, job pressures, conflicts over who does what work around the house. My job most often isn't to be an orgasm coach, it's to help my patients look at the things that get in the way and to empower them to honestly acknowledge, discuss, and deal with them.

I don't do marriage counseling. But I think I have helped women just by sitting down and talking to them about how most problems of orgasm result from stress and respond to relaxation. Improve the quality of the husband-wife association, and you automatically improve the quality of the sexual expression that flows from it. Emptying that overcrowded bed helps. Knowing the nuts and bolts—the kinds of things anyone can get out of a book—helps. But the container the nuts and bolts go in is a loving relationship.

There are endless ways of rekindling the spark of romance. The getaway weekend, the sexy new negligee, boldly trying new positions, even a book that tells her how to have an orgasm without her husband's help (once she's experimented, she can tell him what works best for her) can all make contributions. But truth-telling—not in an angry way, but just to enable the other person to put in corrections—comes first. Too many people don't know how to be honest in that way, so for a lot of men and women the sexual domain remains a wasteland of unspoken desires and unfulfilled fantasies that too few learn to traverse. It doesn't take much to make the desert bloom. You have only to say the right words.

Well, most of the time. Sometimes the problem is purely physical. I recall a young woman in her early twenties who came in to say that she'd been married six months but wasn't really sure that she was experiencing intercourse. She thought she was, and her husband thought so. "But," she added shyly, "he doesn't seem to penetrate very far. So could you examine me and tell me if anything's wrong?"

I put her in stirrups, spread her labia apart, and gently inserted the speculum. It penetrated a half inch and came up against an immediate, "Ouch!" She was still a virgin. She and her husband had, in fact, not yet consummated their marriage. "Your hymen is still intact," I told her when she had dressed and joined me in my consulting room. "It's so imperforate and your vagina is so tight that not even a pinky could be forced through. It's anatomically impossible for you to have coitus."

Her face fell. "Is . . . is there anything you can do to help me?" she asked.

"I'm pretty sure that with a minor surgical procedure we can open it up and allow normal coitus to take place." Her husband was outside in the waiting room. I invited him in. "Boy, this is embarrassing," he said sheepishly, when I explained my finding. "You mean for six months I've been having sex with a virgin and neither of us knew it? How could we be so dumb?"

"I'm as surprised as you are," I said. I explained what was wrong and what could be done about it. Every female child has a hymen—a membrane at the opening of the vagina. The window enlarges gradually—partly because of exercise and activity, sometimes through the use of tampons. By the time a young woman becomes sexually active, it is usually large enough for a penis to pass through. In rare instances, either because of lack of activity or because of an inordinately small pinpoint opening or a particularly tough membrane, the hymen must be removed surgically.

In Beth's case, her vagina was so tight that a second stage was necessary. I had to make a small incision to widen the first inch or so of the vaginal opening. By cutting it sagittaly and sewing it transversely, I was able to enlarge the diameter and caliber of the vagina. I then gave Beth a prescription for a set of graduated dilators—soft flexible plastic dildos of increasing size—which she was able to fill at a medical supply store. Beginning with the smallest, she put one in before going to bed, leaving it in for a few hours or even overnight. Within a few weeks, her vagina was sufficiently dilated so that it could effectively sheathe her husband's penis. Delighted with the change, the couple couldn't thank me enough. They had had an active sex life before. It now became a full and satisfying one.

A vagina that's too tight is rare. One that's "loose" is more common. A stretched vagina can be tightened through an operation known as a perineorrhaphy or a colporrhaphy. Surprisingly, it's an operation that few women know about and fewer still talk about. Probably because sex used to be considered "dirty" and nice girls didn't talk about it even to their gynecologists, we were taught in training that any woman who complained that her vagina was too large should immediately be suspect as psychologically disturbed. We were instructed to do no snugging surgery until we'd obtained a psychiatric consultation.

We realize today that that was advice out of the Dark Ages. A complaint like that from a patient doesn't tell me that, for heaven's sake, she's a nymphomaniac or vaginally obsessed. It tells me that she has fascial (tissue) weakness that occurred as a consequence of childbearing—usually after two or more children, but sometimes after only one, if vaginal tearing and lacerating happened to be severe and/or the episiotomy was poorly performed. Tears sustained during delivery—simply from the stretching process as a 10-centimeter baby's head strains through an opening ordinarily one-fifth that size—can result in a general loss of tissue tone and resilience in the area. Like an elastic waistband, the vaginal tissue can snap back only so many times.

It isn't easy for a woman to say, "Doctor, I think my vagina is gaping. Is there anything you can do about it?" It's no easier for her doctor to ask, "Mrs. White, have you noticed that your vaginal opening is larger than it used to be?"

The subject often comes up on a slightly more comfortable clinical note. My embarrassed patient tells me that she wets her pants when she coughs, sneezes, or goes to her aerobic dancing class. Or she feels something dangling between her legs when walking or during any kind of abdominal straining. Urinary incontinence and prolapsed uterus—sagging of the uterus from its original position in the pelvis into the vaginal area—are the consequences, like vaginal gaping, of the stretched fascia of inordinately traumatic childbirth.

If, on examination, gaping is particularly noticeable, I may ask, "Have you noticed that sexual intercourse is less satisfying than it used to be? Does your vagina feel loose as compared to the way it was before you had children? That's often a problem for women after childbirth. If it is for you, it's a simple matter to restore it to the way it was." Some will deny that it's a problem, so I pass on to the next matter. But many admit, "Yes, I have noticed that. I just assumed that nothing could be done about it."

Years ago that was true. Early literature is replete with scenes of women struggling painfully through their daily chores with ill-supported uteruses dangling from their vaginas. For thousands of years, and indeed as little as thirty or forty years ago, the physician's answer was often the pessary—a curved support fashioned variously out of wood, leather, metal, glass, or, more recently, rubber or plastic. In the middle of the nineteenth century, women were so desperate, the problem was so common, and that solution so unsatisfactory that two kinds of gynecologists were said to have made fortunes with pessaries: those who inserted them and those who removed them. But no longer. Repairing a prolapsed uterus is now safe common surgery. And narrowing the vaginal opening is simpler still—with pain similar to that of episiotomy, with discomfort for a week or two, but pain usually not uncomfortably prolonged.

There are exceptions, of course. A colleague who urged his wife to have the procedure done assured her it would be relatively painless. She was in such agony for four or five days that even Demerol didn't help, and her surgeon was afraid she'd suffered some kind of strange, unidentifiable complication. Her reaction to the surgery was a rare one, but she could hardly be blamed for telling her husband later, "Sure it was painless. For you!"

What is painful to me is having to tell a woman that she has a sexually transmitted disease. Her first question is usually,

"Could it have been transmitted some other way?" When she hears that you can't really get it from toilet seats or towels, or in swimming pools or hot tubs, I can see her retire to the back of her mind, anxiety etched on her face. If she's single, there's the added indelicacy of having to ask whether she's having sex with more than one partner, or with a new person. If she's married, she could have gotten it one of two ways—both of which she knows and I know: Either she's having an extramarital affair or her husband is. She will usually blurt it out if she's involved with someone else, in which case, I suggest she refrain from sex with her husband on "doctor's orders" until the symptoms clear up. She gets a prescription for her and her boyfriend, and that's the end of it. It is, of course, far from the end of it if her husband has symptoms, too.

If a woman has been faithful, this may be her first inkling that her husband is not. That's a more traumatic discovery for some than the diagnosis of an STD. Women handle such a situation in different ways. One who's suspected her husband's infidelity may use this as evidence to confront him—and either begin to heal their marriage or end it. Or she may prefer to overlook it for one reason or another. She'll just go home and say, "The doctor says I have vaginitis, and we both need to be treated." A woman who had no idea that there was any trouble in her marriage will have to handle the seismic shock first. After that, she can either confront or ignore the affair.

Of course, not all husbands or boyfriends are willing to accept the idea that their wives have an innocent case of "vaginitis." The male of the species is at least equally prone to suspicions. Occasionally I get a call from a man asking what his mate has and how she got it. I tell him I can't discuss confidential matters over the phone without the patient's permission and that he should discuss the issue with her directly. That ends it for me, but when I hang up I know that may also end it for the relationship.

This kind of situation is always frustrating. It's uncomfortable telling a woman that if she's been faithful her husband must not be. There's always some slight doubt in the back of my mind that maybe there was no infidelity. Who knows? Maybe the disease came from that one-in-a-million toilet seat where the microorganism lived long enough to be transmitted from one victim to another. Or maybe, in the case of herpes, the woman got it years ago, before her marriage, and the symptoms then were too mild to notice, but now it's flared up, and she thinks it's the first time. If a woman seems absolutely certain that neither of them could possibly be involved with someone else, I will run the test again. It's worth the cost to save a marriage from a false positive test result.

We do get fooled now and then. Like the time a patient seemed to be having repeated cases of trich, one of those ping-pong STDs. She would phone and we'd prescribe Metronidazole, and it would seem to work—until the next infection occurred. Finally, assuming that she and her boyfriend were passing the infection back and forth, I asked her to come in for a test. "You might try a Betadine douche for the odor you complained of," I told her later, "but I'm happy to say there's no sign of any trich in your culture."

"Oh, what a relief!" she exclaimed. "I was afraid that this time we'd have to get prescriptions for all three of us."

Leaves from an Ob/Gyn's Journal

My mask is off. It's all over. The c-section is complete. The new mother squeezes my hand gratefully. "You've got a darling baby there," I say. "Enjoy him."

But my eyes are not on the child. They are on the readout of the instrument monitoring his mother's blood pressure. The numbers are high, an indication that Sharon may be developing postpartum hypertension. Occasionally, a woman registers the kind of high blood pressure after delivery which, when seen during pregnancy, is called toxemia, preeclampsia, or, more recently, pregnancy-induced hypertension.

I explain to Sharon that her blood pressure is up, but that I will be giving her some medication to bring it down and some magnesium sulfate to prevent convulsions. I know that the pressure is almost always back to normal after twenty-four hours of treatment. But I am concerned about that one in a hundred chance that hers won't be. A colleague recently lost a patient from fulminating toxemia in less than twenty-four hours. I order a close watch kept on her.

The next day, I get a call from Jack, who has seen her on rounds. She doesn't look good, he tells me, doesn't seem to be responding to the medication. She has developed leakage from her wound, which he describes as serosanguinous—containing both serum and blood. I feel a sudden tightening in the pit of my stomach. Something's wrong.

I come in to the hospital to find her wound is still draining a lot of the blood-tinged fluid—a sign of imminent disruption of the wound. I call in a surgical consultant to see about taking her back to the OR to resuture the incision, but I am worried about the jaundiced yellow tinge to her eyes—an indication of probably liver dysfunction. I order immediate liver studies and a blood count, and say I think we should move her to the Upstate Medical Center.

The surgeon disagrees. "We can sew her back up and she'll be fine," he insists. "At worst, she'll have a hernia." I respect his opinion, but I'm thinking postpartum toxemia, not repair. My gut fear is that Community, though an excellent general hospital, will be technologically underequipped to handle Sharon's rapidly deteriorating condition. The test results—liver dysfunction and dangerously diminished white blood and platelet counts—warn that she is a very sick woman.

I thank him and step out to the nurses' station to phone Dick Aubry at the perinatal center at Upstate. "I think she has diffuse organ system involvement," I explain. "I'm very concerned, and I'd like to move her there quickly." He agrees. I speak to Sharon's husband, and the transfer is made by ambulance within the hour. She is admitted to Upstate with "atypical toxemia."

Dick calls in a bevy of consultants, but my fears are realized as her condition continues to worsen. Her kidneys begin to fail and urine excretion ceases. Liver function declines further. Bone marrow production of white cells and other elements falls still more. Persistent abdominal distention tells us her bowel is not working. She is bleeding internally.

Officially, she is no longer my patient, but I am intensely interested in her condition and visit frequently. As I stand over her bed, I see a woman who bears no resemblance to the patient I knew. She is bruised all over; her eyes are swollen shut. She drifts in and out of consciousness. I am appalled by the rapidity with which a perfectly healthy young woman can fade away when something goes awry. "Oh, God, please don't let her die!"

The team at the medical center—obstetricians, a nephrologist, surgeons, liver specialists, bone marrow and hematological consultants, virtually every specialty—work doggedly, refusing to surrender her to death. When her bowel fails entirely, an emergency colostomy is done. No magic trick of modern medicine is left untried. I feel intense respect for this team and for the nurses who, with competence and skill, care for Sharon around the clock. But can even they pull her through?

Three months later, Sharon, looking almost her old self, is back in our office, showing off the adorable baby in her arms to the smiling nurses and assistants crowding about her. "I came close to never seeing him," she says afterward with tears in her eyes. "So close. I'm so lucky to have a second chance at life." She presses her new son to her. "It makes you see everything so differently. You know what's really important."

13

Technological Warfare

OF LATE, MEDICAL technology has developed a bad reputation in this country. We like to think how nice it was when people didn't have to be hooked up to machines. When hospitals didn't cost hundreds of millions of dollars to equip. When things were done more naturally.

Well, in those days, Sharon would not have survived. It took the orchestrated excellence of a top-notch medical center to save her even today. So, though I am all for reviving the humanism we associate with the old family doctor's way of practicing medicine, for emphasizing prevention so that technology need not be called on, and for bringing back the comfortable atmosphere of childbirth at home, I'm not for chucking out modern medical technology at the same time. While I've learned—and it took me a while—that medicine is an art, I haven't forgotten that it's also a science.

That's truer today than in the past. Obstetrical doctrine used to be handed down from one generation of doctors to the next, with not much more scientific backing than the old wives' tales that patients passed on. It was taken as gospel, for example, that you couldn't examine a woman vaginally to check progress during labor without dangerously increasing the risk of infection. So everybody examined the cervix rectally, which was uncomfortable for the patient and, because of the hemorrhoids that frequently develop during pregnancy, could be excruciatingly painful. Now we know that the infection rate is no higher when the examination is vaginal. We know that because somebody did a study. Today, most of what we know and do is based on sound scientific data.

Still, there is among patients increasing resistance to technology in obstetrics. Maybe it's because technology is an idea-come-lately in ob or because much of what passed for technology in recent generations was faulty. Then, too, childbirth is not a pathological process; it's a normal one. So not surprisingly, many couples come to my office telling me that they want "a technology-free childbirth": No sonograms. No fetal monitors. No IVs. No enemas. No prepping. No episiotomies. No c-sections. No interventions of any kind. The word "intervention" itself has taken on a negative tone.

It is true that a lot of medical hocus-pocus isn't necessary —the enemas and the shaving and the routine IVs. But it isn't the flowered wallpaper in cozy homelike birthing rooms that has dramatically reduced neonatal and maternal mortality rates in this country. It's the technology in the rooms down the hall. It's the use of ultrasound and fetal monitors and amniocentesis. It's drugs that prevent eclampsia and drugs that stave off early delivery, drugs that prevent infection, and still others that cure it. It's safer anesthesia and sophisticated monitoring equipment when a c-section is needed. It's the ready availability of blood and blood products for transfusing, and techniques for tying off major blood vessels to the uterus to stop postpartum hemorrhage without doing a hysterectomy.

"Natural" childbirth goes smoothly for some women. Not so smoothly for others. For some, it's impossible. It's still the only route in many underdeveloped nations, and the mortality rates for mother and baby are unacceptably high. In primitive societies, a woman can labor for days. The baby rarely survives such a labor. If the mother does, she usually sustains some disabling injury.

When nature goes awry during labor, we don't sit around and watch the damage being done. At one time, "the latest" way to assist in difficult labors was forceps. Dexterously extracting a baby with metal tongs was considered a significant skill, and we young doctors were always proud when we didn't have to turn to surgery. But now we know that midforceps deliveries yield a higher incidence of morbidity and mortality, of minimal brain dysfunction, and of speech disorders, and in general such babies don't do as well as babies delivered abdominally. This is so well accepted that resident obs in most programs no longer receive extensive training in the use of all types of special forceps, but they can do a cesarean section more easily than Caesar could ford the Rubicon.

I don't mean to say that we should be casually unconcerned about the dramatic increase in c-sections, now estimated nationwide at 21 percent. As safe as a cesarean section is today, a woman undergoing one has a 4 in 10,000 chance of dying as compared to a 1 in 10,000 risk for a vaginal birth. Medical peer reviewers *should* challenge ob attendings whose c-section statistics are markedly higher than those of their colleagues. Patients and their advocates *should* address that problem. But the woman who tells her physician she doesn't want a surgical delivery under any circumstances has arrived at the wrong address.

There are plenty of situations, some of them unpredictable, in which a cesarean is not only indicated, but absolutely necessary. When the baby is too big to fit through the mother's pelvis. When the fetus is in distress during labor and that can't be corrected by changing position or administering oxygen to the mother. When the fetus is in the transverse position —crosswise, head to one side, buttocks to the other—which makes it impossible for him to work his way out of the uterus safely. If a mother understands that, then she's as eager as the doctor to get the baby out in the safest way, even if it means she has to submit to surgery. The perfect example of such a mother, a patient I'll never forget, was a courageous air force wife (more about her later) who not only submitted to surgery to save her baby, but to surgery without anesthesia.

There are times when we don't know for sure whether a c-section is absolutely necessary, when we have to make an educated guess. When we add up all the considerations (things like the increased risk to the mother if we do a cesarean versus the even higher risk to a distressed fetus if we don't, and the professional risk that if we don't and something goes wrong, a lawsuit will inexorably follow), sometimes we take a deep breath and reach for the scalpel.

The number of c-sections can certainly be reduced. One way is for doctors to check all possibilities before diagnosing cephalopelvic disproportion (CPD)—which means the baby's head is too big to fit through the mother's pelvis and that a cesarean is a must. There are reasons other than CPD for the failure of labor to progress, and we need to be alert to them. There's maternal exhaustion, for one—in which case a heavy sedative, IV fluids, and a chance to rest may be all that's needed to give mother renewed strength to bring baby down and out. Or, a lazy uterus may need the stimulation of Pitocin. If the problem is a breech (bottoms down) presentation, there's the possibility of manipulating baby into the vertex (head down) position before labor begins, so the delivery can proceed vaginally.

Still another way obs can help stem the cesarean tide is to cross-check indications of distress on the fetal monitor with other tests, so that a c-section won't be done because of misinterpretation of a fetal heart rate pattern. But probably the biggest reversal will come when we recognize the fallacy in the old surgeon's saw: "Once a cesarean, always a cesarean." Repeat c-sections account for a good proportion of the total, but recent studies have demonstrated conclusively that most women who've had cesareans for nonrecurring reasons *can* deliver safely vaginally the second (or third or fourth) time around. If we do do the necessary c-section, but don't do the "automatic c," we can have the best of both worlds.

Sarah Kraft, twenty-five, had had her first baby by c-section because of fetal distress. She came to our office because she knew we did VBACs (vaginal births after cesareans). But when her membranes ruptured and thirty hours later uterine contractions were still sluggish, I was afraid we'd be unable to fulfill Sarah's wish for a vaginal birth. My gut feeling that a little Pitocin would get her lazy uterus going ran head-on into a hospital policy against using the drug for stimulating labor in women who'd previously had cesareans. The literature didn't support such extreme caution; there was evidence that, if carefully monitored, Pitocin could be used.

In a ruptured membrane situation, every hour that passes before labor begins adds to the risk of infection and the need for a cesarean—even with no history of a previous one. Sarah's cervix was soft, thin, and dilated 3 centimeters. Her pelvis was ample. The baby didn't seem to be more than seven pounds or so. And the Krafts remained eager for a natural delivery. So I called the chief of the department and expressed the feeling that this seemed a case for departure from hospital guidelines, and further, that at the next staff meeting we ought to consider changing those guidelines. He consented, a Pitocin drip was begun, and Sarah promptly went into strong and productive labor.

Until a healthy infant lay atop the belly of an ecstatically happy Mrs. Kraft, I remained uneasy. You have to be when you try something that could be challenged later. It's not hard to see why some obs prefer to do repeat c's, motivated by a better-safe-than-sorry philosophy and practicing what's called defensive medicine. But I don't believe that more than a small minority of obs pick up the scalpel for what's been called "the $300 reason." Obs do cesareans because they want the best possible result for mother and infant and don't want to risk a less than perfect one. Some obs deal with any possible patient suspicion of financial motivation by charging the same fee whether the delivery is vaginal or surgical.

There's no doubt that obstetrical technology, like nature, sometimes runs amok and causes more trouble than it cures. But such instances are rare. Not rare are the hundreds of thousands of children who owe their good health, their very lives to technology. I can recall many cases in my own office. A few years ago, a young woman delivered a three-pound baby prematurely. Aided by a lengthy stay in a neonatal intensive care unit, the baby survived. But when the mother became pregnant again, she was concerned that her second child, too, would be premature. So we put her on progesterone from the twenty-fourth week and, when several weeks later she began to go into labor, we hospitalized her and administered drugs to relax the uterus. She was able to go home again and carry her baby to full term.

Clare Krieger was what we call a habitual aborter. Most women have at least one miscarriage in their lives, often without realizing it. They think what they had was a slightly late, particularly heavy period. Most of the time the embryo is blighted and the miscarriage a blessing. But a few women can't seem to retain a pregnancy without help, and Mrs. Krieger was one of these.

After five miscarriages, despairing of ever carrying a baby to term, she had applied to an adoption agency, but that route seemed as fruitless as trying to have one of her own. So she and her husband looked into getting a baby from South America. Then she became pregnant again, and I suggested that this time we try frequent injections of progesterone. She came to the office faithfully each week, got past the critical first trimester, carried through the previously perilous second, and to everybody's surprise and delight, made it all the way. Then, the very week that she brought her healthy new baby boy home, the phone rang—first from South America, then from the adoption agency. The Kriegers had an instant family—a unique set of nonidentical triplets.

Amniocentesis was a major scientific breakthrough only a generation ago, allowing us to diagnose certain conditions in the fetus before birth. One day soon, it may become obsolete. To rule out the possibility of a Down's syndrome baby, a birth defect much more common in older than in younger mothers, we recommend amnio for every woman thirty-five or over. If a woman refuses amniocentesis, we ask her to sign a waiver. The vast majority of tests turn out to be negative and the parents-to-be are happy to know that Down's is one problem they don't have to worry about.

A couple of years ago, one test came back positive. Vikki Meyers was thirty-five and very upset; but she and her husband had decided in advance that if the fetus had Down's she would have an abortion. We sent her to a doctor in town who does therapeutic abortions to the twentieth week, and he agreed to do hers even though she was in the twenty-first. It was terribly traumatic for her. She had been feeling life for weeks, had heard the heartbeat. Now she was going to end that life.

Mrs. Meyers feared becoming pregnant again because she didn't want to go through that ordeal twice. But then she heard about a new test called chorionic villi sampling (CVS) that could be done at eight to ten weeks (sometimes as early as the fifth week) as opposed to the usual sixteenth to eighteenth week for amniocentesis. And CVS doesn't require an additional four or five weeks of culturing to get the results, as do amnios. She and her husband decided to take the risk and conceive. She had to travel to Philadelphia for the test (which was unavailable in Syracuse), but the results were worth it. Not only was the test negative for Down's, but it told her that she was carrying twins. It was almost as though God had arranged to replace that first defective fetus.

Without technology, Mrs. Meyers would probably have delivered the Down's syndrome baby, which might or might not have lived. Had she been able to keep it at home, she probably would not have had the energy to even think about another pregnancy. And if the child had had to be institutionalized, she probably would not have risked another such catastrophe. The Meyers family's wonderful twins are another technological bonus.

The fetal monitor is one of the pet peeves of back-to-nature childbirth enthusiasts, partly because it interferes with mobility and partly because it's a child of technology. When a woman is uncomfortable about it and things are going well, I don't insist on constant monitoring during labor. But the fetal monitor, when read correctly, is perhaps the single greatest reason why it's so rare to lose a baby during labor these days. Fetal heart readings, by warning that the cord is dangerously compressed, that the placenta is compromised and not adequately supplying oxygen to the baby, or that the fetus is being stressed in some other way, allow us time to rescue the child before irreparable harm is done. If there's any sign of a complication, we urge that the fetal monitor remain on for continuous surveillance.

Many a time when I first began practice, I looked at a pregnant woman's abdomen and thought, "If I could only get a look inside . . ." Of course, X-ray was available, but even then voices were being raised in warning against its routine use. Now we can look and learn a lot with equipment which, after a quarter century of trial and not much error, seems to be eminently safe: ultrasound. We can look in early and see if we've dated the pregnancy accurately—which could be important later on in determining when a baby is post-delivery date. We can spot gross deformities. We can check the functioning of certain organs when we have reason to believe there could be a problem. We can often diagnose twins earlier so that we can give the mother appropriate prenatal care.

Where we used to fly blind when we did an amniocentesis, we can now miraculously guide the needle by visualizing it on ultrasound, avoiding accidentally injuring the fetus or penetrating the placenta or its blood vessels. We can define the fetus's exact position as delivery nears, and better estimate its size. Still, for all its benefits and its apparent safety, ultrasound should not be used without sound medical reasons. (A parental wish for a prenatal photo for the baby album or for advance notice of sex so the layette can be purchased in pink instead of blue is not generally considered an appropriate reason.) The use of ultrasound in the United States is governed by guidelines issued by the American College of Obstetrics and Gynecology, and about half of all expectant American women undergo the procedure at least once during pregnancy. It's intervention, but it's the kind of intervention I'm grateful to have on my side.

Among the biggest winners in the obstetric technology game are women who have tried in vain to conceive. The Old Testament records the sorrows of matriarchs Sarah, Rebecca, and Rachel, all of whom apparently had difficulty conceiving. Today we have a veritable arsenal of weapons against infertility. If a woman doesn't ovulate, we may use Clomid to stimulate ovulation. If that fails, we may call out the heavy artillery: Pergonal. We use everything but witchcraft in our manipulations of the cervical mucus to make it favorable for sperm transport. We teach our patients to figure out when they're ovulating so they can time their intercourse for when the odds are in favor of the house. But our best parlor trick is the hysterosalpingogram, an X-ray to determine the condition of the uterus and tubes. If the film shows the tubes to be sound, suddenly, a month or two later, the woman often conceives. No one knows why. She just does.

Of course, not all infertility cases have happy endings. Some couples go through every test, do everything we tell them to do, have intercourse with one eye on the calendar and the other on the clock, but though we can't find anything wrong, all they get is exercise. Sex isn't fun anymore. It isn't spontaneous. It's just calling hubby at the office to plead, "Hurry home—it's time!"

I have one patient now who is forty years old, and desperately wants to get pregnant. I keep going through the steps telling her it's probably not going to happen at her age, particularly when she's been infertile this long, but she insists on trying. Last time she came in, she had cloudy mucus and not very much of it, and I put her on an antibiotic to try to clear it up. I dilated her cervix and put her on a low-dose estrogen, hoping to improve sperm transport. If she's that determined to become pregnant, I'm determined to do everything possible to help.

Ectopic pregnancies are the pregnancies nobody wants. They implant themselves outside the uterus, usually in the fallopian tubes. If they continue to grow, they can burst the tube, causing hemorrhage, shock, and even death. Even if the woman survives, the tubal damage can make her infertile.

We're seeing a lot more ectopics now because of the use of IUDs—which, because they keep pregnancies from implanting in the uterus, increase the risk of implantation elsewhere. The even more widespread substitution of the pill for the condom —stimulating freer sexual life-styles—has increased the incidence of chlamydia-induced pelvic inflammatory disease (PID), which can damage tubes, making the perilous journey of a fertilized egg to the uterus still less likely to succeed. In the past, women often died before an ectopic pregnancy could be diagnosed. That still happens, but diagnosis has improved so much that it's a lot less likely.

Not long ago, a family friend called me at home late one night in considerable pain.

"Where does it hurt?"

"In my abdomen."

"In the middle, on one side, or both?"

"One side."

"Have you missed your period?"

"Yes, and I've been staining."

"Are you wearing an IUD?"

"Yes, a Progestercert."

"Meet me at the emergency room in twenty minutes."

My first sight of Linda coming into the emergency room supported my original hunch. She was bent over in obvious pain, barely able to walk. Step by step, the case for ectopic pregnancy grew. A pelvic exam discovered a tender and somewhat bluish cervix, and a uterus slightly enlarged and a bit softened, suggestive of early pregnancy. After that was confirmed by a positive pregnancy test, I did a culdocentesis —inserting a needle into the cul-de-sac behind the cervix to draw 10 cc of blood. The blood didn't clot, and that indicated internal bleeding, yet another factor pointing to an ectopic pregnancy.

There remained one final step. Linda exhibited none of the signs of shock, so we were able to anesthetize her and do a laparoscopy. With a trocar, I punctured her skin just below the navel, creating an opening about the diameter of a ballpoint pen. I inserted the scope—a marvelous fiber-optic instrument that lights up the reproductive organs like a movie set—into the channel.

There it was, clear as the freckled nose on Linda's face, and one of nature's worst mistakes: like a car driven into a wall of the Lincoln Tunnel instead of straight through it. One of the fallopian tubes was bluish, swollen, and leaking a small amount of blood. Diagnosis confirmed: ectopic pregnancy. I performed a laparotomy to excise the damaged tube.

That's not a happy chore for an obstetrician. It's wonderful to be able to relieve pain, but painful to do it by removing part of the machinery for making babies. The best thing about the technology is that if what the scope shows is simply an infection treatable with antibiotics, I can sheathe my scalpel and spare the tube. So laparoscopy doesn't just make laparotomies easier, frequently it makes them unnecessary.

Technology has an equally important role in the other half of ob/gyn: the gyn part, from the Greek, *gynaikos*, or "woman." The most important part of that is something that wasn't possible thirty-five or forty years ago: the early detection and swift obliteration of cervical cancer.

What we've noticed in the years since the Pap smear became a standard part of the periodic gyn examination is that women rarely die of cervical cancer anymore. Many of them don't even have to go through what used to be the standard treatments: radical hysterectomy, or extensive radiation therapy. Now we can catch the early signs of cervical change before the disease becomes invasive and life-threatening.

In the old pre-Pap smear days, a woman would come in with hemorrhagic foul-smelling gross lesions of her cervix. By the time we saw that, it was usually too late for any cure but mutilating surgery or devastating radiation, which destroyed her vagina and ovaries and made her a surgical or radiation cripple. And Miss or Mrs. Jones was lucky to be a cripple instead of a mortality statistic.

When Ms. or Mrs. Jones comes in today—and for many women it's as routine as going to the hairdresser—her Pap smear is sent to a cytology laboratory, where a cytotechnician examines it under a microscope. Abnormal cells are instantly given away by their flamboyance. Their nuclei are vividly hyperchromatic, as colorful as a Jackson Pollack painting. When the lab report tips us off to the fact that abnormal, or dysplastic, cells are present, we immediately phone our patient and call her in for a follow-up colposcopy.

''Now for the salad dressing,'' I remark in a not very funny but occasionally successful attempt to relax my anxious patient, as her cervix is stained with a vinegar solution. I examine it through a magnifying lens. Normal cells are pink and unremarkable. But in dysplasia, abnormal patterns of blood vessels occur, producing what is called ''punctuation.'' Appearing as though a child with a pencil has dotted them enthusiastically, they often form telltale mosaic tile patterns. I gently biopsy the suspicious area. If it reveals nothing more than a dysplasia, with my patient's consent I prepare to destroy that early abnormal cell growth, usually—though the options of heat cauterization and laser are also available—by means of cryosurgery.

No hospitalization is needed. I simply trigger a sci-fi-like instrument that is, in effect, a Cold Gun. All Ms. Jones feels is a momentary cramping. An ice ball forms over the diseased cells. In five minutes, they've been ''frozen to death'' and slough off over a period of several weeks. Normal new cells regenerate to replace them. The dreaded gross lesions of runaway cervical cancer never get a chance to appear. With continuing Pap smear surveillance every six to twelve months, they never will.

When thermography for breast cancer diagnosis was introduced at an ob/gyn convention, Jack and I were much impressed. The experience of French investigators who had used it for five years promised the ideal early detection system for breast cancer: one that didn't expose patients to radiation as does mammography. We envisioned its doing for breast cancer what the Pap smear did for cervical cancer.

We bought and installed the impressive-looking machine and developed educational materials to describe its pluses and minuses to our patients as an early detection screening device. We told them that the technique was new and that, in effect, we were doing a clinical trial. Thermography, we explained, is a body-heat measuring test that tells us that something is abnormal in the breast, just as a fever tells us something is abnormal in the body. It's a nonspecific test. A feverlike hot spot detected in the breast doesn't shout, ''Cancer!'' But French studies indicated that one woman in three with a hot Class 4 or 5 thermogram would go on to malignancy in five years.

In theory, that was extremely valuable information. In

practice, we got a lot of false positives—cancers that weren't confirmed either by manual examinations or mammograms. I started to feel very uncomfortable about laying on an otherwise blithe spirit the anxiety that she had a one in three chance of getting cancer in the next five years. Particularly when we couldn't be sure this was scientifically sound.

Even more disturbing to Jack and me were two cases in which patients had cold (thus, supposedly normal) thermogram readings, but early malignancies were picked up by manual exam or baseline and backup mammograms. We knew that cold cancer lesions are less biologically active than hot ones—meaning that they are less likely to grow rapidly and spread quickly. But that was small comfort if we might miss them entirely because of our diagnostic technique. So we mothballed our thermography machine and returned to screening by mammography.

Which turned out to be a good move. In the interim, better cameras and faster film had so greatly improved the technology that today the mammogram can do for breast cancer what the Pap smear did for cervical cancer: get it early before it requires major surgery. Unfortunately, many women are still afraid of regular mammography ("X-rays are bad for you, aren't they?") and doctors have to do a lot more to educate them to the need.

One out of every eleven women will develop breast cancer in her lifetime. That lifetime will be a lot longer once women understand that what they need to fear is an ominous lump, not an occasional low-dosage X-ray equivalent to a dental bite wing. With proper staging of mammography surveillance (baseline films at age forty, then repeated, depending on family history, every couple of years until age fifty, and annually thereafter), the danger from X-ray exposure is minuscule compared to the benefits of early diagnosis.

A skillful mammogram made with the state-of-the-art equipment now available at modern diagnostic centers can, like a Pap smear, pick up cancer in well nigh microscopic stages. I'm talking about pinhead-size calcific lesions so small—barely one millimeter—that to ask a surgeon to remove it is like asking him to do an appendectomy on the Invisible Man. But we've found a way.

Under fluoroscopic or X-ray guidance (and, of course, under local anesthesia) a fine needle is inserted into the breast up to the edge of the cancerous calcium-containing particle seen on the mammogram. The patient is rolled into the OR with the needle still in place. The surgeon then excises down to the tip of the needle and removes the lesion. The speck of excised tissue is rushed off to radiology. If the lesion shows up on X-ray, the surgeon's done the job and the tumor has been removed. Removed long before the patient could find it herself in the shower or the doctor in the examining room. The risk of spread—metastasis—is virtually nil. Further minor preventive surgery may be recommended: perhaps some axillary node dissection and possibly some localized radiation therapy, but certainly not mutilating mastectomy. The breast remains intact.

Technology doesn't specialize in bad news. It can also reassure us that things are going well—as it did when I had the remarkable experience of using a diagnostic CAT scan for the first time. Mrs. Harris was post-op after major gyn surgery and making worrisomely slow progress. Could she, I wondered, have a pelvic abscess that was retarding recovery? I talked to my nuclear medical consultant, Bill Goldman, about the possibility of doing a radioactive gallium scan, a test I hadn't used in years. "Why?" he asked. "It would take two to three days to get a result with gallium. We're now using the CAT scan to make that diagnosis."

Later that day, from a control room that, with its vast array of computers, switches, dials, and gauges, looked like Space Center in Houston, I watched in awe as attendants slid Mrs. Harris into a huge stainless steel cylinder, resembling a space capsule. Minutes later, I had my answer. There was no abscess, no need to reopen Mrs. Harris for drainage. I could continue the present conservative management of my patient's recovery. Thanks to a $200 test we avoided the cost and the stress of additional surgery.

There was good news for Anne Romano when I did an exploratory laparoscopy. She was experiencing a lot of pelvic pain for no apparent reason. Was it psychosomatic in origin, or perhaps caused by endometriosis or adhesions from previously unrecognized pelvic inflammatory disease? Through the magic of fiber-optic technology, I was able to view Mrs. Romano's internal pelvic organs through a pen-sized opening as well as if I had opened her up in major surgery and was able to assure her that her pain was not organic. Knowing that eased her tension. The pain gradually disappeared.

Of course, there's such a thing as doing too many diagnostic tests and procedures. Health economists and peer reviewers who monitor health care costs think so, and I certainly agree. But where automatic shotgun testing only runs up larger hospital bills, appropriate tests can yield life-saving information. I recently had a patient who complained of heavy bleeding. She had very large fibroid tumors and surgery was indicated. But were the fibroids the cause of her bleeding, or should I, remembering May Martin, a maternity patient I'd operated on many years earlier, order clotting studies to be on the safe side?

Years earlier, Mrs. Martin's normal vaginal delivery had unexpectedly been followed by sudden and intractable postpartum hemorrhage. With my scrub suit soaked with her blood, I fought to control the hemorrhaging, but simply could not locate the source. I was forced to do a desperate, last resort hysterectomy. Several years later, after a minor procedure, the same patient developed a large and baffling hematoma. Only then did I discover that she had a rare bleeding disorder: Factor 8 was missing from her blood.

This time, I ordered a simple and inexpensive test on the fibroids patient to make certain she wasn't a bleeder. Her clotting time and other coagulation studies were normal, and we were able to proceed with her surgery without fear of serious and unexpected coagulation problems. Conclusion: In ordering tests, it's necessary to seek a balance between keeping costs down and keeping patients alive.

Advances in anesthesiology have made surgery much safer than in years past. Not long ago, the error tolerances in anesthetic drugs were so narrow that the wise patient gave as much thought to choosing the anesthesiologist as the surgeon. Anesthesiologists were in Class V, the highest malpractice insurance risk category. But the safety of anesthesia and the techniques for monitoring it have improved so dramatically in the past several years that anesthesiologists have moved down three liability risk levels to Class II. This is good for me, for my patients, and for New York State anesthesiologists.

My good and modest friend Bill Dwyer, who frequently orchestrates the anesthesiology when I operate, waxes positively euphoric when he talks about the changes for the better.

"It was," he says, "a lot more stressful in the old days."

I remember those days. The only thing anesthesiologists I worked with used to monitor a patient's condition was a precordial stethoscope. Now they have an alarm that goes off if the patient's blood pressure rises too high or falls too low. Another one buzzes if the pulse is too fast or too slow. Still another indicates the concentration of oxygen the patient is inhaling—and an alarm goes off if she's not ventilated for five seconds. If a tube should accidently disconnect, yet another alarm signals. And for the rare patient subject to malignant hyperthermia (high body temperature), there's a tiny electronic black spot pasted to her forehead that makes her look like an Indian princess while automatically printing out her body temperature. Bill likes to say that with all these "idiot monitors," he could teach the average ten-year-old to do his job. Maybe. But I'd rather have Dr. Dwyer.

Technology doesn't always come in gadget or drug form. It can be as simple as a bar of soap. To cut down on skin and wound infections, I have my patients scrub the entry area with an antiseptic solution for three consecutive nights prior to surgery to reduce the bacterial count. And I suggest that they shower several days before admission with an antiseptic soap like Safeguard to cut down the body colonization of staph bacteria. Between the Betadine scrubs and the showers, they come in for surgery squeaky clean and less likely to develop infections.

Technology can continue to reduce stress for the surgical team and trauma to the patient even when surgery is over. Instruments used in surgery aren't counted. It's up to the surgeon and assistant to be sure they don't absentmindedly forget a pair of scissors or drop a hemostat inside the wound cavity. But sponges and needles—more numerous and much harder to keep track of—are counted. Occasionally, as surgery nears the end, the scrub nurse who keeps the count announces that we're short a sponge or a needle. The missing item could be misplaced somewhere in the folds of one of the cluster of disposable drapes covering the patient. Or the count could have been incorrect from the start.

But there could be a far less desirable reason for a short count. To rule it out, a portable X-ray machine is summoned —usually after the peritoneum has been closed and before the skin is sutured. Most of the earliest malpractice suits, in the good old days for doctors when few people ever sued, were for the clear-cut carelessness known legally as *res ipsa loquitur* —or, let the thing speak for itself. When a sloppy or inexperienced surgeon left a sponge or needle inside his patient, usually the error went undetected until the patient had complained of postoperative pain for weeks, months, or even years.

Sometimes, much later, another surgeon would operate and find the cause—often triggering a lawsuit. As a result, for years sponges have been tagged with radio-opaque material. And, since the metal needles are naturally radio-opaque, the post-op portable X-ray will spot them, too. I've never had to reopen a patient to remove a foreign object, but like most surgeons, I appreciate X-ray technology. Without it, we'd spend a lot of sleepless post-op nights on pins and needles.

The more scientific we become, the more humanistic we need to be. The gleaming new pieces of equipment, awesome to me, can be frightening to the patients who are hooked up to them. That means we must introduce patients, not just attach them, to the machines that will be their companions as they travel together through pregnancies or illnesses. We need to provide step-by-step explanations, respond to concerns, answer questions without impatient glances at our wristwatches.

My patients know that I've become a noninterventionist. I prefer doing a delivery naturally—essentially the way it's been done for thousands of years—to doing it with drugs and instruments the way it was a generation ago. But they also know that I won't hesitate to call upon the best of modern technology when the situation departs from the normal, that I will do everything necessary to get a good result. I let them know that up front, so that if problems arise in a delivery, they won't be shocked to see a fetal monitor attached or upset to have an IV inserted and preparations for a cesarean begun.

It's the same in all aspects of medicine. The more we can do naturally, the better. If I find a patient who is having pelvic pain for no apparent reason, rather than tell her to take two Advils and call me in the morning, I suggest that she examine the stresses in her life.

If she and her husband argue a lot, I urge her to take responsibility for telling him exactly how she feels so that he gets the message. Ask him for what you want, I advise, and encourage him to tell you what it is that he needs and wants. There are sure to be differences in the way they view things, but unless each partner knows what the other is thinking, there's no way they can understand each other and come to any kind of agreement. I urge honesty because I've found myself that our lives work best when we tell the truth. It's a hammer that breaks down the thickest walls, and its consequences are never as dire as we anticipate. Telling it often opens doors and options for us that we never knew existed.

There are other effective methods of stress reduction —meditation and exercise among them. The brand name doesn't matter. It can be TM, Benson's relaxation response, autogenic therapy, or biofeedback. It can be brisk walking, jogging, bicycling, swimming (though that doesn't give women the weight-bearing exercise that benefits their skeletal structure and helps ward off osteoporosis), cross-country skiing in season and aerobic dancing out of season: whatever turns her catecholamines and endorphins on. Exercise can produce a sense of relaxation and euphoria that beats Valium by a country mile.

I feel about prescribed drugs almost as strongly as I do about street drugs. It makes more sense to keep a woman well by modifying her life-style than to wait until her life is at risk, and it's better to work at keeping her heart healthy than to plead for a transplant.

An emphasis on prevention is still difficult for many physicians to accept. For one thing, we can't prevent everything. For another, the use of drugs and high technology is what sets us apart from other healers. No one else is licensed to prescribe and to perform surgery. For still another, some of our patients aren't all that eager to listen to life-style modification sermonettes. They expect an Rx or the recommendation of a procedure that will effortlessly cure what ails them. To tell them, "My prescription is for you to improve your diet, start exercising regularly and aerobically, and quit smoking," doesn't sound like their fifty dollars' worth. Not when they can get the same recommendations for $14.95 in any one of hundreds of self-help books.

Nevertheless, that's what we have to tell them. We can't sit back and let *American Health* and *The Runner* run the health promotion movement. Not only should we participate in it, we should lead it. Because no one knows better than we that the miracles of modern technology can't cure everything.

Leaves from an Ob/Gyn's Journal

"I'm scared to death of the tube that doctor's going to shove down my throat. If I go down there, I know I won't come back . . ." The speaker is a strapping twenty-eight-year-old man admitted for a bronchoscopy scheduled for the following morning. His voice is shaky, his hands clammy.

I try to reassure him: "This is a minor procedure. Your attending has done hundreds of them. You'll not only come back up, you'll come back with a smile on your face." But he is not reassured, and when I leave his room, I am worried, too. As an intern, I'm new at this. Is his profound fear normal?

I talk to the night nurses. They tell me they've seen a lot of anxious patients, but Don Jones is the worst by far. They feel that postponing the procedure might be a good idea, but neither one is willing to risk being upbraided for calling the doctor at home after hours. I fear that if I call, the doctor will think I'm a bigger flake than his patient. Still, the terror in Mr. Jones's voice haunts me. So, finally, I pick up the phone.

"Of course, he's nervous," the doctor says sharply. "Everyone's nervous before something like this. But the procedure is necessary. There's no other way to find out what's causing his problem. And," he adds more gently, "there's nothing to worry about. The man works for a trucking company. He's as strong as an ox."

I know he's seen a lot more patients than I have, and I hang up feeling foolish. But all the same, I wish he'd come and talk to the patient one more time.

The rest of my tour is filled with activity, and when I wearily sign out well after midnight, I sleep the sleep of the intern. Next day, I look in on Jones for a cheerful I-told-you-so. There is another patient in his bed. I am about to ask where he is when the younger of the two nurses approaches me, an odd look on her face.

"Did you hear what happened to Mr. Jones?" she asks in a small awed voice. "He arrested during the bronchoscopy. He died on the table."

14

Scared to Death

I LEARNED LONG ago never to consider surgery, even routine surgery, "routine." Surgery is an invasion of the body which, no matter how far we've come with scientific medicine, presents risks. The body fights any trespass, any disturbance of its stasis. It's as though a silent alarm goes off when a burglar pries open a window. From the moment that the first spurt of Pentothal is injected, the first tube inserted, the first cut made with the scalpel, the body rallies resistance forces which we may never fully understand. So recommending surgery—or even a nonsurgical but invasive diagnostic procedure like bronchoscopy—is a serious responsibility.

I discovered that when Donald Jones died. I relearned it a short time later during my surgical rotation.

The patient was scheduled for surgery of the upper spine. The night before, he asked me to check his blood pressure and read aloud a few passages from his Bible. "I was hoping that would calm me down," he murmured when I finished. "But I just don't feel right. I don't feel like I'm going to get through this." Again I talked to the nurses on the floor. None of them thought his reaction was significant, and I thought, maybe it's just me, and went on my way. But I caught him on early rounds before going off duty next morning, discovered that his pressure had climbed another 40 points, and suddenly remembered Donald Jones. I paged the attending neuro surgeon and told him, "I don't know what you'll want to do about this, doctor, but I thought you should know that your patient is scared to death."

"He needs the surgery," he said evenly, "and I'm already in the OR waiting to do it. Send him down."

I thought, why doesn't he at least come up and talk to him? Frustrated, I watched the orderlies wheel the patient to the elevator. The surgery was technically successful. The patient died in the recovery room.

Three years after I opened my practice in Syracuse, I was tragically reminded of the awesome grip of fear and the power of negative thinking.

I had admitted a thirty-year-old mother to the hospital for uncomplicated surgery to repair a prolapsed uterus. Lower back pain frequently incapacitated her, and she felt her uterus protruding from her vagina when she walked. She seemed anxious when I visited her the evening before her operation, and I asked what was troubling her.

"I'm frightened," she admitted. "This is the first time I've ever had surgery. I know you're going to think it's irrational, but I have a premonition that I'm . . . that I'm . . ." Tears flooded her eyes.

I reached for her hand and pressed it. "That's okay," I reassured her. "Just cry it out." There was a box of tissues beside the bed. I plucked a handful.

She dried her eyes, blew her nose, and with an effort, finished her sentence: ". . . that I'm not going to leave this hospital alive."

"Mrs. James," I reasoned, "I understand the way you feel. It's normal and natural to worry about surgery. Everybody does. As a matter of fact," I added, hoping to get her to smile, "if you weren't concerned about surgery, I'd be concerned about you."

My patient looked no less glum. I rose from the chair beside her bed and tried again. "Just relax," I said, "and get a good night's sleep. I'll see you first thing in the morning. Everything's going to be just fine."

I was right about the surgery. It was uneventful and uncomplicated. All vital signs were stable and I was happy to assure Mrs. James when she came out from under anesthesia that she would be home with her family in less than a week.

But thirty-six hours later, I was awakened at 2 A.M. by a phone call from the nurse on the floor. "Something's wrong with Mrs. James, doctor," she said. "She's hysterical and thrashing about like a crazy woman. It's all we can do to hold her down."

I ordered a tranquilizer and broke all speed records to the hospital. A nurse grabbed my arm as I rushed into my patient's room. "Doctor," she said. "I'm sorry. You're too late. She's dead."

I didn't believe her. It wasn't possible. How could it be possible when she had been coming along so well? I looked down at the bed. My patient lay motionless, her pupils dilated, her skin cold, her wrist pulseless. I checked for heart tones. There were none, nor did her pupils respond to the penlight I flashed in her eyes. So it was true. She was dead. A victim of fear and her own self-fulfilling prophecy.

I telephoned her husband and asked him to come to the hospital as soon as possible. I was in the nurses' chart room, writing my notes, wondering what I could say to him, how I could explain the unexplainable, when I heard hurrying foot-steps down the hall. At 3 A.M., it was unlikely to be anyone else. I walked out to meet him. He looked disheveled and fearful. "Mr. James," I began, "there's no easy way to say this. I don't know why or how, but your wife has died."

He flung himself at me, grabbing me by the collar. "Murderer!" he exclaimed hoarsely. "Murderer! You killed my wife!" He shook me angrily. I pushed his hands away and tried to calm him down. A resident and two nurses who had rushed out at the first sounds of the scuffle restrained him gently.

"You sonovabitch, what do you mean my wife is dead? What did you do to her?"

It was a valid question. Had I done something wrong? I knew that couldn't be. Everything had gone perfectly. But his anger, his anguish were understandable. The unexpected death of my patient was professionally painful, but the family tragedy was far worse. A husband losing the wife he loved. Three young children suddenly motherless. Even if it was not my fault, I had to know what had gone wrong. When Mr. James was calm enough to be rational, I told him the only way we'd know what had caused his wife's death was to order an autopsy.

It was far worse than anything I had experienced in the morgue at PGH during internship. This was no aged cadaver whose best years were part of his distant past. This was my patient, and only forty-eight hours earlier I had told her she didn't have a thing to worry about. But there is, as a Scottish proverb puts it, "nae medicine for fear."

The autopsy findings were professionally reassuring. There had been no error or wrongdoing on my part. Her sudden death was, indeed, inexplicable. And the rationale for the surgery had been justifiable. But that was scant comfort when I considered that if I had taken her premonition more seriously and scrapped the surgery, perhaps called in a psychiatrist to talk to her before proceeding further, she might still be alive.

Hindsight, though more acute than foresight, can only be employed after the fact. I use it now. In visiting a patient before surgery, I preview everything that's going to happen every step of the way. Let there be no surprises. I don't leave until I'm sure that everything's complete for my patient in a process that, much as I hate to use the analogy, resembles in many ways the classic stages of dying. It's a process that begins long before hospitalization. First comes denial—when the patient in my office is told something she doesn't want to hear: "You need surgery." Despair and anger often follow: "But why me?" Then comes resignation: "That's the way it is and I'll just have to go through with it." And finally acceptance: "This surgery is going to make me feel better. I'm glad I'm going to have it."

Even then there are troubling questions: "Am I going to survive?" "Will I be able to do the things I've always done?" And the details of surgery: "How long will I be in there?" "What about possible complications?" Once that's all been processed, there's nothing left, and the patient is ready. There's just a clear space that says, "Here I am. Let's get it over with." That's the space I want to find before I pick up the scalpel.

While ideally the surgeon's goal should be to allay fear, we are, these litigious days, legally required to create it. Something called informed consent—which is one of those multimillion-dollar spears lawyers love to impale us on when we fail to dot an "i" or cross a "t" in explanation—has doctors today sounding like drug side-effects warning labels. Simply stated, if anyone anywhere has ever had A,B,C, or D happen to them as a result of procedure X and the surgeon fails to warn you of each and every possible dire consequence before he performs procedure X, he could be liable for thousands or even millions of dollars if A,B,C, or D happens to happen to you. And his failure to strike fear in your heart prior to surgery and obtain your informed consent in writing would be called malpractice.

As a result, I now spend considerable time in my office informing patients of all possible complications, sudden death not excluded. No matter how gently I try to put it, it's a litany that cannot help but make the bravest blanch. And it takes as much courage for me to broach the subject as it does for them to hear me out.

The last thing in the world a surgeon, especially one who's seen patients "scared to death," wants to do is alarm someone about to put her life in his hands. It's like administering a mood-depressant when what's needed is a cheerful and optimistic frame of mind. And it's not all that wonderful for us professionally. Just to talk about possible complications is to raise in a patient's mind the question: "Hmm, have I got the right doctor for the job? If this operation is that dangerous, shouldn't I go to the Mayo Clinic?"

Imagine requiring your waiter at Maxim's, as he announces the specials of the day, to solemnly warn: "Messieurs et Mesdames, please note that rich high-cholesterol foods like those from which you are about to choose may lead to your untimely death from atherosclerosis, stroke, or intestinal cancer." Yes, it could happen. But the odds—for that particular main course as for this particular surgical procedure—are so much in your favor, why talk about them and scare you away from a dinner you flew thousands of miles to enjoy or surgery you need?

But, of course, our responsibility goes beyond delivering the bouillabaisse. And not talking about the consequences that we ourselves are aware of—which is the way it used to be—is clearly too paternalistic. I just wish that somewhere between paternalism and alarmism there was a better way.

Since there isn't, we have to make the best of it. And one of the things I've come to realize is that honesty—truth in surgery—may be the best of all policies after all. Instead of the surgeon as God, it makes possible a shared enterprise, a kind of trinity: the two of us and God. And this will sound hokey to some. But I really have the feeling that the three of us in partnership together can achieve the kind of result that the two of us want. And that I think God wants, too.

I let my patient know that while complications are possible, I don't want them to occur any more than she does. And that I'm committed to their not occurring with a conscientious 100 percent effort supported by a lot of years of experience. But I make it clear that that's not enough—that a patient's attitude is as important as a doctor's skill. Her intention and determination to get well are going to make a difference, for if Lederle or Searle could synthesize courage and optimism and distill them into an injectable aqueous solution, it would be the best medicine of all.

When I talk to my patient the evening before her morning of surgery, I want to know that she's on my side before we start, committed to recovering rapidly and getting out of the hospital and back to a normal life as soon as possible. I want to empower her to feel that she can help me. When I talk that way, something happens to make the doctor-patient relationship different from what it was when I kept my own counsel, when only I knew the dangers ahead. We become two travelers going on an adventure together—not knowing exactly what the outcome is going to be, but both committed to giving it our best shot and confident, as confident as one can be as a human being, that it's going to turn out all right.

Without commitment—without their knowing I'm committed to them and my knowing they're committed to helping me get a good result—it doesn't feel the same. I'm not happy about embarking on such a journey alone. It's too perilous. But when I sense that strength of purpose in my patient, then I know it's going to be okay.

I felt that strength recently from a patient who developed a post-op bowel dysfunction and fever that, while not life-threatening, hung on persistently, prolonging her hospital stay. I was very unhappy about her discomfort and the added expense, but when I went to her room to cheer her up, it was she who encouraged me: "Oh, don't worry, Henry. I've got two insurance coverages and I don't have any money concerns. I know it's going on longer than you thought it would, but however long it takes, it's going to work out fine." *She* was telling *me* not to worry—an example of the kind of partnership that can happen when people trust, respect, and care about one another. And, indeed, everything did work out as she predicted.

We can wish wistfully for the good old days when patients trusted their doctors implicitly, but we can't wish them back. All we can do is try, one patient at a time, to re-create that trust. With some patients, it happens without our even trying —in one recent case, oddly enough, because my patient felt that clothes make the surgeon.

The patient, whom I operated on for a fibroid uterus, thanked me for doing a good job and then explained why she trusted me. "I wouldn't buy a cake in a bakery with a lot of dirty sawdust on the floor," she said. "It's the same principle with a doctor. I noticed you always dress neatly, so I figured you would probably do a neat surgical incision. I was right, too," she added proudly. "I won't show my friends the incision, but I'll certainly tell them how pretty it is."

Sometimes trust isn't earned that easily. It comes naturally in women with whom I've had a long doctor-patient relationship. But it can be a while coming in the new patient, particularly one who is anxious about the whole hospital experience and worried about what we're going to "do" to her.

Even so simple a matter as starting an IV for a woman in labor who may soon require a cesarean section can raise hackles between us. How I handle it makes a major difference —but I only learned that recently. At one time, the scenario would have gone this way:

ME: Mrs. Grey, we're going to establish an IV now. Nurse Richards is going to be inserting a needle in your vein.

MRS. GREY: But I'm deathly afraid of needles.

ME: Well, Mrs. Grey, it's necessary, just in case you should need a c-section.

MRS. GREY: I don't want an IV and I don't want a cesarean.

ME (*feeling my blood pressure rising*): Mrs. Grey, don't be ridiculous. Nurse, I'm going outside. Get the IV started, please.

Now I patiently hear the patient out and just as patiently explain my actions and decisions. I accept her fear, grant its presence and its reasonableness, and very often, that done, it—or at least her resistance—vanishes:

MRS. GREY: I don't want an IV. I'm deathly afraid of needles.

ME *(gently):* I understand your being nervous. I'd be nervous in your position, too. Lots of things scare me, but I need to do them, scared or not. It takes courage to do something when you're afraid. And I would just like to tell you that I believe you have the courage. I know you do.

MRS. GREY: But why not hold off on the IV until you're sure I need a cesarean?

ME: Well there is some indication on the monitor that your baby is undergoing stress. If the abnormal readings continue and other tests verify distress, then we may have to do the surgery in a hurry. With the IV in place, that will be possible. So the IV is important to help your baby. And even though you hate the idea, it will help you, too. You've been in labor for a lot of hours with nothing to eat or drink, and this will allow us to get some fluids into you—so you won't dehydrate.

I'm learning. Same situation. Same doctor. Different attitude. Very different result.

Sometimes the resistance is much stronger, and it's a struggle to develop trust. Like the woman—Jack's patient, not mine—I examined for the first time in her thirtieth week of pregnancy. Gladys Graham was a Syracuse woman who had married and moved to the south but had returned home to have the baby she planned to give up for adoption. Coming north to do it made it easier: fewer questions from friends and relatives at home. Jack was away for a few days, so it fell to me to see her. I palpated her abdomen routinely, then repeated the procedure. I wanted to be sure.

"Your baby is in a breech position," I said finally. "It's very possible that it will turn, but it might need some help. My nurse can demonstrate some exercises that sometimes work. Another possibility is a fairly new technique where the doctor tries to turn the baby around, monitoring the process for safety with ultrasound. I've never done it and neither has Dr. Yoffa, but I've seen babies turned with its help, and there's a fifty-fifty chance it would work. I'd be willing to try it if he doesn't want to. Or, if you prefer, we could send you to the perinatal specialist at Upstate Medical Center.''

I sensed that I had her attention but not her trust. We had no ongoing relationship. She was wondering where Jack was, and why this stranger had suddenly become her doctor.

"If your baby doesn't turn," I continued calmly, "we'll have to do a c-section.''

She flushed with sudden anger. "I don't want a c-section," she declared firmly. In the back of her mind, I guessed, she was thinking, Dr. Yoffa wouldn't force a c-section on me. I knew she was wrong, but until Jack's return, it was up to me to address her problem.

I had heard that indignant battle cry often enough in the past half-dozen years so that it no longer upset me. The response that leapt to mind was one I couldn't give: "When you flew here from Atlanta, did you tell your pilot how to fly the plane?"

What I said instead offended her almost as much: "I'm sorry, Mrs. Graham, but if your baby remains in a breech position, a c-section is the only way we'd be willing to deliver you. If you're totally opposed to that, you might consider finding another office to be responsible for your care." That came out sounding harsher than I intended. "Of course," I added, "I don't want you to take my word for it. Feel free to get a second opinion. But if you have a breech, I don't think anyone in this community will deliver you vaginally."

I paused for her reaction. She was tight-lipped and hostile. Well, I thought, say goodbye to any relationship with this patient. But with a little luck, she'll get Jack for the balance of her pregnancy and for her delivery. Maybe she'll listen to him.

Six weeks later though, it was my turn again. I learned that Jack had sent her to Upstate's perinatal center, but that the defiant little fetus was still in a stubbornly breech position. I did my best to warm up our relationship, but I couldn't change the baby's position with a smile. I didn't change it either when I concluded after the examination, "Nothing seems to have worked, and you're only a week or ten days away. I'm sorry, but it does look as though it's going to have to be a c-section." I explained that vaginal delivery of a first baby in breech position is, with a few exceptions, no longer considered prudent practice because of possible damage to the infant at the time of delivery.

She left still harboring resentment. An hour later, I took a phone call from her mother in Syracuse, who made no effort to conceal her annoyance. Why, she asked, couldn't we deliver her daughter naturally? Why did we have to do a cesarean? Half an hour later, I heard from her husband in Atlanta. He was overtly antagonistic. "It's well-known," he informed me, "that doctors are doing unnecessary c-sections for their own convenience and for larger fees. How," he asked, "can I be sure that's not the case here?"

By the second phone call, I was feeling a bit hostile myself. I confined myself to politely summarizing what I'd told my patient and telling both callers that I'd be happy to rediscuss it next time she came in. Actually, nothing would have pleased me more than for Jack to be on her case from here to maternity.

But Mrs. Graham was now in her last month and coming in weekly. So two weeks later, I saw her name on my appointment schedule. I got a sinking feeling, then realized suddenly that I'd been going about this the wrong way. It was far more important for me to work on my personal relationship with her than on the nuts and bolts of how she was going to be delivered. I needed to create some trust. How? Maybe with a little honesty.

"Look, Mrs. Graham," I began after the preliminary greetings, "I may have to be there when your baby is born. It doesn't feel good for me to be working with you when I know that you would prefer another doctor. I want you to know that the way things are now, it would be just as uncomfortable for me as it would be for you. And I don't like that feeling. If I'm there with you, I want to feel welcome. And I want you to know that if I'm there, I'm going to give you the best that I have and nothing less than that.

"We may disagree about some of the details, but I feel we can handle disagreement as long as we share a common goal: that you have a healthy baby and come out of it well yourself. When I told you that you needed a c-section and I suggested that you get a second opinion, I wasn't being sarcastic. I really meant it. I wanted you to have freedom of choice—to make it possible for another obstetrician to have some input. I sense that you felt I was putting you down or not caring about you. That wasn't what I intended, and if the way I acted or what I said caused you to feel that way, I'm truly sorry."

The young woman's eyes brimmed with tears. I could feel her hostility washing away. Suddenly we were together, in an entirely new relationship: genuine partnership.

"I really did have a lot of negative feelings about you," she said after a few moments. "And I was worried about your being there at the delivery." Impulsively, she leaned forward and touched my hand. "But I'm not anymore."

Ten days later, I delivered her baby. We were partners in a great experience. Because we had been honest with one another, we were able to share one of life's most wonderful moments. Because I had won her trust, she was able to go through an experience she had dreaded calmly and without fear.

Leaves from an Ob/Gyn's Journal

It is 1963 at the Air Force Base Hospital in Dover, Delaware. Donna Maxwell hunches into the labor room doubled over like a fighter who has just been punched below the belt. But she is smiling through her misery. This low blow is only the latest in a long series of uterine contractions, and if all goes well, in a few hours she'll be cradling a new baby in her arms.

"Hi, doc," she says breezily. "I guess this is it. I've got contractions—lots and lots of contractions. They hurt. But"—she smiles up at me—"they hurt good."

Donna straightens up and begins to unashamedly peel off her clothing. "I thought I'd be shy and modest when I got here," she says, laughing. "Now all I can think of is to shuck this stuff as fast as I can so I can get this ordeal over with." The nurse helps Donna into a hospital gown and eases her into bed. I lean over and briefly apply my stethoscope to her abdomen.

"Your baby's heart sounds are good," I report. "A solid 135 beats per minute. And"—I pause to check her cervix—"you're dilated a good two fingers. Two or three more hours of contractions and you should be ready for the big time. Cathy will stay here with you, and I'll check in periodically to see how the baby's progressing."

Twenty minutes later, I return. Donna's contractions are closer now, and she is progressing nicely. But this time my stethoscope reading is cause for concern. Baby Maxwell's heart rate has plummeted alarmingly and now hovers around 100. Anything below that is considered fetal distress. Usually these drops are temporary and self-correcting, so there's no point in agitating the mother. I say nothing. But when I recheck five minutes later, the heart rate has continued to slide. It is now 60 and remains there even in the interval between contractions. The thick greenish matter in the amniotic fluid indicates the fetal bowel has relaxed and passed meconium, another sign that the baby is not getting enough oxygen. I order maternal oxygen and spend the next two minutes bent over Donna, listening through the contractions for signs of improvement in my other patient—the tiny one I've never met. There are none.

I bounce up barking orders to the nurse: "Call Dr. Pasquale in the clinic and tell him to come up immediately, that I need him to assist on an emergency c-section. Get someone to call Edwards and to keep on calling till they locate him. Tell him we need anesthesia for a cesarean right away, and it's an emergency. Page nurse Jones and have her scrub, and let's get an IV going and have Mrs. Maxwell typed and cross-matched for two units of blood. And put a Foley in her bladder right away. When you have the catheter in, get her right into the OR."

I turn to explain the sudden flurry of activity to my patient, but she has already guessed what's wrong. Her reaction is not the panic that I had feared. She lies there quietly, the fingers of both hands spread lovingly over her abdomen. "Is it the cord?" she asks.

"Probably," I say. "His pulse is way down. Last reading was 40 and dropping. The oxygen should have restored the rate to normal, but it didn't do a thing. If we're going to save your baby, I'm going to have to do a c-section right away. The problem is . . ." I pause, overwhelmed by the enormity of the thought forming on my lips. ". . . our anesthetist is off duty, and if he's off the post, it's going to be a while until we reach him. I can give you a spinal, but that will take time, and time is something we don't have. We've got to get your baby out fast."

Mrs. Maxwell's face is pale. "Just do it," she says.

"Are you sure? I've never done a c-section without anesthesia. It's going to hurt like hell. And it's risky for you."

"It doesn't matter," she says quietly. "I want you to save my baby."

Mrs. Maxwell has taken the decision out of my hands. I turn to the nurse. "Captain Pasquale should be here any second to assist. Keep trying to reach Edwards."

I find Pasquale scrubbing and quickly explain the situation. "A cesarean without anesthesia?" he asks. He looks shell-shocked but doesn't argue.

I'd like to know what the baby's pulse is now, but there is no time to listen. If we don't get it out fast, there'll be nothing to listen to. Without oxygen, brain damage or death could occur within minutes. Blood has been drawn for cross-matching. The IV is in. So is the catheter. We drape the patient and, skipping the usual ten-minute prep, the nurse splashes antiseptic on the mother's exposed abdomen. There are going to be a lot of short cuts, and I begin taking them immediately.

I make the first incision down to the fascia without clamping any blood vessels in the skin, dreading the reaction from my patient. But Mrs. Maxwell does not cry out. Could she have passed out or gone into shock from the pain? As blood begins to flow, I glance at her quickly. I am amazed by what I see. She is fully conscious. And she has not even winced.

Encouraged, I continue feverishly. I incise the fascia and, as it falls apart, separate the muscles to expose the grayish membrane that is the peritoneum. The catheter has already drained and collapsed the bladder, which lies over the lower portion of the uterus. That gives me more room to maneuver and lessens the risk that a slip of the scalpel will damage it. My assistant lifts the peritoneum with two pairs of forceps so that, in incising it, I don't simultaneously incise the bowel. I widen the incision with Metzenbaum scissors.

As I cut, I talk to my patient. "How are you doing?" I ask. "Fine," she replies through gritted teeth. "Don't worry about me. Just hurry!"

I'm moving faster now. Pushing the bladder out of the way, I make a half-inch incision in the muscle of the uterus at the midline, slip in both index fingers, and spread it wide enough for a baby's head and shoulders to exit. I rupture the membranes, make way for the flood of amniotic fluid that spurts forth, and slide my hand into the lower uterus, insinuating it under the baby's head. My fingertips probe the infant's neck and locate the cause of its respiratory distress. Quickly, I scoop out the baby's head, carefully untangle the compressed cord, and with my assistant pushing from above, deliver the shoulders and the rest of the body. The infant does not look good. There is a pale bluish cast to its features. But my left hand covers its chest as I extract it, and I am overjoyed to feel the tiny heart beating slowly beneath my palm.

I hand the limp child to the nurse, and she cradles it while I cut the cord that has preserved it in life for so many months, only to threaten it at the moment of birth. She passes it on to the pediatrician, who has just arrived. I hear a faint cry as he suctions it and administers positive pressure oxygen. We have won. "Ninety seconds, doctor," says the OR nurse. "I watched the clock. That took ninety seconds from the first cut."

I look at Mrs. Maxwell and marvel at the strength God gives women. I have just cut her open without anesthesia of any kind. Blood is pooling in the raw gaping wound in her abdomen. Her face should be distorted with pain. Instead there is a contented smile on her lips and the sweet serenity of a madonna. I am in awe. This is the kind of woman who fought Indians and wrestled mountain lions when her young were endangered, who would summon the superhuman strength to lift an automobile if her child were pinned beneath it. But this is no time for fifty-cent philosophy. We've saved the baby—I don't want a mother in shock from loss of blood. Pasquale and I sponge it away and begin to stem the scarlet flow, tying off blood vessels.

In the corridor behind us, I hear running footsteps. I look over my shoulder. The anesthetist sticks his head in the door and quickly surveys the scene: the woman open on the table, the baby in the pediatrician's arms. "Oh," he says, "I'm too late. But then, how . . . ?"

"I'll explain later," I tell him. "First, how about giving Mrs. Maxwell something for her pain so we can close? I think she's bitten the bullet long enough." From the other side of the delivery room, there is good news from the pediatrician. "The five-minute Apgar's 9," he calls out. "This little guy is doing fine."

I smile down at my patient. "Yes," I say, "I forgot to tell you. It's a boy."

15

The Lawyer in the OR

"THERE'S A GENTLEMAN in the waiting room with a summons for you," my nurse said. She brought the news as though offering me a dead fish at arm's length.

That's the way Montgomery vs. Eisenberg began, with a process-server handing me a summons and complaint from a New York City attorney accusing me of malpractice against a Syracuse woman and her baby.

I tell this painful story of a trial I would just as soon forget largely as a case in point—to explain why doctors are practicing defensive medicine these litigious days; why so many obstetricians, no matter how much they love what they do, are abandoning the delivery room; and why the whole system needs reform. But I'd be lying if I didn't confess another reason: the chance to tell in full, without courtroom interruptions, my side of the story.

This is, of course, the way I saw and see it. If Mrs. Montgomery (that's not her real name) should read this chapter, she may well feel I have distorted the facts of the case. That's understandable. Our accounts of the events, seen from opposite poles, are bound to differ.

Her delivery six months earlier was still fresh in my mind when the summons arrived. It had been traumatic for both mother and child, but considering the far more dire results avoided, I'd never expected a lawsuit.

Mrs. Montgomery had been my patient for half-dozen years when, on the evening of October 1, 1973, I met her and her husband at the hospital to deliver their first child. A small woman, she'd gained forty-nine pounds during her pregnancy though I'd repeatedly cautioned that her pelvis might be unable to accommodate a large baby. In the labor room, the baby's estimated weight of eight to eight and a half pounds seemed likely to make a reluctant prophet of me. "We may have to do a cesarean section," I told her.

But there are four times more maternal deaths from c-sections than from vaginal births, so following prudent obstetrical procedure, I gave nature a chance. Mrs. Montgomery's trial of labor progressed nicely. The early phase was rapid, a hopeful sign that everything was fine and delivery would be easy. The active phase, too, was well within normal limits, a second signal that a c-section would probably be unnecessary. I relaxed.

As the baby's head was pressing against the perineum, the anesthesiologist administered a low spinal block to relieve Mrs. Montgomery's pain and prepare her for delivery. I did a wide episiotomy to avoid the tearing and rupturing to be expected from the anticipated fairly large baby and, with the head crowning, positioned my forceps, then commonly used to ease the baby out. The head emerged routinely—another good sign. When the head, generally the broadest part of the infant, descends, the rest of the body usually follows easily.

I leaned forward to deliver the front-facing shoulder. It didn't budge. I tried the posterior shoulder. Again, no movement. The chin, which had appeared momentarily, suddenly sucked back in. I slid my hand inside to determine the problem. The baby's shoulders were firmly impacted in the mother's pelvis. The ob's nightmare: shoulder dystocia. Trouble, I thought. Big trouble.

Shoulders too large to slide easily through the bony pelvis were the midwife's nemesis long before they became the obstetrician's. In frontier days, when small Indian women were raped by large white men, a painful lingering death for mother and child from dystocia was so common that victims routinely practiced early abortion to avoid giving birth to oversize "half-breeds." In 1914, dystocia, a baby killer second only to syphilis, was the cause of one in every six infant deaths at a leading eastern hospital. Modern obstetrics allows us to deal more safely with shoulder dystocia, but it still complicates from three to a dozen of every 2,000 births. And as overnutrition causes average birth weights to increase, those numbers will probably rise.

Shoulder dystocia is insidious. The head usually moves along nicely, and all seems well. Then, unexpectedly, too late to do a c-section, the wide shoulders come along and stick. Medical literature is full of possible corrective maneuvers dating back fifty years and more, bearing the names of obstetricians long gone, memorials to their desperate struggles to save unborn infants. But in most cases, we dislodge babies by rotating the shoulders with a corkscrew motion, today's procedure of choice. On the three or four earlier occasions I'd faced shoulder dystocia, I worried and sweated and manipulated, and finally managed to dislodge the baby that way without permanent injury to mother or child. But, ob textbooks warn, the prescribed maneuvers don't always work, no matter how many you know and try. I prayed this wouldn't be one of those times.

Sliding my left hand into Mrs. Montgomery's vagina, I tried to rotate the baby in the corkscrew maneuver. The slippery little shoulders refused to budge. I tried again, then again, using every variation I knew, had learned, or could improvise. Dammit. What now? If I didn't get this baby out quickly, it was going to die or be brain-damaged. A compressed umbilical cord in the birth canal, a few minutes without oxygen, and cerebral palsy or mental retardation could blight a lifetime.

"Fundal pressure!" I said urgently.

Anesthesiologist and ob nurse pushed inward and downward on Mrs. Montgomery's abdomen, as though trying to force a cork out of a flexible bottle. The hope was that their weight against the fundus, the upper portion of the uterus, would compact the shoulder blades and create an expulsive force, allowing me to extract the infant from below. With luck, the network of neck and shoulder nerve fibers known as the brachial plexus would be uninjured.

But fundal pressure wasn't working. God, if only I could stuff this baby back inside its mother's uterus and do a c-section. But the birth canal is a one-way street, and Baby

Montgomery had passed the point of no return.*

There was one final option. Fracturing the baby's clavicle. Reaching in and snapping it like a chicken bone. That would collapse the infant's shoulder blades, narrowing their girth and facilitating delivery. It was mentioned in obstetrics textbooks, but I'd never done it and didn't know anyone who had. In any case, so tightly was the Montgomery baby wedged in that the maneuver seemed impossible. I might be able to do it by surgically cutting the clavicle. But that was a procedure of last resort, a desperate measure that could sever a major blood vessel. It was generally reserved for infants already given up for dead, and I wasn't giving up on this one. Not yet.

I slipped my hand into Mrs. Montgomery's vagina and again attempted to rotate the axis of the shoulders. No movement.

"Press!" I shouted hoarsely to my colleagues. The shoulders remained jammed. "More pressure," I urged, trying to keep cool admidst the pandemonium of grunts, lurches, and cries from the team above me.

They pushed suprapubically from above. I tugged gently but firmly from below. Finally, with an almost audible pop, his emerging broad shoulders explaining the difficult delivery, the baby appeared. His face and skull were misshapen, as is usual with babies subjected to extreme pressures during delivery. I knew that within a matter of days the head would return to baby roundness and the swelling would recede. The limp arm, though, was disturbing. The brachial plexus in the axilla might be torn. If so, the nerves would not regenerate, and permanent palsy and some degree of atrophy would occur. I hoped they were just stretched and swollen. They often are in traumatic dystocia deliveries. In that case, the arm would recover in

---

*Interesting. A few days after writing these words, I came across an article in the January 1986 issue of *Contemporary Ob/Gyn* that could make them obsolete. Obstetrician-authors James A. O'Leary and David L. Gunn reported four cases in which they'd successfully used a new option for shoulder dystocia cases that they call cephalic replacement. After all possible extraction maneuvers failed, the two doctors pushed the baby's head back into the vagina "by exerting firm, constant pressure with the palm of the right hand while depressing the posterior vaginal wall with the left hand." Then they performed a c-section. So I spoke too soon. If other obs replicate that heroic O'Leary-Gunn maneuver, a mother's birth canal will no longer be a one-way street, and a lot of infants will be spared death or serious injury.

anywhere from a few hours to a few days.

What mattered was that we'd gotten Mrs. Montgomery's little boy out alive. His initial Apgar score was a worrisome 2. But the anesthesiologist resuscitated the infant quickly, and thank heavens, oxygen deprivation had been brief. At five minutes, his Apgar was an almost perfect 9. I toweled away the cold sweat. If every birth were like this one, I'd be an old man at fifty.

Maybe sooner. I noticed a ribbon of crimson swirling into the catheter the nurse had routinely inserted in Mrs. Montgomery's bladder after the delivery: blood mixing with the urine. Swiftly, I explored the uterus. There was no trace of a hole that would explain the bleeding. But bloody urine from a traumatized bladder following a difficult delivery isn't unusual. It generally clears up within a few days. I ordered the catheter left in place and put my patient on large amounts of intravenous fluids. Flushing out her urinary tract might do the trick.

But my hopes for both mother and child were soon dashed. The baby was seen by a pediatric neurologist, who reported that the nerve injury was most likely permanent: a condition known as Erb's palsy. Physical therapy might help, but one arm would always be relatively useless.

Then, on the third day after delivery, Mrs. Montgomery complained that she was leaking urine. I called in a urology consultant. X-rays revealed a vesico-utero vaginal fistula—a perforation between the uterus, bladder, and vagina caused by pressure from the baby's shoulder. There would be no permanent damage, but it could not be surgically repaired for three to four months. In the meantime, between her son's disability and her own discomfort—Mrs. Montgomery would have to be on antibiotics, sleep only on her stomach, and might leak some urine even while continuing to wear a catheter—my patient was in for an uncomfortable and discouraging time.

Only, suddenly, she was no longer my patient. She didn't want me to be her doctor anymore, she told the urologist. If I'd done a c-section, she said bitterly, all this would not have happened. Could he recommend another ob/gyn? Her angry words were not reserved for the urologist's ears alone. She contacted a local lawyer, who placed a call to the office of one of the country's best-known malpractice firms. Not long afterward, the process-server paid me a visit.

I was bitter, too. I deserved to be sued, even to be stripped of my license, if I had been drinking or was high on drugs, if I had been poorly trained and didn't know what I was doing, or if I was downright careless. But none of that was so. I had done everything I possibly could to deliver the Montgomery baby in perfect condition. Maybe somewhere there was a doctor who could have done better, maybe not. Certainly the outcome could have been far worse.

The sick feeling returned to my stomach whenever I thought of the summons, but for a long time I heard nothing more. Perhaps, I thought hopefully, after her initial outburst of anger, Mrs. Montgomery had realized that she was a victim, not of malpractice, but of an unfortunate and unavoidable result. I heard welcome news from a patient who knew the Montgomery family: the boy was bright, doing very well in school, and, though unable to raise his weak arm over his head, had fairly good movement in it, and pretty good motion in his fingers. Maybe her attorney had told her that she had no case.

But then one day, some five years later, when my wishful thinking had almost lulled me into believing the case closed, the attorney assigned by my professional liability insurer phoned. A New York City lawyer would be in Syracuse in a few weeks to take pretrial depositions—testimony under oath, by the parties to the case and the witnesses, in response to questions by the attorneys on both sides. Review your notes and the hospital files carefully, he said. It's only pretrial, but it's important.

After five years, a lot of the details had receded into the fog-banks of memory. I told what had happened to the best of my ability, but the subject of the clavicle option never came up. Neither attorney raised the question, and since fundal pressure had finally done the job, I didn't think to bring it up.

But things had gone pretty well, I thought. And the subsequent malpractice screening panel mandated by the State of New York in medical malpractice cases—usually made up of a judge, a physician, and an attorney appointed by the state—went even better. Based on a reading of relevant depositions and office and hospital records on the case, the panel brought in a unanimous verdict that I had not been negligent—evidence that my attorney could introduce into the record in a trial or, even better, might use to persuade the plaintiff to drop the case. I was elated.

When there was another long silence out of New York, I persuaded myself that the plaintiff's attorney had indeed decided to forget the whole thing. But then came another phone call from my attorney, and nine years after the delivery of Baby Montgomery I walked up two flights of stone stairs, turned left, and walked down the corridor to enter the courtroom and take my seat behind the long dark oak defendant's table in the Supreme Court of Onondaga County. I wasn't handcuffed, but I felt eerily like one of the criminals escorted by police officers I'd passed in the lobby below.

I was confident of exoneration. I'd done what any prudent physician would do under the circumstances. The malpractice screening panel had absolved me of culpability. But still I was nervous.

In spite of eight or nine hours of preparation by my attorney, I felt completely out of place in a courtroom. I had read and reread the chapters on shoulder dystocia in every obstetrical textbook in the Upstate Medical Center library, but I should have boned up on malpractice law. And I should have attended a malpractice trial or two.

Until we find ourselves trapped in a sticky web of litigation of some sort, most of us are pitifully ignorant of the law. Bad guys get theirs. Good guys get off. Justice, that beautiful blindfolded lady with the perfectly balanced scale, always prevails. But as I discovered in the next five weeks, justice doesn't just happen. It takes hard work, diligence at digging out and explaining the facts, experience, and knowledge of both human nature and the subject matter to make a case in court.

Jack had volunteered to see my office patients for me. I saw hospital patients at early rounds each morning before taking my seat in the courtroom to wait and wonder. Would the judge assigned to the case be what my attorney called a "plaintiff's judge" or a "defendant's judge"? When, finally, a name was announced, I thought I detected a frown on the other attorney's face. My lawyer looked pleased. Our judge, he confided, was known to be both fair and knowledgeable.

Would the jury be sympathetic to the plaintiff or the defendant? Piercingly, I studied each potential juror, as my attorney asked me in hushed tones what I thought of this one or that one. Would men or women be more sympathetic? If women, should we opt for older women or childless women, rather than those in childbearing years who might identify with the plaintiff? Could a schoolteacher take an unbiased view in a case involving an injury to a child?

I quickly realized that I was no Sherlock Holmes. I hadn't the faintest clue how anyone was going to think, or how age, sex, or occupation would affect judgment. I left it to my lawyer to decide. By the end of the week, six jurors—two women and four men, plus a couple of alternates—had survived examination by both sides and were seated. I felt particularly good about the younger of the two women. At lunch break, before she was chosen, she'd given me a big smile and a friendly hello as she walked by.

These six lay people held my fate in their hands. They would decide on the basis of complex medical and scientific evidence marshalled by Mrs. Montgomery's advocate and mine, whether or not I had been negligent. One of the two attorneys was certain to be more eloquent and persuasive than the other. I hoped it would be mine: low key and a kind of young Jimmy Stewart. But what if it was the plaintiff's attorney, older and far more seasoned?

He knew every psychological game in the books. As we sat on opposite benches in the corridor during a long recess, he addressed me unexpectedly: "Pardon me, doctor, you have two different color socks on." Startled, I looked down. Both socks, I assured him, were blue. "Oh," he said, "I guess it was just the light."

Later in the day, he stopped me to say what a terrible shame it was that I had to spend so much time away from my patients. On the other hand, he declared cheerily, he liked our community and his hotel, and wouldn't mind staying a couple of months. "But of course, doctor," he added with a sardonic smile, "the longer I stay, the bigger the stakes in the game."

That was only a preliminary skirmish. The following day, apparently displeased with the way things were going, he requested a conference in chambers and accused the judge of showing prejudice toward him in his preliminary rulings. It was a gutsy gamble, and it worked. When the astonished magistrate responded angrily, the attorney coolly asserted that this unjudicial display of temper in front of his client had just proven the judge's bias. Faced with the hint of an embarrassing motion that he be disqualified, the judge voluntarily withdrew from the case.

In his opening remarks before a new judge, the plaintiff's attorney carefully ticked off what he called "the facts." To me, they were a stew of distortions, exaggerations, and statements taken out of context, and I couldn't wait to get on the stand to rebut them. Finally, two days later, the clerk called my name and the bailiff swore me in. After nine years of waiting and worrying, battle was about to be joined.

The size and structure of Mrs. Montgomery's pelvis was an issue, so the large anatomical model the attorney unveiled came as no surprise. He hoped to persuade the jury that her pelvis was inadequate for an eight-pound baby, that I should have performed a c-section. In describing the pelvis, he made a couple of anatomical mistakes, which, trying hard not to look smug, I corrected. "Well, doctor," he said looking uncomfortable, "you know what I mean." But I felt from the smirks on several jurors' faces that they didn't think he knew what he meant.

As the morning wore on, and I became used to the hot seat, testifying became more comfortable. I began to enjoy the verbal duel, and by the way jurors' heads nodded when I spoke, I sensed that I was getting through to them. Madalyn leaned forward to catch every word. I smiled and absorbed the loving energy she transmitted in return. Hey, maybe this wasn't going to be so bad after all.

The plaintiff's attorney, seeming to sense my growing confidence, interrupted his examination to ask the judge's permission to put on an expert witness from out of town. This visiting professor, he said, had to return to New York City. He could only be heard at that moment. Again and again, our opponent skillfully found ways to halt my testimony, break my concentration, and make any easiness I developed on the stand slip away.

In the days that followed, the plaintiff's attorney paraded his witnesses with consummate artistry. He embellished the child's neurologist's description of the boy's arm as 95 percent dysfunctional with a word picture of what that meant: a child who couldn't play baseball with his dad or participate in team sports with friends, who would even have trouble boarding a public bus with a briefcase in his hand. "And how do you suppose this boy will feel," he asked the physiotherapist, "when he's older and he's rejected by a girl for someone with two working hands?" It was pure conjecture, beyond the expertise of the witness. But overruling my attorney's objection, the judge allowed it. My despondence grew with each passing moment. Only a jury chiseled from Appalachian granite could fail to respond to his dramatic appeal. Even I, on the other side, was moved.

A nurse who had assisted at the delivery followed. She had been present at thousands of deliveries since the birth of Baby Montgomery nine years earlier. But because she didn't remember those five minutes nine years earlier, the plaintiff's attorney charged her with being part of "a conspiracy of silence." I knew our day in court was still to come, but my head felt as though it had been battered by a policeman's billy already.

Perhaps the judge had sensed my discouragement. Or maybe it was just customary at a trial's midpoint to try to save the court's time. He called us into chambers and urged my attorney to make a settlement offer.

The insurance company, said my lawyer, had authorized him to go as high as $50,000. The plaintiff's attorney immediately denounced the offer as an indication of our bad faith and gross callousness. Then, coming after me like a heat-seeking missile, he declared that this case was worth far more than the face value of Dr. Eisenberg's one-million-dollar professional liability insurance policy. He would personally see to it that any assets or resources I owned were seized in a verdict exceeding the amount of my policy. Furthermore, if the jury found a cause of action against me—in effect, found me guilty as charged—he intended to report me to the Board of Regents of New York State and see to it that my license to practice medicine was revoked.

I'd seen enough of our opponent's courtroom dramatics to know that storm and bluster were part of his style. But it didn't help to tell myself that his performance in chambers was just more of the same. I left the room badly shaken.

The possibility that a million-dollar insurance policy might be inadequate had never occurred to me. Now my mind reeled at the consequences. Our home, our sons' college funds, retirement savings: everything I'd worked for could instantly go down the drain. All that was required was for this jury to say the word.

When court was adjourned for the day, Madalyn hurried to the defense table in the front of the courtroom. We held each other silently for a long moment. "I sat there all day with my heart pounding,'' she said as we walked down the courthouse steps. ''It was all I could do to keep from screaming. The way that attorney was trying to prove a conspiracy at the hospital . . . trying to make you sound like a terrible doctor. I wanted to say something really outrageous and walk out of the courtroom.''

I told her I was glad she hadn't. But I shared her anger and understood her frustration. I had been under stress in medicine often, but rarely more than a few hours at a time. This trial, well on its way to lasting five weeks, was becoming a stress marathon. In the courtroom and at home, messages from my body that it was unhappy with what was going on were delivered with increasing regularity: frontal headaches, painful eyes, tight neck, periodic chills. Sleep had always been easy for me. I could nod off anywhere: on a couch, on the rug, on a bed of nails. Now my rest became fitful and disturbed.

On weekends, tension letdown and depression gripped me. When friends called, I didn't want to talk to them. When Madalyn persuaded me to accept a Saturday night party invitation, I moped in a corner. I refused the glass of wine our hostess offered. What if it impaired my memory?

On days when court adjourned early, I headed for the office for a breath of fresh air. On one such day, after hours, I sat down for a serious talk with Jack. ''I think we should give up obstetrics,'' I said. ''It's not worth the stress. And I don't want to have to do unnecessary c-sections in self-defense every time I think there *might* be a problem.''

''That's not you talking,'' Jack said. ''It's the trial. Let's not make any hasty decisions. When it's over, you're going to feel a lot differently.''

Mrs. Montgomery's testimony did nothing to change my mind. Responding to her attorney's carefully constructed questions—''You didn't have good rapport with him? You couldn't discuss things?''—she replied, ''He was very cold.'' When my attorney objected, the answer was stricken. Well then, had she discussed her problems with me after her son's birth? She replied that I was ''unapproachable.'' On cross-examination, my attorney counterattacked. She admitted that she had been seeing her ''cold . . . unapproachable'' doctor for five years. Her explanation: ''I didn't know enough to change.'' Thinking about our good relationship over all those years, I felt saddened and disheartened.

She admitted, too, that though she claimed I'd told her I would do an automatic c-section if her baby were larger than six pounds ten ounces, she hadn't raised the question even after I'd estimated its weight at more than eight pounds. And in answer to the "Any special concerns?" question on the hospital admission form, she'd written not a word.

I breathed a little easier. But then the plaintiff's attorney introduced into evidence the minutes of the monthly hospital staff meeting at which the Montgomery delivery had been discussed. The physician member of the malpractice screening panel that later exonerated me had been present, he said indignantly. Not only, he accused, was this doctor a hospital colleague of mine, but he had been privy to discussions of my case. Pursuing his conspiracy theory, the attorney asked that both the verdict of the malpractice screening panel on which the doctor had served and his upcoming testimony as one of my two expert witnesses be thrown out.

The judge's agreement left me angered but impotent. Why couldn't he have put us under oath first to try to determine the truth? He would have learned that neither of us had any recollection of that staff meeting almost ten years earlier, and that we were not only not bosom buddies but periodically clashed at hospital meetings. "Don't worry," my attorney whispered. "The judge should have taken testimony. This gives us grounds for an appeal if we lose."

"Lose?" I didn't want to hear that word. But I began to see that it was a distinct possibility. In any case, I had lost a powerful spokesperson for the defense. When the jury, which had been out during this discussion, returned, the judge immediately told its members to disregard the medical malpractice screening panel mentioned by the defense attorney in his introductory remarks. I don't want you to speculate as to why, he said, just to erase it from your minds. Once again, the plaintiff's attorney rose to score a point. "Thank you, Your Honor," he said. His message to the jury was clear: The judge has granted something I requested. We're the good guys. They're the bad guys.

Maybe not bad, but certainly not smart guys. Why on earth had we called Dr. Thornton as an expert witness? Of course, because he was one of the most respected obs in town. But he was also my hospital colleague. That should have alerted us to the possibility that, although we knew him to be beyond reproach and above suspicion, he would be vulnerable to attack by the opposition.

The plaintiff's attorney continued to plant innuendos, which, once uttered, can never be wholly stricken from a juror's mind, not even on a judge's orders. The first meeting of Community General Hospital's peer review committee had taken place several months after Mrs. Montgomery delivered. He suggested that the reason for the committee's formation was my poor performance, and promised to subpoena the committee's chairperson to prove it. Then, perhaps learning that my case had never been brought before the committee, he dropped the issue as suddenly as he'd raised it.

Next, having found articles in obstetrical medical literature dating back to 1960 on the uses of ultrasound, the opposing attorney declared that the hospital had been negligent in not providing ultrasound capabilities for its staff thirteen years later. A sonogram, he asserted, would have revealed that the Montgomery baby was oversize and required c-sectioning.

But there is a big difference between journal articles on experimental procedures and actual clinical use. During the lunch recess, my phone calls to New York Hospital–Cornell Medical Center and to Dr. John Hobbins at Yale, a pioneer in obstetrical ultrasound, confirmed that as late as 1975—two years after the Montgomery delivery—only 10 percent of U.S. university medical centers used ultrasound, and then only to date the length of gestation. Not until 1977 were fetal weights estimated with it, and then only experimentally.

At no time had it been possible to accurately measure shoulders or to publish any kind of shoulder dystocia risk chart. In a 4,000-gram (8½-pound) infant, Dr. Hobbins's technique could come within a pound—which, he added, any good clinician can do without ultrasound. This information, passed on to the judge, resulted in the plaintiff's attorney dropping the issue. But again, damage had been done.

My sole remaining expert witness was until his recent retirement perhaps the most beloved and respected ob/gyn in Syracuse. In spite of the fact that he was nervous on the stand, as inexperienced in the courtroom as I had been, the plaintiff's attorney couldn't trip him on the facts. So the attorney took a different tack and asked the doctor why he had agreed to testify. Our expert, who had been president of the county medical society and for years headed the county's maternal and child health committee, responded that he was there "to protect obstetricians" from unjustified attacks. Mrs. Montgomery's attorney pounced joyously on that remark, shaping it to fit his medical conspiracy theory. Why, he demanded, wasn't this witness there to aid in the search for truth?

Why, I longed to demand aloud of the attorney, was *he* not interested in the truth? Of course, I was being naive and unrealistic. As an advocate, his principal truth was that his client had been injured. His search was for as many ways as possible to prove me responsible.

In the middle of the night following that courtroom exchange, Madalyn awoke with pains in her chest. "Henry," she said, squeezing my arm, "wake up. I think I'm having a heart attack."

I checked her pulse. It was racing. I drew my wife to me and stroked her hair. "We could go to the emergency room," I said, "but at your age and with all the running and bicycling you do, I doubt there's anything wrong. Considering all the stress you've been going through, it's much more likely to be an anxiety attack than a heart attack."

"Oh, Henry," she sobbed, her defiant front crumbling at last. "It's all so horrible. I hate what those people are doing to you in court. And that attorney . . . He said he was going to ask for a verdict over the limits of your insurance policy. They could take away our house and everything we own. And for something that wasn't even your fault. It's so unfair."

She fell asleep in my arms. Next morning her internist did an EKG and assured her that she not only didn't need a heart transplant but would make a great donor. When the judge gavelled for the last time, she'd be fine.

We had tickets to see the Rolling Stones the following Saturday night. The afternoon of the concert, I lay in our bedroom, head buried in my pillow, totally depressed and unable to move. Now it was Madalyn's turn to come to the rescue. She came upstairs and got me to talk it out. An hour later, I felt better, and we went to the concert and had a great time.

A few days later the little plaintiff himself came to court. His attorney had sketched such a pathetic picture of a boy whose life I had ruined at birth that even I was surprised when this adorable youngster, all smiles, was called to the stand to demonstrate the extent of his injury. He took off his polo shirt unaided, slipping his weak arm in and out. My principal feeling was relief. This child was not going to be left behind by life. He would be able to make his own way. Nothing else that could happen at the trial was more important to me than that.

The little boy's demeanor supported his pediatrician's earlier testimony that the child had had a happy well-adjusted early childhood. I wondered if the attorney's grim description earlier might backlash, making his whole case less credible. But I felt torn. Yes, it would be great if this boy could receive something to compensate for his injury. But that could only happen if negligence on my part was proven, and I felt strongly that I had committed no malpractice. Still, if I won, I knew it would be with mixed feelings.

The last day of the trial, the final day of the most difficult five weeks of my life, fell on my fifty-first birthday. A settlement offer by the insurance company and considered fair by the judge had been rejected by the plaintiffs the previous evening. They were going for broke. Finally, the summations and the judge's instructions ended. I watched as the jury filed out of the box and the door closed behind them. With the confidence of ignorance, I had begun my trial innocently optimistic. Now, I had lost my innocence, and after five weeks of seeing a masterful plaintiff's attorney put my witnesses and my case through his shredder, I was no longer optimistic.

What if the decision went against me? The one thing I couldn't afford to do was draw any negative conclusions about myself as a physician or a person. That would compromise my ability to carry on with my life and practice, and I couldn't allow that to happen.

But what if the verdict exceeded my insurance coverage? A letter from a lawyer I'd retained on the judge's advice in midtrial had already put the insurance company on notice. Its early unwillingness to settle could make it responsible for any verdict beyond $1 million. Madalyn and I reassured one another as best we could with the thought that most of the things we "what if" about never happen.

The verdict for the plaintiff came late the next afternoon after fourteen hours of deliberation. I was relieved that it was all over. I was anxious to get back to my life, my practice, my patients. But the size of the award shocked me: $813,000. What could the jury have been thinking?

A few days later, I found out—from the jury panelist who'd smiled at me in the corridor the day before she was chosen. A magazine had asked my writer-brother for an article on how jurors think in medical malpractice cases, and she was the first person he called.

The jurors, she said, had been astonished that they, without an economics major among them, were responsible for fixing the monetary award: "We assumed the court did that. The only figures we had to work with were the ones that the plaintiff's attorney wrote on the blackboard during his final summation. More or less based on that, we each came up with what seemed a correct figure and then divided the total by six to get an average. When we got to 'loss of consortium' for the husband, nobody knew what that was. We sent a note to the judge to ask. Then Joe, another juror, said the going rate on the street was twenty-five dollars a shot. We said, okay, three times a week is the national average: seventy-five dollars a week for a year. That's what we gave him."

The juror volunteered that she didn't like the style of the plaintiff's attorney ("pompous") or the way he kept interrupting my testimony ("everything got so disjointed"), but that this didn't sway her one way or another. That was as it should be.

In the end, she explained, it all came down to the baby's collarbone. Working backward from my failure to discuss my thoughts about breaking it in my pretrial deposition, the plaintiff's lawyer got his expert witness to state emphatically that when all else fails, you can always reach in and break the clavicle.

Did his expert ever break one? I doubt it. It's more obstetrical theory than practice. But when I tried to make the point on the witness stand that I had thought about breaking it but felt there was insufficient space to effect the maneuver, the plaintiff's attorney objected and the judge sustained. What I was thinking, he said, wasn't relevant. It was what I did that mattered. He ordered my response stricken from the record. And, declared the juror, on that single judgment, the case turned.

"We talked a lot about the maneuvers you did," she explained. "How you tried to move the shoulder here, the arms there, tried to do this and that. Someone said you should have broken the collarbone. I said that you'd considered doing that—but when we listened to the testimony, it wasn't there. As far as the others were concerned, no collarbone was broken, so you didn't do anything right.''

I dreaded opening my local newspaper on Sunday, the day after the verdict. To my relief, there was no mention of the trial. Monday and Tuesday's papers ignored it, too. The plaintiff's attorney had said he'd gotten what he came for and had no intention of talking to the press. I began to hope that the worst was over. But on Wednesday, there it was—a big black three-column headline in the *Syracuse Herald-Journal:* JURY AWARDS $813,000—MOM, SON HAD SUED LOCAL DOCTOR. The newspaper's court reporter had come across the case, and there, without a mitigating word or comment, no explanation that this was what had been alleged, not what had been proven, were all the dramatic pretrial allegations that plaintiff's attorneys customarily make.

I wanted to hide, to disappear, to stay home and lick my wounds. But next morning I had to face my patients, knowing that they'd read it, too, wondering what they were thinking as I examined them, wondering how many appointment cancellations the headline would trigger in the weeks ahead. I'm sure there were some newly pregnant women in Syracuse that day and other women with gyn problems who said, ''Well, that's one doctor I'm going to stay away from.'' But my appointment schedule remained full, and our patients seemed unperturbed. A few old friends commented sympathetically. Most patients, as embarrassed to discuss it as I, said nothing. By the end of the week, as sanitation trucks carted away the last of Wednesday's newspapers, Madalyn, the boys, and I were probably the only people in town who winced at the recollection.

Heads you win, tails I lose, I thought bitterly a few months later, when a downstate jury found another obstetrician guilty of breaking the collarbone in a shoulder dystocia case. Where is justice, I had to wonder, when one plaintiff's attorney wins his malpractice case by arguing that an obstetrician *broke* the baby's clavicle, while 200 miles away another plaintiff's attorney wins his by arguing *failure to break* the clavicle?

It was easy for me to dislike the plaintiff's attorney for the wringer he put me through. But under our advocacy system, he was just doing his job. It's possible that I'd have felt he was the greatest lawyer since Daniel Webster, had he been on my side.

Since he wasn't, I couldn't help but feel resentful knowing that he and his law firm would deduct legal fees of one-third of the award—more than a quarter of a million dollars—and then pile trial costs on top of that, before writing their clients a check for the balance.

But negligence attorneys operate on no-win-no-fee contingency arrangements, often laying out as much as $50,000 to take a case to trial. If they demanded $25,000 retainers, only the very wealthy could afford to take their cases to court. So the contingency system may be imperfect, but it's the only way we've got to assure that even the poorest of the poor can have their day in court. What might happen without contingency fees is seen in criminal court. There, with no pot of gold at the end of the trial, the poor are all too often represented by court-appointed hacks. Meanwhile, skillful legal maneuvering by teams of expensive lawyers wins acquittals for rich white-collar manipulators and the criminal elite.

What happens in a malpractice trial is painful. It's also very human and understandable. For parents, the first prize in the delivery room is a healthy baby. For those who don't get that, society and our legal system have developed a consolation prize: a malpractice award. I can understand Mrs. Montgomery's anger at the universe. Her pained cry, as she lived with his handicap day in and day out, of "Why my child?" And her "Why me?" as she walked around for three months with an uncomfortable and foul-smelling appliance strapped to her thigh. Could the answering cry, from sympathetic friends and relatives, of "Why not your doctor?" be far behind? Especially when an insurance company with deep pockets writes the check.

Of course, when an insurance company writes any check (for the luggage stolen from a car trunk, an automobile fender smashed in the parking lot by a party unknown, or a malpractice award), the money comes not from some monolithic entity known as The Insurance Company. It comes from you and me and everyone else who pays insurance premiums.

Jack and I pay a combined total of $60,000 a year* for our malpractice insurance. The figure is already twice that for a single obstetrician in south Florida—where recently in one

---

*It is anticipated that this figure will rise to almost $100,000 before the end of 1986.

up-in-arms community five out of every six ob/gyns voluntarily discontinued obstetrics. Because they have to make a living, chances are many of those doctors will return to ob. But like stores with high shoplifting bills and pharmaceutical companies marketing high-risk products, doctors will have to pass this cost of doing business on to the "consumer"—you, me, and anyone else who visits a doctor. For obstetricians, that could mean raising the cost of a delivery by $1,000—which won't bother the family with good insurance, but could play havoc with those insufficiently protected by their policies and will mean that those with no insurance better use good birth control methods.

Patients are going to pay in other ways, too. Doctors in the high-risk specialties are going to become hard to find. Doctors who don't drop out will increasingly practice defensive medicine. New procedures that could conceivably save lives will be performed less often. Excessive testing will be performed more often—to protect the doctor, not the patient. "Safe" options—cesareans, for example—will be chosen over others that might be preferable but that carry a significantly higher risk of legal action. Today, given a situation like Mrs. Montgomery's, I'd be under a lot of pressure to do a c-section.

It's not easy to practice medicine when you know the patient on the examining table is thinking, "I want the best possible care from a doctor I admire and trust. But if anything goes wrong, for whatever reason, I'll sue the hell out of him."

I've had plenty of time to think about the malpractice dilemma since my trial. I don't have any easy answers, but I have a thought or two. A major part of the problem is that when a bad outcome occurs in medicine, there is rarely any relief for the unfortunate victim unless malpractice money is pursued. I'm no expert on either law or economics. So now I don't know if it would work. But it's been suggested that there could be bad-outcome insurance, a kind of earthbound flight insurance patients would pay into as part of their fee before surgery, childbirth, or any other even slightly perilous procedure. The rates—say, $20 to $200—could be calculated on a sliding scale according to the risk involved. If a bad outcome occurred, no one would have to look to the courts for financial healing. This might not make lawyers happy, but it would protect patients. All injured patients, not just the few whose doctors were found guilty of malpractice.

Bad-outcome insurance wouldn't be intended to get the negligent physician off the hook. When a doctor has been negligent, he should be held responsible. But it seems to me that there must be a better way to go about assessing liability and responsibility than in a three-ring circus of a jury trial, with expert witnesses—we call them hired guns—who are paid $1,500 a day to testify and attorneys who build their cases as much with melodrama as with facts. A my-lawyer-can-beat-up-your-lawyer situation in which the best actor often wins, and presentation counts more than content, doesn't seem the road to equal justice for all.

Heaven knows, somebody's got to do something, and if 'twere done, 'twere best done by doctors and patients together in partnership. On the patient's side, there should be a willingness to become informed, to talk about problems, and to ask questions. Doctors *aren't* infallible. The patient who raises questions about a prescription, a course of treatment, or anything else she has doubts about may prevent a malpractice on its way to happening. On the physician's side there must be caring, keeping current, and the will to listen, to explain (even to difficult patients), and to refer the patient elsewhere when the relationship isn't working.

We must do a better job of self-policing, too. That won't stop malpractice suits, but it will protect patients from dangerous practitioners. We've begun the job. Hundreds of bad apples—addicted, alcoholic, or less than competent doctors—have been threatened with loss of license, and scores have been stripped of the right to practice. But not without repercussions. Doctors serving on peer review committees are often subjected to multimillion-dollar damage suits by the outraged doctors whose hospital privileges they attempt to revoke. It's not easy to dispose of an apple that bites back.

But the alternatives are getting uglier all the time. Like the screen-your-new-patients services recently available to doctors out west that are sure to spread east. You tell the service the prospective patient's name. Instantly, the service tells you if she's ever filed a malpractice suit. If she has, you say, "Sorry, Ma'm, you're not my kind of patient." Consumer groups will, of course, soon play the same game. They'll search court and insurance records for the names of doctors who've been sued, and steer patients to the offices of doctors who haven't. In obstetrics, that's not going to be easy.

Why is the malpractice crisis most severe in my specialty? Why have seven out of ten ob/gyns already been sued? Is it because only three out of ten of us are competent, caring, and capable of performing a laparoscopy or delivering a baby? Are obstetricians almost universally practicing bad medicine? Not according to the statistics. Just look at the drop in the newborn mortality rate over the years these same doctors have been practicing. Last year was the lowest ever in this country. Even women in high-risk categories—those with diabetes or hypertension—are having healthy babies. Maternal mortality is dropping, too. We must be doing something right. In fact, studies show that it's the absence of a doctor that's most dangerous to an expectant mother's health. The more frequently a woman sees her ob/gyn during pregnancy, the better chance she has of a good outcome.

But it's precisely because good pregnancy outcomes have become so routine that the ob is a prime malpractice target. When the rare bad outcome occurs, patients feel that somehow the doctor must be at fault. The feeling is understandable, but it fails to take into account the fact that though the science of obstetrics is better than ever before in history, nature is still the same as it was when we lived in caves. It still gives us compressed cords, unexpected dystocias, unwanted hemorrhages—and all the other complications that can occur around the time of birth. No matter how good obstetricians get, we will never be able to guarantee healthy babies and safe deliveries for every single patient. We may enjoy playing God, but we can't perform miracles.

Being an ob/gyn these days may be riskier than being an ob/gyn's patient. Nevertheless, I've picked myself up and climbed back on the horse. I'm back doing deliveries and gyn surgery and enjoying both. And I'm trying not to let the Ghost of Malpractice Past run and ruin my practice. Recently I recognized that grim specter in my examining room, standing behind the chair of Martha White, a trim attractive mother of three in her early thirties. "I have a problem that I'm embarrassed to talk about, doctor," she began. An athlete, she found herself wetting her pants when she ran or did aerobics, a difficulty that I explained was not all that uncommon. Once we'd ruled out an old bladder infection or a nervous system difficulty, the probable cause was stress incontinence: an anatomical derangement in the connection between the neck of the bladder and the urethra, which often occurs as a result of childbirth.

When a week of Kegel exercises to strengthen the muscles around the vaginal opening didn't help, I examined her further and did the appropriate diagnostic studies to verify the need for surgery. When it was clear that there was no other alternative, I began to have second thoughts, though I'd done the procedure throughout my career with excellent results. "Then why am I hesitating?" I asked myself. "Because," myself answered, "if you get a bad result, you might get sued."

I discussed my concerns with Jack, who had asked Mrs. White to see me in the first place. "By all means, refer her to an incontinence specialist," he agreed. "I know I can do it, and do it well. I referred her to you because, frankly, I was afraid of getting sued."

I thought about Mrs. White a lot that night. The next morning, I awoke knowing that it would be cowardly to refer her. And unnecessary. It was a fairly simple procedure: a matter of putting a few stitches around the urethra and tying it to the pubic bone. The possibility of effecting a significant cure for a patient is half the joy of medicine. It was a half I didn't want to lose. But for moral support, I got Jack to scrub with me.

I sometimes wonder what would have happened that day in 1961 in the hospital at Dover Air Force Base if I had been a civilian instead of a military doctor, and if malpractice suits had been as epidemic then as they are now.

Donna Maxwell was thrilled with her live healthy son. She risked normally unbearable pain to save her baby with a courage that, I'll always feel, deserved a medal for valor as surely as any soldier ever did on the battlefield. But I sometimes think it was foolhardy to take the chance I did. I didn't stop to think that I might be disciplined, possibly court-martialed, for doing surgery without anesthesia, or what would have happened if something had gone wrong. All that mattered was saving that baby.

It would be nice if all a doctor had to worry about in a crisis was the patient. Nice. But today, naive.

Leaves from an Ob/Gyn's Journal

The electronic warble of the phone beside my bed awakens me from a sound sleep. Its impact on my snugly pillowed head is that of a semitrailer truck crushing a crate of eggs.

As always, my first conscious thought is "No, I don't want to . . ." But I shift swiftly to "Yes, I want to," because there is no room for "I don't want to" when you do what I do.

What time is it? I refrain from reading the luminous clock face beside the bed until I've mentally placed my bet—a minor diversion invented to transform rude awakenings into fun and games. I guess 3 A.M. Usually I am close. This morning, my internal clock is way off. It's only a few minutes past one. Why do babies choose to be born at such indecent hours?

The voice I hear when I pick up the phone, that of a nurse from labor and delivery, is splintered with urgency and anxiety: "Ellie would like you to come right away. She's just delivered Mrs. Mann, and there's a retained placenta. The patient is bleeding heavily." Her message is an ice-cold shower. "I'm on my way," I tell her.

Through my bedroom window, I can see that this is a better night for dogsleds than for doctors. Four fresh inches of snow have fallen during the day, and now the narrow winding road outside is being treated to a freezing rainstorm. Stopping only to pick up my twenty-three-year-old Alaskan parka, the remaining nostalgic souvenir of my air force career, I hurry downstairs. As my radials fight icy slides and skids in the race to the hospital, my mind races, too, considering the possibilities ahead.

This is a patient who has just been delivered of her fourth child. That makes her an ideal candidate for a placenta accreta—one that grows into the wall of the uterus, becomes one and inseparable from it, bleeds from the disturbed edge, and for which the only treatment is the knife. An emergency postpartum hysterectomy can be very risky. It's been ten years since I've had to do one.

Nearing a red light. I brake gingerly, crane both ways, then speed through. Even police cars are in the garage on a night like this, but I wouldn't slow down if they weren't. I pull into the hospital parking lot and brake at the robot arm blocking the driveway. I slip my plastic ID into the toll machine, the arm rises obediently, and I gun through and park in front of the white Community General building complex. I slam my car door, burst into the hospital, and as on so many other occasions, sprint down the corridor. The elevator is waiting, and I take it to the delivery floor. I push through the swinging doors and head for the labor and delivery suite. The area is dimly lighted and unusually quiet. No one is behind the desk, and except for the name of my patient, the "In Labor" board is bare.

I proceed to the doctors' locker room and quickly change into surgical scrubs. When I reach the delivery room, I find the anesthesiologist starting the first of three units of blood to replace what my patient, her face almost as white as the upper half of the sheet beneath her, has lost.

The lower half of Mrs. Mann's sheet is crimson, with large clots of blood staining the area between her legs. All three nurses in the room look grim. So does the woman on the table; she is aware of what is going on around her. Ellie looks harried and frightened. Jack and I screen our midwife's patients to be sure that her deliveries will be routine and uncomplicated. Mrs. Mann's was supposed to be one of those. Ellie approaches me as I begin to scrub. "I'm worried about a placenta accreta," she says. "Of course," I say shortly, "I'm worried about it, too." I hear the edge of irritability in my voice and immediately regret it.

Hurriedly, I begin to scrub and then realize resignedly that before I order the patient anesthetized and attempt to remove the placenta manually, I must attend to the legal details. Both the patient and her husband have to be warned about the possible need to do a hysterectomy if I find what I think I might find. In an emergency like this, there's no time for lengthy discussion and the signing of informed consent forms. But some protection is necessary. Overlook it entirely, and I could find myself hit with a lawsuit not only for malpractice but for battery as well.

After quietly telling Mrs. Mann what I plan to do and what I may have to do if all else fails, I brace myself for the meeting with her husband in the waiting room. An intimidating figure, several inches over six feet, he is strongly built and formidable. As I explain the situation, I am filled with an unsettling sense of discomfort. His reticence and grim jaw suggest that he does not fully trust me to deal with a crisis that, I am obliged to tell him, could result in serious injury or even death for his wife.

But there is no time for a second opinion, and I know that whatever must be done I can do. We wheel Mrs. Mann into the c-section room, which is better equipped for surgery should that prove necessary, and quickly intubate and anesthetize her. I regret that, though she is our office's patient, I have only met her once before, and then only briefly, early in her pregnancy. She preferred a midwife rather than an obstetrician for her delivery, so we have had no real relationship. Yet suddenly her life is in my hands, with no time or opportunity to shop around for anyone else. This is it for her and for me.

I say a quiet private prayer, then watch the scrub nurse wash Mrs. Mann's bloody perineum with an antiseptic solution and drape her thighs and abdomen. I insert my gloved hand in her vagina. My hand has traveled this route many times before and requires no map. It maneuvers slowly through the narrow but elastically yielding tunnel that is her vagina, through the cervical opening, and bending at the wrist, up into the upper reaches of the uterus. I grope cautiously about, my arm now in almost to the elbow.

With a rush of relief, I find that 85 percent of the placenta has already separated from the wall of the uterus. It is a simple matter to insinuate my hand between the uterus and the remaining portion of the placenta. I silently pray that it will be equally simple to detach it. There is no resistance. With just a little coaxing, the placenta separates completely.

I want to shout, "Hurray!" but this is a hospital operating room, not the Carrier Dome. I grasp the spongy mass firmly, tug downward, and dump it on the table like a hated enemy. I hear a chorus of relieved sighs, my own among the loudest. The drama is over. There will be no hysterectomy.

The bleeding is now controlled, and I carefully check for lacerations elsewhere in the vagina and cervix. There are none. Ellie, our midwife, has done a fine job of delivery. I order intravenous antibiotics to prevent infection and insert a catheter into the bladder to monitor the patient's urinary output over the next six to eight hours.

Ellie is elated, but still shaken. "I keep telling myself," she says wearily, "that having a baby is a normal process—95 percent of the time."

This night Ellie has experienced how swiftly an uncomplicated situation can turn catastrophic. I hug her. We both feel good. I hurry to the waiting room, this time without foreboding. There is good news for Mr. Mann, and I know my pleased smile is communicating that even before I say a word. An answering smile breaks out on his face. I wait for my patient to awaken from anesthesia, share the happy outcome with her, change my clothes, and walk quietly back down the long corridor to the parking lot for the drive home.

Back in bed by 3:30 A.M., I curl up contentedly against Madalyn. She has slept through another of the countless high dramas that have occurred in the twenty-seven years we've been together. She is happy to nestle in our warm and comfortable bed and sleep through them. I'm twice as happy—to be married to her and to have been chosen this night for the special privilege of saving a life.

I roll over to set the alarm. In three hours, I'll visit Mrs. Mann and see how she and her baby are doing.

16

The Journey Continues

WHY DO I wake most mornings with an indefinable sense of dread? Why do I sometimes want to crawl back under the covers and stay there? That one night, so much like a thousand others, explains it as well as any other. From the first tweet of the phone to the last sigh of the mattress as I roll over and contentedly close my eyes, it defines the responsibilities and risks of my chosen profession: the ones that make me want to stay in bed. It defines the rewards and satisfactions, too: the ones that persuade me finally to throw off the covers and that leave me a happy man when I slip under them each night, whether at 10 P.M. or 4 A.M.

But unease is a presence more of the time than I would wish. When I switch from plain Henry Eisenberg in bed with his wife to Henry Eisenberg, ob/gyn, I don't become Superdoc. I climb into my trousers aware that any error I make in the day ahead or the night that follows could be fatal for a woman or a baby. When something goes wrong, will I be able to make it right?

If I can't, I worry a lot about the patient, but lately I also worry about an invisible presence in every delivery and operating room: the attorney looking over the doctor's shoulder. That presence is why I had no choice but to take the time to explain Mrs. Mann's condition to her husband—though I knew it was important to move quickly to find the cause of her bleeding and remove it. We used to talk about interesting medical cases in the doctors' locker room. Now we talk about alarming legal cases, why, and for how much, and have you written to your state senator yet to urge him to vote for tort reform?

That snowy night we were lucky. Everything turned out well. It almost always does. But as fingers probe or scalpel slices, a worst case scenario always runs through my mind. Will the fetus in distress die before I can complete the c-section? Will the mother, unexpectedly hemorrhaging after delivery, succumb before I can stabilize her? Will the Emergency Room patient's probable ectopic pregnancy burst and send her into irreversible shock before my diagnostic testing is completed?

Such outcomes are unlikely with the technology at hand, but knowing that doesn't ease the anxiety. When the technology isn't at hand, when we don't have the answers or the skills, the anxiety intensifies. That's what compounded Ellie's stress that night, and compounds mine when a challenge outstrips my skills or knowledge, or rolls the dice at the outer limits of medical science.

Behind almost every move we make, every Rx we write are the questions: Is this the best way to go? Is there something better? Will today's miracle drug or accepted truth be tomorrow's catastrophe?

Like radiation, the treatment of choice for the grotesquely bulging neck goiters so common before salt was iodized. The same doctors who pronounced their patients cured of goiters after X-ray therapy later had to pronounce many of them dead of thyroid cancer.

In my own field, the DES prescribed for expectant mothers in the 1950s to prevent miscarriage triggered cervical and vaginal cancers years later in some of the very daughters the treatment had been intended to save. Diuretic "water pills" were universally recommended for mothers-to-be thirty years ago for what was then believed to be a worthwhile medical purpose: the prevention of edema (a fluid buildup causing swelling of ankles and feet, and sometimes hands and face), thought to be a precursor to the deadly pregnancy complication, toxemia. Now we know that ordinary edema is not only harmless, it serves a worthwhile medical purpose: increasing body fluids required by the pregnancy. We used to put expectant mothers on low-calorie diets to keep babies small for easier delivery—limiting weight gain to under twenty pounds. Today we believe that calorie-restricted diets are risky in pregnancy, that undersize babies are less likely to survive and are at greater risk of poor health than larger ones.

Despite innumerable medical journal articles to the contrary, those of us on hospital welcoming committees remain stubbornly convinced that middle-of-the-night babies—like Mrs. Mann's—are more numerous than daytime arrivals. The journal articles say that's just an old doctor's tale—that fetuses can't tell time, and contractions play no favorites between day and nighttime hours. Still, we'll always be unpersuaded. The baby who arrives between 9 A.M. and 7 P.M. is all in a day's work. The baby who comes later upsets dinner plans, interrupts lovemaking, devastates a good night's sleep.

I remember in medical school hearing fellow students talk about choosing specialties that wouldn't get them up in the middle of the night, like opthalmology or radiology. I'm not sorry I chose ob/gyn. But sometimes, like one night last week, I'm pretty tired.

I had admitted Sue Sanders and Diane Bergman in labor early that morning, assuring them that they'd be mothers by dinnertime. "You're my kind of woman," I joked with Sue, "the kind who has her baby during the day, so I can get a good night's sleep." But God prints his own timetables. The Pitocin drip I'd finally had to resort to brought Sue to the delivery room—and a ruddy little baby boy—shortly after midnight, but even that biochemical spur didn't help Diane progress. After eight hours of ineffective Pitocin administration, I explained to her that, since her membranes had ruptured nearly twenty-four hours earlier and there were early signs of intrauterine infection, it was in her best interests and the baby's to consider a c-section.

While she was talking it over with her husband, the emergency room phoned. "We've got a young woman here who's bleeding, with lower abdominal pain, and a temperature of 101," the ER doctor told me. "She says she missed her period last month and a pregnancy test was positive. Could be an ectopic. Can you take a look?"

"First chance I get. Meantime, send her to Radiology for an ultrasound. If it's an ectopic, there's no time to waste."

The sonogram was gratifying: no evidence of a dangerous tubal pregnancy. But it was initially puzzling: Though the uterus was enlarged, it was not as large as it would have been in a normal pregnancy. I looked further. Instead of a gestational sac, all I saw were the remains of a disturbed pregnancy, indicative of an incomplete miscarriage. Now what had happened was clear. Residual tissue fragments in the uterus had become infected. The young woman's uterus must be quickly evacuated and antibiotic therapy begun, or the consequences could be serious. I explained the problem, reassured her that what had to be done was quick and relatively simple, obtained informed consent, and had her readied for a D & C. Upstairs, in Labor and Delivery, Diane was prepped for the c-section.

I found a quiet place to meditate for a few minutes. Jack was away, and this was the fourth night in a row that I'd been on call. I felt spacey—the way you do at the end stages of a marathon, when you shuffle along as fast as you can, knowing you're not going to quit but not knowing how you're going to finish either.

When, toward dawn, on mental automatic pilot I aimed my car homeward (at times like that, it seems to know the way on its own), I felt tired. But as I evaluated my night's work—two robust babies, two healthy mothers, and a young woman whose temperature would soon subside and whose pain and bleeding were under control—I also felt a sense of exhilaration.

That kind of three-alarm fire doesn't light up my life every night (Jack, Ellie, and I usually take turns on call), but neither is it rare. You learn to live with the assault on your biological clock, even, in an odd way, to enjoy it. To enjoy the silence of the hospital when almost everyone else is asleep, and a special sense of being alive, uncrowded by the swifter flow and busier schedules of the daylight hours. Jogging at dawn after a 4 A.M. delivery—just me and the sunrise and the birds greeting the sun and each other with contented, happy-to-be-alive tweets and chirps.

It's a law of nature: If emergencies don't happen when you're sleeping, as Mrs. Mann's retained placenta did, they happen when you're having fun, have something special planned, or are just plain pooped. If you're a plumber, somebody's pipes burst when you've got tickets for a show; if you're a sanitation worker, a snow emergency requires you to work right through your anniversary party; if you're a locksmith, someone always gets locked out of his house just when you start to make love to your spouse. If you're a doctor

. . . well, take the other evening. Madalyn and I were out for dinner with friends, and the waiter had just brought the salad plates when my beeper messaged: "Four-one-four. Patient with abdominal pain. Call the ER." My first reaction was, "Dammit, not now!"

But in the thirty-minute dash to the hospital, mind and body fell into line. I began to sort out the possible diagnoses and how I might treat them. I reminded myself that the patient's life was interrupted, too. And that she was probably frightened and worried in addition to being in pain. By the time I walked into the ER to deal with the pelvic pain, I was ready: This patient needs me. I'm here. I'm going to give her everything I've got.

Sometimes Madalyn has to remind me. Like when I start moaning about missing a Syracuse-St. John's basketball game. "Forget it, Henry," she'll say. "This is it. Life isn't always the way we want it. Resist and you'll be miserable. Surrender to the way it is and you'll be happy." I surrender.

There's no time then for what my good-natured father frequently advised: "Coast along, Henry." (He never did, but he thought his sons should.) When you're racing the stork or have a patient, like Mrs. Mann, who is hemorrhaging, fly along is more like it. Most ob/gyns would enjoy second careers as race car drivers. Early in our careers, we all learn the fastest route to the hospital. Sometimes, out of habit, I drive as though I'm going there when I'm not. There've been weekends with my family in the car when a sudden emergency call interrupted whatever we were on our way to do. When the boys were young, they liked my driving Indy 500 style, running red lights and darting in and out of lane. They loved it when, stopped by a police car, I acquired an escort with flashing lights and sirens. There is, I confess, still something of the boy in me. Anytime I run red lights, I'm mildly disappointed when I'm not stopped. It's such a kick to be momentarily above the law—like playing a part in an old "B" movie and being given the privilege of uttering that wonderful cliche: "But, officer, I'm on my way to the hospital to deliver a baby."

Racing to the hospital with pulses pounding and adrenaline flowing is stressful. But it's over in fifteen minutes and forgotten. Communicating bad news to a patient or her family can be over quickly, too, but it's not as easily forgotten. You never get used to telling a husband that his wife's condition is critical. Or telling a woman, "That lump in your breast could be malignant" or "It may be necessary to remove your uterus." Or giving a couple the crushing news that their baby isn't normal. I'd hate to be in oncology, where sorrow shares the patient's bed in almost every room you visit.

One reason I chose obstetrics and gynecology was that I found it a happy specialty: Most patients weren't sick and few died. That's even truer today. Pregnancy and childbirth are so safe that the expectant mother has a 10,000 to one chance of coming out of the experience alive, and even better odds than that if she's a low-risk patient. The chances for her baby's survival are better than ever, too. Still, even that one maternal death in 10,000 is devastating to her family and friends, and any child who is abnormal or doesn't survive brings grievous, lasting pain.

The first time I delivered a seriously deformed child was heartrending—very different from my experience in medical school of seeing an anomaly as a curiosity in a bottle. It has never gotten any easier. Especially when, as a father, I understand how difficult it is for the parents, who often are guilt ridden, disappointed, and grief stricken, but sometimes display great courage in deciding to love and care for their abnormal infant.

We're seeing fewer anomalies these days. Since the advent of routine amniocentesis for women over thirty-five—to rule out chromosomal defects and the possibility of a child with Down's syndrome—I haven't delivered a single child with what used to be called "mongolism." A careful sonogram can usually pick up other gross malformations—missing limbs, for example. And simple alpha-fetoprotein tests now help to screen out infants who may have spina bifida or other neural tube defects. When prenatal diagnostic tests are done early enough and a catastrophic defect is found, a couple can choose to abort the pregnancy and try again—though not all of them avail themselves of that option.

Immunizations have all but wiped out congenital rubella (German measles) and the deafness, cataracts, heart disease, and appalling microcephaly (abnormally small brain) associated with it. Thanks to routine testing and treatment, we don't see congenital syphilis anymore either. Many of the defects we do see—things like hydrocephalus, cleft palate and hare lip, heart abnormalities—can be corrected (sometimes even before birth) surgically or through other procedures. We take all these things for granted, but research scientists deserve our thanks. Their work has helped countless babies lead normal or near-normal lives, spared a lot of mothers and fathers a great deal of heartbreak, and made it easier for obs.

There's reason to believe that improved maternal nutrition, too, has helped to reduce the incidence of birth defects. (I tell my ob patients that this is the ideal time to modify poor eating habits—for pregnancy and for the rest of their lives—now, when they're motivated to protect their unborn children.) But there's still much that we don't understand, and a lot more to learn about the occasional catastrophes that strike the fetus during its nine months of growth and development.

So, every now and again, the ob is faced with the grim need to tell unsuspecting parents that their child is imperfect or didn't make it at all. When a baby is stillborn, I generally suggest that parents see and hold it, even if its appearance is painfully grotesque. Specialists in the grieving process tell us this is best for the couple. In the past, I'd have said, "I'm sorry, but your baby is not normal. You may not want to see it." I used to think that was compassionate, but such couples, left with an unfinished pregnancy, must wonder always, "What did our baby look like? Did he tell us the truth?"

Two hundred years ago, telling a pacing father in the next room that he'd just lost his wife, or his new baby, or both, was almost as common as the favorable report that, "Mother and baby are doing well." Today, it's extremely rare to have to pass along bad tidings. But because expectations are so high, bad news may be that much harder to bear.

Unlike obstetrical complications, gynecological cancers are all too frequent. One in eleven women will have a malignant breast tumor at some time in her life; and each year invasive cancer strikes an estimated 75,000 women in the reproductive tract. For me to tell a patient she had cancer used to be as difficult as telling her she was going to die. In most cases, that's what it meant. No matter how I word it, "You have cancer" is still a painful message to deliver. But the prognosis for most gynecological cancers today is so favorable that, particularly when the diagnosis has been made early, the bad news can often be cushioned with good news of the encouraging results of newer treatments and less disfiguring surgery.

Sometimes, though, patients are caught between conflicting medical opinions. Then they often tend to buy the one they want rather than the one they need. Ten years ago, Amy was a vivacious woman in her early thirties, so full of life that I always enjoyed her visits. The visit at which I had to tell her I felt a small lump in her breast wasn't at all pleasant. And her suspicious mammogram led the consulting surgeon to do a biopsy that resulted in an immediate mastectomy.

The surgeon was confident that he'd "gotten it all" and that chemotherapy wouldn't be necessary. But her family insisted that she visit Sloan-Kettering in New York, which recommended chemo plus some additional therapy. Amy, dreading the unpleasant side effects of nausea and falling hair she'd heard about, chose to believe the local surgeon. When she came into my office about eight months after surgery, she looked wasted. Distressed, I recommended another drug that might help, but Amy turned that down, too. She died within a year of the surgery, leaving her family and friends (I count myself among them) saddened, sorrowful, and terribly frustrated that Amy had resisted therapies that, just maybe, might have saved her.

Sometimes when I sit in the doctors' lounge in the middle of the night, waiting for a special delivery, I remember the way I was and how ob/gyn was when my nervous novitiate began, and compare it to the way it is now, when we know and can do so much more so much better.

Some of that is thanks to the brilliant Dr. Edward Hon, who, when I began my residency at Yale in 1957, was patiently logging thousands of hours in laboratory and delivery rooms with catheters designed to measure the force of uterine contractions. His since perfected device, the now familiar and invaluable fetal monitor, allowed us to know what was going on inside the laboring uterus and to rescue the fetus when something went wrong. During those years, ultrasound, amniocentesis, and chorionic villi sampling have also come along to change the face of obstetrics.

But the technical explosion came into direct conflict with another movement for change in ob/gyn, led for the most part not by doctors and researchers, but by women, consumerists, and childbirth educators. When that Irresistible Feminine Force met the traditionally Immovable Object of the medical-hospital complex, it was the IO that retreated, abandoning a maternity floor Maginot Line it had stubbornly manned—and been stuck in—for decades. One by one, out-of-date rules that had persisted "becausethat'sthewaywedothingsaroundhere" were challenged and eventually withdrawn. Childbirth education classes not only proliferated, they were sponsored by hospitals. Neglected and maligned breast-feeding went from "barbaric" to "beautiful." It became okay to invite husbands into labor and delivery rooms as coaches and baby-catchers. And, spurred by competition, hospital birthing rooms and freestanding birthing centers multiplied like rabbits on the fertility pill.

Pain relief during labor used to come primarily from injections. Now pain is eased more often with caring support, breathing techniques, empathy, and lots and lots of attention. In a difficult labor, there are times when even Lamaze-trained patients require medication or regional anesthesia, and that's okay, too. Fortunately, labor and delivery nurses are better than ever. I know loving nurses (and that includes our own nurse-midwife, Ellie) who go through every labor as though it's their own and who, by offering patients calming compassionate care, transform what was once a scene of panic and fear into one of quiet and acceptance.

When there's progress, of course, there are always trade-offs. These days, most of our practice's deliveries are in the birthing rooms, which, compared to the well-lighted, well-equipped delivery rooms we used to use, are on the primitive side. I know expectant mothers love them. Still, it's a treat once in a while to bring a baby into the world in a good old-fashioned, brightly lighted delivery room—where any emergency can be dealt with instantly and where the vagina is properly illuminated for a precise, neat, painless-as-possible episiotomy repair.

Doctors used to take their patients for granted. With the doctor surplus and the coming of the HMOs, that complacency is gone, never to return. Patients used to take the authority and knowledge of their doctors for granted. The patient-education revolution changed that. Consumerism started by challenging big business, but it wasn't long in getting around to the medical profession. Second opinions to eliminate unnecessary surgery are one aspect of that change, and I think they're often a good idea. In spite of all the advances in modern surgical and hospital care, any operation is a possible complication and a possible death as well as a possible cure and a happy patient. So I want to make certain that my patient understands the risks as well as the benefits, and knows about alternate methods of treatment. If I sense any doubts, I don't hesitate to say, "I won't feel hurt if you seek a second opinion."

One way to be sure my own opinions are accurate is through continued education. Medical knowledge has been growing exponentially each year. One of the medical profession's answers to challenges from consumerists about the need for doctors to stay current in their knowledge rather than stand pat with what they learned years ago has been both voluntary and compulsory continuing education courses. So I take courses in new techniques periodically, and frequently attend the Grand Rounds presentations sponsored by our university hospital's ob/gyn department. Sometimes that can be pretty humbling.

I attended one the other day at which a professor from St. Louis discussed applications for a gonadotropin-releasing hormone called GNRH. Endocrinology presentations are very esoteric, a kind of hothouse knowledge that's valuable to superspecialists but not extraordinarily useful to a garden variety clinician like me. I felt pretty good listening to it and being able to understand perhaps three-quarters of the lecture. That three-quarters, reinforced by some boning up in journals, will enable me to talk intelligently to an academic consultant if ever I have a patient this new knowledge can help. And if it's new and helpful, I want to know about it.

The one thing that doesn't change is the refreshing enthusiasm of ob residents in training—more and more of them bright young women—who now want to be me, as once I wanted to be the attending in the three-piece suit. I notice they no longer stuff stethoscopes in the side pockets of their white coats as we used to do. They've learned from TV that the thing to do is wear them necklace-style. But, alas, as the hospital health care team has grown, the status symbolism of the stethoscope has declined. Everybody wears them now but the social workers and dieticians. It's hard to tell who is the nurse, who's the respiratory therapist, who's the physician's assistant—and who's the doctor.

More changes have probably taken place in me personally over the years than in hospital labor and delivery departments. I've learned that if you really want to serve people, you really have to listen to them. That the ob's role is not to manipulate nature, but to help it run its course. That pregnancy isn't a disease to be treated with diuretics and other pills, but a natural state in which a woman can feel better than she ever has in her life. That in the many stages of labor and delivery, the woman's the real star, the ob just a bit player. And that it's possible to enjoy the birthing process even more playing second fiddle than playing God.

I've learned, too, that the old adage about an ounce of prevention is every bit as appropriate for modern medicine. That treating illness is only a small part of what an ob/gyn does, and the words he speaks are often more important than anything he scribbles on a prescription pad.

I enjoy practice more as a result. When I was young, my greatest satisfactions came from neatly removing a diseased uterus or skillfully wielding a pair of forceps. Now there is pleasure in moments like one recently when, with snow falling outside and the temperature at fifteen degrees, I ran laps inside Syracuse University's Manley Field House.

As I jogged past an elderly gray-haired lady in yellow cap and sweater and sweatpants who was walking rapidly with an older gentleman, I thought, that's what I like to see. I turned around to get a better look and realized she was a patient of mine—a woman who, though just five feet tall, had weighed in at her last visit at 180 pounds. It's not too late to change, I'd told her, even at age sixty-one, and with your high blood pressure, it's dangerous not to. I'd exhorted her about how she could change her life-style if she really wanted to. I explained how by going on the Pritikin diet and gradually increasing her exercise, she could lose weight, lower her blood pressure, and extend her life. Her lean and obviously fit husband had nodded enthusiastic agreement at my every word.

When I passed her again next time around the field house, she had begun jogging, nearly as fast as I. We slowed to a brisk walk so we could talk. "I walk five fast laps, run one, and then walk some more," she said proudly. "I've lost twenty pounds since my last visit to your office. And I'm eating better, too. Not only that. My blood pressure's down to 120/80—without pills." I congratulated her on how well she looked, and we began jogging slowly again.

"My husband's been trying to get me out here for ages," she said, as I speeded up and started to pull away. "But it was you who motivated me, and I can't thank you enough. I feel terrific."

I felt as though my team had just won the Super Bowl.

Epilogue

Winter 1985 (continued) . . .

TIME TO START thinking about retirement?'' Madalyn's words as I linger in bed keep coming back. They represent an easy escape from fear and responsibility. But more than that.

A nerve receptor switch clicks on in my mind, and suddenly I am reliving a vacation scene on a Swiss mountain slope. My wife and I have just checked into our hotel, skis clumped over our shoulders, late in the afternoon after a long train ride across France. "Let's not unpack," I say. "Let's just go skiing."

"But it's snowing!"

"That's why we should go."

We go, she under protest, with heavy new snow beginning to fall. We catch the last tram to the summit, the only people aboard. "Henry," my wife, who has had time to form a decision of her own on the twenty-minute ride up the mountain, says decisively, "this is crazy. I am not going down that slope. I'm taking the tram back down to the hotel."

"See you there," I say airily. "I came a long way to ski this mountain, and I'm skiing it now."

I push off, the wind biting my cheeks, snowflakes melting on my lips. I swoop down the side of the mountain, dart like a snowbird along the broad path winding through the evergreens, kilometer after wonderful kilometer, until I find myself back at the clearing near our hotel. By the time Madalyn returns, I am lolling in our room enjoying a cup of Swiss blueberry yogurt.

Now, at home, I think of all the slopes I haven't had the time or opportunity to ski, and what fun it would be to ski them. But maybe I'll only semiretire. If they like the idea, and if I can do it without being a domineering patriarch, why not go into some kind of business with Jordan and Bruce—and Ned, who'll be out of college in a few years? Eisenberg & Sons. I like the sound of it. And wouldn't it be great to work 9 A.M. to 5 P.M. instead of 9 P.M. to 5 A.M.? To throw off the shackles of responsibility for other people's lives?

Or would it be? I look down at Madalyn, who's dozed off again in the crook of my arm. In spite of the ever-present stress, in spite of the fears, it's been a wonderful life. The days in the office seeing patients and in the operating room healing them, followed by the nights in labor and delivery, have been more than just tiring. They've been challenging and rewarding.

I've been able to give strength to the frightened, like the young woman with a breech baby afraid of a cesarean. And strength of purpose to the patient who finally decided to become fit after sixty.

I've gained strength from the strong. Like the courageous air force wife who underwent a cesarean without anesthesia. And the brave young woman whose husband cried when I told him the bad news of her metastasized uterine cancer, but who, hearing the news herself, confidently declared, "Don't worry about me, Henry. I'm going to beat it." And with that kind of determination, it's possible she *will* overcome the odds.

With each birth, I undergo a kind of rebirth. Watching and helping a brand-new life check into the world just may be the most powerful human experience of them all. Often it's high drama. Always it's high emotion. It's the rapt wonder of fathers and the excitement and relief of toe - and finger-counting mothers. Whether the new parents cry tears of joy, shout their happiness, or, not caring who hears, declare aloud their love for one another, it's hard not to get caught up in the emotions of the moment. More than once, I've wiped away tears of my own.

Newborns are so close to the moment of their creation that just being with them, looking down at them, thinking how serene and uncluttered and unprogrammed their minds are, how fresh and full of potential, reminds me of the potential in me. In us all. Who will this one be thirty years from now? I wonder. An Einstein? A Gershwin? A Gandhi? Or a drug dealer? Genes I can't see have something to do with it. The parents in front of me will have even more to do with it. There's new hope for the future in every newborn. When I look at one I've delivered, I want to go on practicing medicine until I can't walk without a cane.

I get out of bed, head for the bathroom, shower, and start to shave. My eyes are puffy and I feel like the morning after New Year's Eve. I narrowly miss cutting my upper lip as, reminded of a classic *New Yorker* cartoon, I smile broadly. It's a sketch of a plump middle-aged man in his bathrobe standing barefoot on a checkered linoleum bathroom floor, toothbrush in one hand, arms thrust heavenward in the triumphant pose of kings and conquerors. "Ah," he exults, "another day! A new opportunity for fame and fortune. Onward fearless warrior! Forward into battle! Make way, world! It is I."

I dress quickly, adjust my tie in the mirror one last time, bend over to kiss Madalyn. I turn toward the garage. Make way, world! It is I. And it's time for hospital rounds.

Oops. Forgot something. I scoop my beeper off the bedside table. Hmm, I think, as I back out of the driveway, some fine summer evening I'll throw a party and invite all our friends. At the height of the festivities, I'll invite them all into the garden. There, with pomp and ceremony, I'll make a little speech, dig a little hole, and then take my beeper, wrapped in velvet and encased in a cigar box, and bury it forever.

But not yet. What could I possibly do when I retire that would be better than what I'm doing now?

The true story that became a national bestseller

NURSE

PEGGY ANDERSON

8 weeks in the life of "Mary Benjamin," R.N.

The shocking, inspiring, surprise bestseller. NURSE is the story of 8 weeks in the life of a real nurse in a large urban hospital. It reads like a novel.

But it strikes with all the impact of a real experience—because it is.

0-425-09959-8 — $3.95

Please send the titles I've checked above. Mail orders to:

BERKLEY PUBLISHING GROUP
390 Murray Hill Pkwy., Dept. B
East Rutherford, NJ 07073

NAME _____

ADDRESS _____

CITY _____

STATE _____ ZIP _____

Please allow 6 weeks for delivery.
Prices are subject to change without notice.

POSTAGE & HANDLING:
$1.00 for one book, $.25 for each additional. Do not exceed $3.50.

BOOK TOTAL	$_____
SHIPPING & HANDLING	$_____
APPLICABLE SALES TAX (CA, NJ, NY, PA)	$_____
TOTAL AMOUNT DUE PAYABLE IN US FUNDS. (No cash orders accepted.)	$_____